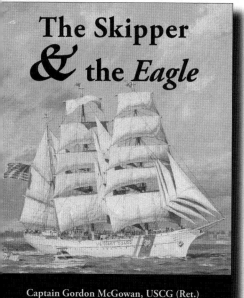

The Skipper & the *Eagle*

Captain Gordon McGowan, USCG (Ret.)

Introduced by Adm. Robert J. Papp, Jr.
Commandant, US Coast Guard

"This rousing yarn of how the US Coast Guard barque Eagle *sailed from war-torn Germany to become 'America's Tall Ship' makes good reading for all hands who care about the traditions of American seafaring and the brotherhood of the sea."*

—WALTER CRONKITE

New edition features an Introduction by Admiral Robert J. Papp, Jr., Commandant, US Coast Guard, and will be available through the National Maritime Historical Society's store at www.seahistory.org.

Sea History Press • 255 pages, 36 illustrations • $25.00, hardcover

Join us for a voyage into history—become a member of the National Maritime Historical Society and discover *Sea History*, the preeminent journal in the maritime heritage field. Each issue brings new insights and discoveries, highlights important people and vessels, and covers the world of maritime museums and sail training with a national focus and an international scope. To join NMHS—and receive your quarterly *Sea History*—visit our web site at www.seahistory.org.

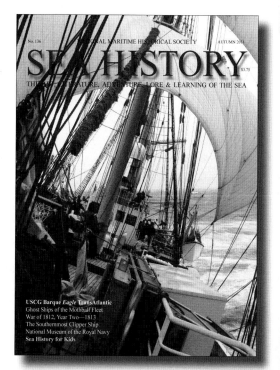

No. 136   NATIONAL MARITIME HISTORICAL SOCIETY   AUTUMN 2011

SEA HISTORY

$3.75

THE ART, LITERATURE, ADVENTURE, LORE & LEARNING OF THE SEA

USCG Barque *Eagle* TransAtlantic
Ghost Ships of the Mothball Fleet
War of 1812, Year Two—1813
The Southernmost Clipper Ship
National Museum of the Royal Navy
Sea History for Kids

NATIONAL MARITIME HISTORICAL SOCIETY • www.seahistory.org
Tel 914 737-7878 • 5 John Walsh Blvd. PO Box 68 Peekskill NY 10566

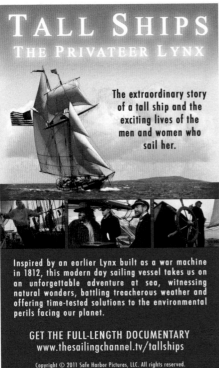
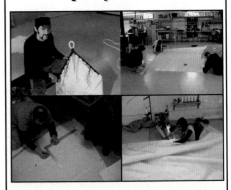

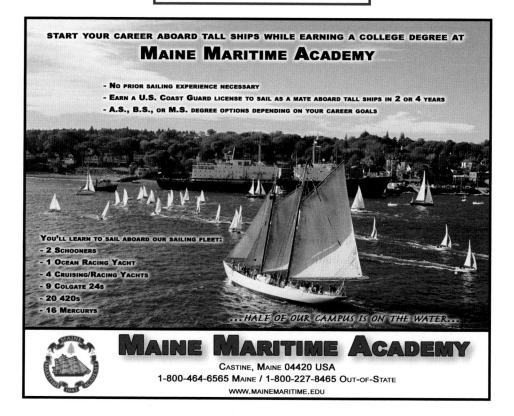

TALL SHIPS CHALLENGE® 2012 - Atlantic Coast
TALL SHIPS CHALLENGE® 2013 - Great Lakes

A series of sailing races, cruises, crew rallies and maritime festivals organized by
Tall Ships America in cooperation with US and Canadian ports on the
Atlantic Coast of North America and in the Great Lakes.

Tall Ships America
Adventure and Education Under Sail®

TALL SHIPS
AMERICA.

TALL SHIPS CHALLENGE® Atlantic Coast 2012

Halifax
July 18-23, 2012
and Nova Scotia Outports
July 24-30, 2012

Newport, Rhode Island
July 6-9, 2012

Greenport, New York
May 24-28, 2012

Charleston
South Carolina
May 10-14, 2012

Savannah, Georgia
May 3-7, 2012

TALL SHIPS
CHALLENGE®

SAVANNAH, GEORGIA

will proudly serve as the official starting point for the
Tall Ships America® TALL SHIPS CHALLENGE® 2012 Atlantic race series.

Please visit our website at
SavannahTALLSHIPSCHALLENGE.com

The Savannah TALL SHIPS CHALLENGE® and Festival will take place on the historic banks of the Savannah River in May, 2012. Join us in recognizing Savannah's nautical heritage while also commemorating the War of 1812. Enjoy participating in the magnificent display of international, domestic and military vessels. These fully rigged, multi-masted tall ships will grace our historic riverfront returning it back to the rich maritime history enjoyed for more than 280 years.

Serving over 11 million visitors per year, Savannah was named **"Best Southern City"** by Southern Living Magazine and **"Top 10 U.S. Destinations To Visit"** by Condé Nast Traveler.

Volunteer, Vendor and Exhibitor opportunities still available.

Savannah
TALL SHIPS CHALLENGE®
May 3-7, 2012

TALL SHIPS
AMERICA.

39th Annual Conference on Sail Training and Tall Ships

Safety Under Sail Forum ~ Education Under Sail Forum

Crew Development
Awakening the Next Watch

Navigating the Regulatory Seas
New Program Showcase
Apps for Caps
The Future of Marine Weather Prediction Technology
Risk Management
Social Media
Hot Topics in Marine Science
Ships to Save the Waters
and More!

January 30 - February 1, 2013
Newport Marriott
America's Cup Avenue
Newport, RI

Go to www.tallshipsamerica.org to register

TALL SHIPS
AMERICA.

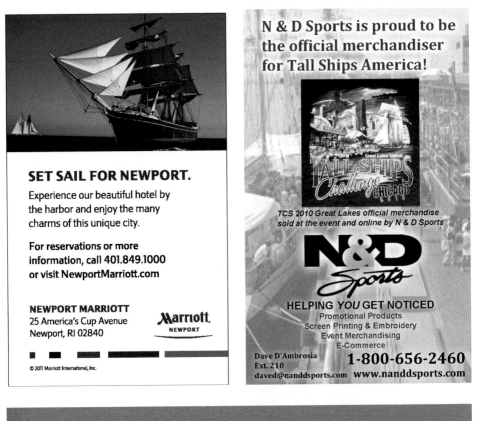

At sea, they gracefully catch the wind.
Docked, they capture the imagination of thousands.

Join us for Tall Ships® Nova Scotia 2012 for adventure by the sea

TALL SHIPS®
NOVA SCOTIA
2012
Waterfront Development

Waterfront Development is proud to host the 2012 TALL SHIPS CHALLENGE® and showcase the best that our city and our province has to offer. Famous for our hospitality, and a favourite port of captains and crew from the world over, we invite you back in 2012 to experience our rich maritime culture and seafaring traditions.

JULY 19-30 • NOVA SCOTIA CANADA

TALL SHIPS CHALLENGE®

Great Lakes 2013

LAKE SUPERIOR

LAKE HURON

LAKE MICHIGAN

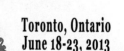

LAKE ERIE

Toronto, Ontario
June 18-23, 2013

Duluth
Minnesota
July 26-28, 2013

Chicago
Illinois
August 9-11, 2013

Bay City
Michigan
July 12-14, 2013

Erie
Pennsylvania
September 6-8, 2013

Battle of Lake Erie
Put In Bay, Ohio
August 30 - September 2, 2013

TALL SHIPS CHALLENGE® Great Lakes 2013
Commemorating the 200th anniversary of the
major military events that took place in the
Great Lakes during the War of 1812.

Schedule is preliminary and subject to change

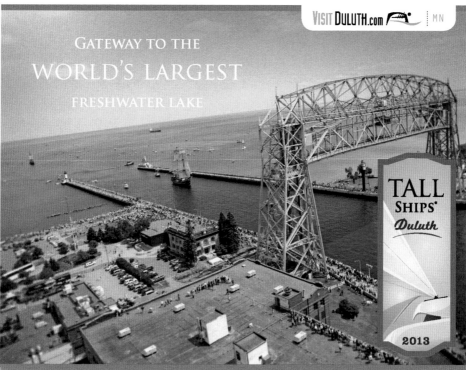

Battle-of-Lake-Erie BICENTENNIAL

Aug. 30 through Sept. 2
2013

Nearly 200 years ago 557 brave men set sail from Put-in-Bay to engage in an historic battle.

YOU can sail in their place and honor their service in securing our freedom.

Sponsored by The Perry Group a 501c3 organization

Experience history FIRST HAND in one of the largest celebrations ever to take place on Lake Erie!

JOIN THE CREW...

Take part in the battle, Sept 2, 2013, as a Tall Ship Crew Member!
Spaces are <u>Limited</u> ~ Enlist Today!

Join us in honoring the patriots who secured our freedom.
Enlist today at…

www.BattleofLakeErie-Bicentennial.com

As one of the finest maritime museums in the nation, the Erie Maritime Museum is a must-see destination on the Great Lakes.

The museum's star attraction, the Flagship Niagara, provides educational day sail opportunities for individuals of all ages!

Julie A. Wagner
Operations Manager
Flagship Niagara League
150 E Front Street
Erie, PA 16507
814-452-2744 Ext. 222
website: www.eriemaritimemuseum.org

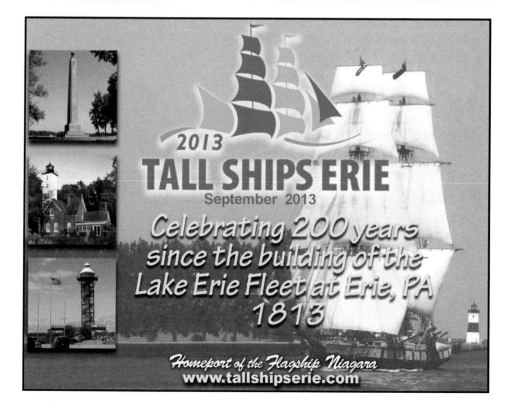

2013
TALL SHIPS® ERIE
September 2013

Celebrating 200 years since the building of the Lake Erie Fleet at Erie, PA 1813

Homeport of the Flagship Niagara
www.tallshipserie.com

Tall Ships America
The New Face of ASTA

TALL SHIPS AMERICA.

PROMOTING SAIL TRAINING TO THE NORTH AMERICAN PUBLIC:

Since 2000, **60** TALL SHIPS CHALLENGE® events have been held in **32** cities across North America with over **500** member vessels participating.

18 MILLION people have visited our **TALL SHIPS CHALLENGE**® events since 2000, generating **$1.4** BILLION in economic impact for our host ports, and **$13.5** MILLION in economic impact to our member vessels.

39 Annual conferences on Sail Training and Tall Ships

19 Editions of Sail Tall Ships! A directory of Sail Training and Adventure at Sea

AND SUPPORTING EDUCATION UNDER SAIL:

SERVICES PROVIDED TO 180 MEMBER VESSELS ANNUALLY:

- Tall Ships America® Billet Bank
- Insurance programs for vessels and crew
- Berth Placement Agency
- Website/bulletins/blogs
- e-Running Free, our monthly e-newsletter

TAKING THE LEAD WITH GOVERNMENTAL AND REGULATORY AGENCIES:

- Sailing School Vessels Act of 1982
- ADA regulations
- 3rd party rig inspections
- Incidental discharge regulations
- STCW –compliant licensing schemes
- Marine Events of National Significance

TALL SHIPS AMERICA.®

TALLSHIPSAMERICA.ORG

2011 Thad Koza
Youth Photography Contest
Grand Prize Winner
Jane Kim

From August 14th to August 19th, I sailed on the Flagship *Niagara* with the Project YESS (Youths Empowered to Succeed through Sailing) Program in the company of 13 other selected students.

It truly was a life changing experience. The program went far beyond our initial expectations, and we returned with so much more knowledge, courage, strength, and friendship than we started with.

Dedicated in Memory of

Thaddeus J. Koza
1940 - 2010

In Memory of Thad Koza

In this, the 19th edition of *Sail Tall Ships!*, we remember our friend Thad Koza. With us in spirit are the countless friends and colleagues that Thad inspired around the world through his lifetime of art and craft and devotion to tall ships and sail training.

Thad was the official photographer for Tall Ships America, and in that role, Thad was everywhere. At every function, at every Tall Ships® event, Thad was there, capturing the moment and preserving for us the sense of intimacy and community that inspires us all as we carry on with the day-to-day challenge of sustaining this movement we call sail training.

Thad traveled the world to capture the majesty of tall ships with his art, and he packaged it in calendars, books, and online so that it could inspire the next generations of seamen. His work is ubiquitous, as was his personality. Every where that Thad went, he made friends and enlisted them in his work, even as he shared with them so generously the results of his art.

His legacy is so much more than his body of work, globe spanning and decade spanning as it may be. His true legacy is the community of friends and the fellowship of tall ships that he fostered, and of which he drank so deeply for his own inspiration. He was one of us, in his own special way, and he will be with us, always.

Thad's friendships were many and deep, wherever tall ships are found all over the world. His friendships were always personal, never just opportunistic, his generosity being proof positive of his authenticity.

That was Thad's way. He pursued his art to satisfy his own inner passions, to be sure. He made a living at it, he pursued it like a craft as necessary, and he amassed a great body of work and worldwide recognition. But for Thad it was always more about the moments, and the people. Certainly, he would share his latest photographic masterpiece with friends, and revel in the artistic achievement, but he would mostly talk about the circumstances of the ship, the people, the sailors, that led him to that moment with the camera.

That is what we will miss. In his gregarious but solitary way, Thad moved around the world and connected us all, across oceans, on every continent. His wide and varied experiences and travels in pursuit of his art provided for us a continuity of story and so of community. We will all miss him for that.

We remember him here in this directory, and the record of his work will take care of his reputation for posterity. More than anything else, we will remember his generosity, his devotion, his friendly spirit, and the indelible mark it made in our lives.

About Tall Ships America

Adventure And Education Under Sail®

The mission of Tall Ships America is to encourage character building through sail training, promote sail training to the American public, and support education under sail.

Tall Ships America
PO Box 1459, 29 Touro Street
Newport, RI 02840 USA
Phone: (401) 846-1775 Fax: (401) 849-5400
E-mail: asta@tallshipsamerica.org
Website: www.tallshipsamerica.org

Many of the photographs in this edition of *Sail Tall Ships!* have been generously donated by the family of Thad Koza.

The following registered trademarks and service marks are owned by the American Sail Training Association:

Tall Ships®
Tall Ships are Coming!®
TALL SHIPS CHALLENGE®
Tall Ships America®
Adventure and Education Under Sail®

TALL SHIPS
AMERICA.

TALL SHIPS
CHALLENGE.

Compiled and edited by Lori A. Aguiar, Director of Operations, Tall Ships America
Design by Artinium Inc., www.artiniuminc.com
Consulting by Pucino Print Consultants, 631 Fletcher Rd, North Kingstown, RI 02852
Printed in Canada by Dollco Printing, www.dollco.com
ISBN 978-0-9799878-2-3
Cover photo: Privateer LYNX, Photo by Thad Koza

Table of Contents

Board of Directors and Staff

Officers
Chairman – Captain Michael J. Rauworth, Esq. – Boston, MA
Vice Chairman – Eric Shaw, Ph. D. – Newport, RI
Vice Chairman – Caleb Pifer – Erie, PA
Secretary – Captain Christopher Rowsom – Baltimore, MD
Treasurer – Dexter Donham – Dover, MA
Executive Director – Captain Bert Rogers – Newport, RI

Class of 2012
Captain Jonathan Boulware – Branford, CT
CAPT. John Gaughan, USCGR (Ret.) – Bethesda, MD
Ms. Karen Helmerson – New York, NY
Mr. James Kerr, Esq – New York, NY
Captain Ken Neal – San Francisco, CA
Mr. Dan Stetson – Dana Point, CA
Ms. Gail Thacher – Newport, RI
Ms. Alix Thorne – Camden, ME
Mr. F.C. "Bunky" Wichmann – Charleston, SC

Class of 2013
Dr. Raymond Ashley – San Diego, CA
Mr. Daveneet Bakhshi – Boston, MA
Mr. Kevin Dykema – Bay City, MI
Captain Jonathan Kabak – Kings Point, NY
Mr. Richard Hawkins – Hyannis, MA
Mr. James Hiney, Esq. – Middleburg, VA
Mr. John Jamian – Bloomfield Hills, MI
Captain Doug Prothero – Montreal, Quebec, Canada
Ms. Meghan Wren Briggs – Port Norris, NJ

Class of 2011
Captain Les Bolton – Aberdeen, WA
Mr. Terry Davies – Montreal, Quebec, Canada
Captain James Gladson – San Pedro, CA
Captain Jennifer Haddock – Woods Hole, MA
Mr. Norman Lemley – Arlington, VA
Mr. Paul Madden – Middletown, RI
Dr. David Niebuhr – Yorktown, VA
Mr. Barclay "Tim" Warburton IV – Newport, RI

Commodores Council
Mr. Henry H. Anderson, Jr. – Mystic, CT
Mr. Bart Dunbar – Newport, RI
Ms. Nancy H. Richardson – San Pedro, CA
Captain Christopher Rowsom – Baltimore, MD
VADM Thomas R. Weschler, USN (Ret.) – Mystic, CT
CAPT David V. V. Wood, USCG (Ret.) – Newport, RI

National Advisory Board
Captain Richard Bailey – Wellfleet, MA
Mr. Hal Barstow – Anaheim, CA
Ms. Beth Bonds – Mt. Pleasant, SC
Ms. Alice Cochran – San Rafael, CA
Mr. Chuck Fowler – Olympia, WA
Mr. Chris Freeman – Mystic, CT
Mr. Thomas Gochberg – New York, NY
Mr. Andy Hammond – East Boston, MA
Mr. Mike Jehle – Fairfield, CT

Mr. Perry Lewis – Newport, RI
ADM James Lyons – Alexandria, VA
Captain Joe Maggio – Coconut Grove, FL
Mr. Jeff Parker – McLean, VA
Mr. Jed Pearsall – Newport, RI
Mr. Nigel Rowe – Gosport, Hants, UK
Captain Walter Rybka – Erie, PA
CAPT Christopher Sinnett, USCG – Ledyard CT
Mr. Howard Slotnick – Bay Harbor Islands, FL

Staff
Captain Bert Rogers – Executive Director
Ms. Lori A. Aguiar – Director of Operations
Ms. Jennifer Spring – Operations Coordinator
Ms. Darlene Godin – Office Manager/Bookkeeper
Ms. Patti Lock – TALL SHIPS CHALLENGE® Director
Ms. Erin Short – TALL SHIPS CHALLENGE® Coordinator

Foreword: Bert Rogers, Executive Director

I am pleased to announce that the American Sail Training Association has changed its name to Tall Ships America. As a valued friend of the organization, we hope you will share our excitement about our new public identity. Our mission is unchanged, and just as we have done since our founding in 1973, Tall Ships America will **encourage character building through sail training, promote sail training to the North American public and support education under sail.** And of course, we will continue to operate the TALL SHIPS CHALLENGE® series of races and public maritime festivals every year.

In the nearly forty years since our inception, our member fleet has grown to more than 200 vessels, our races and maritime festivals reach millions of Americans, and our member programs now provide more than 1.9 million participant-days at sea each year. We are the acknowledged hub for tall ships expertise, information and activity in North America, and we are designated by the United States Congress as the national sail training organization representing the United States.

As Tall Ships America, we will proudly carry our mission forward under a bright new banner, one that will capture the public imagination for the 21st century. We hope you will continue to be involved with Tall Ships America for the next leg of our epic voyage - we are bound for distant horizons of adventure and education under sail.

Bert Rogers, Executive Director
Tall Ships America

Tall Ships America: A Brief History

"This is the Great Purpose of sail training - that the greatest handiwork of man, the sailing ship, shall be borne across the greatest handiwork of God, the sea, to bring together our young people in friendship"

Barclay Warburton III

TALL SHIPS AMERICA.®

Tall Ships America was founded in 1973 as the American Sail Training Association. In the summer of 1972, Barclay Warburton III of Newport, Rhode Island, his two sons, and several friends, sailed his brigantine *Black Pearl* across the Atlantic Ocean to participate in a tall ships race from Cowes on the south coast of England to Malmo in Sweden, organized by what was then known as The Sail Training Association. He was so inspired by the enthusiasm and spirit he saw in that international gathering of tall ships and young people that he set out to create a similar organization in order to bring the same kind of spirit to the United States. Through his efforts, the American Sail Training Association (ASTA) was founded the following year. ASTA soon became the first national association to formally affiliate with what eventually became known as Sail Training International.

The Tall Ships Races in which the *Black Pearl* took part had first been held in 1956, when a London solicitor, Bernard Morgan, had the idea of bringing what he imagined to be the last of the world's great square-riggers together for a race as a last hurrah—a farewell salute—for the Great Age of Sail. A committee was formed, and with the support and assistance of the Portuguese Ambassador in London, a race was organized from Torbay, on England's Cornish coast, to Lisbon, Portugal. Five square-rigged schoolships entered the race: Denmark's *Danmark*, Norway's *Christian Radich* and *Sorlandet*, Belgium's *Mercator*, and Portugal's first *Sagres.* The event proved to be anything but a funeral procession, however, and it has since grown into an annual series that would astonish its original organizers. Today, hundreds of tall ships from around the world come together annually for friendly competition in international and regional Tall Ships Races organized by Sail Training International in Europe and national affiliates such as Tall Ships America. These races, along with waterfront festivals in designated start and finish ports, bring together the ships and young people of most European countries, Russia and the former Soviet states, the Americas, and the Pacific Rim. The key elements uniting these events are an emphasis on youth—from the beginning, tall ship racing rules have required that not less than half those onboard participating vessels be between 15 and 25 years of age — and a formula for rating participating vessels which allows vessels ranging in size from the largest square-riggers down to yachts of 30 or more feet in length.

Tall Ships America's efforts in its first decade were primarily focused on organizing tall ships races on the European model, but from the mid-1980s to the mid-1990s, it worked on a multitude of activities broadly aimed at promoting sail training and supporting education under sail in North America. Thus, at the beginning of the 21st century, Tall Ships America has evolved into an organizer of tall ships races, a strong industry association for the growing numbers of vessels involved in providing opportunities for people of all ages to take part in deep water sailing experiences, and a public charity which makes sail training more available and affordable for young people.

With an organizational membership of over 200 vessels, Tall Ships America serves as a forum for information exchange, professional development, and program standards. Through such initiatives as the Council of Educational Ship Owners, which worked successfully for the passage of the Sailing School Vessels Act of 1982, and the Sailing School Vessels Council founded the following year, Tall Ships America has continued to work with the US Coast Guard and other agencies to create and maintain a friendly regulatory climate for the development of sail training.

Safety at sea has been an enduring emphasis, and in conjunction with the Australian bicentennial gathering of tall ships in Sydney in 1988, a group of Tall Ships America members organized the first international discussion on safety standards and practices, and equipment for sail training programs. Since 1992, Tall Ships America has organized an annual Safety Forum, which regularly draws professional sail trainers from around the world. Also in the 1980s, Tall Ships America developed the concept of the Sail Training Rally, a competition among crews both at sea and ashore, which provides trainees with an opportunity to demonstrate their seamanship skills in a friendly but competitive format. During shore side events, the general public can observe the sort of teamwork and maritime skills that are learned on board sail training vessels at sea.

Over the years, the Tall Ships America has undertaken many other projects to meet the needs of a rapidly growing sail training community. These include a variety of publications such as *Sail Tall Ships! A Directory of Sail Training and Adventure at Sea*, an Annual Conference on Sail Training and Tall Ships which attracts international interest and participation, a Billet Bank to assist vessels in finding qualified crewmembers, a growing program of scholarships and grants to support trainees, vessels, and professional crew, and a constantly expanding website and social network. In 2001, Tall Ships America launched the TALL SHIPS CHALLENGE® Series, an annual series of Tall Ships® races and maritime port festivals that informs the general public about tall ships, our maritime heritage, and the incredible power of sail training to change lives.

Why Sail Training?   By CAPT David V. V. Wood

ASTA's decision this year to re-brand itself as Tall Ships America prompts the question, Why was it called "sail training", anyway? It always did sound a bit like something one had to endure in order to prepare for an occupation—but then, perhaps that's because it started out that way. In the mid 19th century, when steam power began to replace sail as the principal means of propelling ships around the world and shippers came to demand more predictable schedules, ship owners began to discover that nothing could replace the skill and seamanship that their crews had learned under sail. So sail training began—probably with the Swedish brig Carl Johan around 1849—as a means of providing formal training under sail for young men intending to become seagoing officers.

It was an idea that lasted for more than a hundred years, until the last of the big Cape Horners left commercial service following World War II; and not coincidentally, as noted elsewhere in this book, the British Sail Training Association was created in 1956 to create what has been known ever since as the Tall Ships Races. By then, a number of the world's navies (which gave up sailing ships long before the merchant shipping industry did) had recognized the value of training officers under sail, and purposely built big sailing ships to provide the sort of training in leadership, teamwork, and discipline that is required of a naval officer.

Perhaps more to the point, the real seed of the modern sail training movement had been planted in Britain in the dark days leading up to World War II. Kurt Hahn, a German Jew and a pioneering educator who had been a proponent of what we now call experiential education, or expeditionary learning, had fled Germany for England in the early 1930s. In 1940, after war had broken out in Europe, Laurence Holt, part owner of the Blue Funnel Shipping Company, was looking for a training program for young sailors who seemed to have lost the tenacity and fortitude needed to survive the rigors of war and shipwreck, unlike older sailors who, because of their formative experiences on sailing ships, were more likely to survive. Holt teamed up with Hahn, and the result was the birth of Outward Bound at Aberdovey, Wales—a program that very much set the pattern and served as a beacon for many of today's sail training programs. Holt's interest was, of course, in preparing young men to be seafarers; but Hahn saw it as more than that—preparing young men for life.

> After all, the principal qualifications for positions of responsibility in all walks of life are much the same. One may call for the exercise of a slightly different talent from the other, but in the main it is character and common sense that count. There is no sounder ground for the cultivation of that than the sailing ship.
>
> Alan Villiers

Adventure And Education Under Sail©

Even before Hahn and Holt teamed up to create Outward Bound, a number of pioneering adventurers had, in the 1930s, had a similar idea, but in a somewhat different vein. With the maritime industry in the doldrums because of the worldwide Great Depression, sailing ships were laid up by the score, and people like Alan Villiers and Irving Johnson, as well as two less remembered today— Warwick Tompkins and Adrian Seligman—acquired ships and undertook long voyages with young people as paying crew. These remarkable adventures— each recounted in a book—involved the ship *Joseph Conrad*, the brigantine *Yankee*, the schooner *Wander Bird*, and the barquentine *Cap Pilar.*

By 1956, then, "Tall Ships" may have outlived their commercial usefulness— indeed, even ocean liners were fast disappearing (later to be replaced, of course, by cruise ships) with the advent of reliable long distance air transport— but the human fascination with a heritage of exploration and travel by sailing ship remained as strong as it had ever been. Indeed, it was perhaps even stronger, reinforced by the many great authors who had been to sea under sail and later wrote about it; think of Herman Melville, who was not much read in his own lifetime, but whose *Moby Dick* is now universally deemed one of the great books of American literature; or Joseph Conrad, or of Richard Henry Dana's classic, *Two Years Before the Mast.* And of course, the currency of the term "Tall Ships" owes much to John Masefield's poem "Sea Fever."

> I must go down to the sea again, to the lonely sea and the sky,
> And all I ask is a tall ship and a star to steer her by,
> And the wheel's kick and the wind's song, and the white sails shaking,
> And a grey mist on the sea's face and a grey dawn breaking.
>
> John Masefield

And who has not felt the pull of that song? "Tall Ships" have never lost their ability to conjure up visions of lofty white sails on the horizon, the rousing sound of sea shanties wafting across the water, the clank of an anchor chain slowly hove up by jolly tars at the capstan bars, soon to be bound away for sea, toward who knows what exotic ports or tropic islands, over weeks or months of empty ocean.

By the time the tradition of Tall Ships Races that began in Britain in 1956 was imported to America by Barclay Warburton in 1972, further dimensions had been added to the already rich mix of nautical skill, adventure, and character development. Modern society was waking up to the importance of the oceans, the science of oceanography was in ascendance, and sailing ships were (as they had always been) ideal platforms from which to study the watery part of the planet. By 1972 the Sea Education Association was already getting underway, and other similar organizations would soon follow in its wake. Then, with the celebration of the American Bicentennial in 1976, there was a revival of interest in historic ships, and maritime heritage became yet another reason to introduce young people to the long human tradition of seafaring under sail.

Today, the handful of programs and vessels appearing in Tall Ships America's first directory has been augmented many times over by literally hundreds of tall ships of all sizes and rigs around the world. Despite the variety of programs described in the pages of this book, however, and the continuing evolution of what we still call Sail Training, all of them continue to build on the same fundamental belief: that the experience of going to sea as part of the crew of a vessel that is designed to move solely by the natural force of the wind and is dependent on the skill of its crew to conduct it safely and efficiently to its destination is, more often than not, a life-changing experience. More than ever, in a world where almost anything can be experienced vicariously and instantaneously, without getting up off the couch, through the media of streaming video, instant messaging, on-line video games, etc. etc., the opportunity to actually, physically do something challenging and adventuresome—and to realize the benefits only through that effort--seems essential. Indeed, a major study of sail training programs done by the University of Edinburgh in 2007 concluded the following:

> We are convinced that young people consistently experience increases in their sense of confidence about themselves and their dealings with the world, following participation in sail training voyages . . .

It is worth remembering that, not so long ago in human history, sailing ships were the equivalent of today's space ships. When they set off on a voyage,

Adventure And Education Under Sail®

everything they needed for their crews to survive had to be carried along, often (at least in the early voyages of exploration) without assurance that vital things like food and water could be replenished when needed. Navigation was uncertain, the weather unpredictable, communication with the shore virtually non-existent, and the outcome of the voyage sometimes in doubt. It took great skill, courage, teamwork, and self-reliance to make those voyages, and despite the enormous advances in technology we have seen in the last half-century, those are still qualities that our society needs. Perhaps the late Harvey Oxenhorn said it best in his account of a 1981 voyage aboard the barquentine *Regina Maris*, then operated by the Ocean Research and Education Society:

> In the manic pursuit of gaining and becoming, what is lost is the capacity for simply being: with each other, with nature, with ourselves. Not surprisingly, when we think of freedom, we locate it outside our daily round. We define it as escape. What I discovered aboard *Regina* is that we have it backward. In exercising self-restraint, in accepting the kind of limits that I had previously squandered so much energy evading, I experienced a kind of solidarity I'd never known before. I had gone far off to bring what mattered closer–gone to sea and come back feeling grounded–relieved of the burden of specialness, reprieved from the lonely ego, released but also re-engaged.
>
> Harvey Oxenhorn in Tuning the Rig, 1990

So what are you waiting for? There's a program for you in the pages of this book, a tall ship waiting for you to sign on. Pull the plug on your computer, turn off your cell phone, and hurry down to the waterfront; it's high time to get to sea!

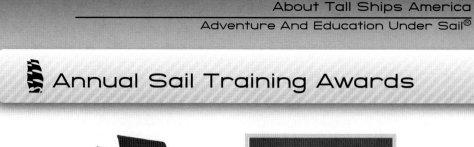

Annual Sail Training Awards

Each year at the Annual Conference on Sail Training and Tall Ships, Tall Ships America honors a select group of sail trainers and supporters who have been recognized by their peers and fellow sail trainers for their outstanding contributions to the world of sail training.

The annual award recipients are nominated by the Tall Ships America membership and the final winners selected by the Tall Ships America Board of Directors and staff.

Lifetime Achievement Award

Awarded to an individual who has dedicated his/her life's work to getting people to sea under sail and who has worked to preserve the traditions and skills of sail training.

2009 Lifetime Achievement Award Recipient: Captain Jonathan Bacon "JB" Smith

(left to right) Mike Rauworth, JB Smith, Bert Rogers, Alix Thorne

With a career at sea longer than most Tall Ships America member organizations have been in business, Captain JB Smith is one of the early leaders of sail training. He is an educator and an inspiration, an explorer and a leader, a father and a friend and a shipmate. For many young people aspiring to master of sail, it has become a "rite of passage" to spend time under his command. Many of Tall Ships America's member vessels have his protégés as Captains with more coming along every year.

Since 1995, he has been a part of the Ocean Classroom Foundation (OCF). As Senior Captain, he has sailed thousands of miles on board the schooners Harvey Gamage, Spirit of Massachusetts, and Westward. There are literally thousands of students who have experienced a voyage with JB, and the memories that he created will live with them forever. Above all, he has been a role model influencing both crew and students to continue with careers in sea education and sail training.

Tall Ships America is proud to honor Captain Smith for a lifetime of dedication to taking kids to sea - bringing them home stronger and better prepared for life whatever they choose to do.

Lifetime Achievement Award

2010 Lifetime Achievement Award Recipient: Captain James Gladson

(left to right) Bert Rogers, Jim Gladson, Lori Aguiar, Mike Rauworth

As an innovative teacher at an alternative school in the early 1970's Jim Gladson was a pioneer in getting kids out of the classroom box and on the water. He took an early retirement and started the Los Angeles Maritime Institute in the early 1990's to increase youth access to education under sail.

Jim Gladson has always seen a bigger picture, like building not one but two brigantines specifically designed for youth education under sail. Jim is known for sharing his vision, as an inspiring speaker at Tall Ships America and STI conferences and adding his insights to the Tall Ships America Board. If your mission is to get youth out on ships, you could count on his full support 30 years ago, and you can count on it today.

Jim Gladson and the programs he has captained, developed, supported and delivered over the past 30+ years have positively impacted thousands of lives. Thousands more have been enriched because of his unwavering passion and dedication to education under sail.

Sail Trainer of the Year

Awarded to a Tall Ships America member whose contribution has been a demonstration of leadership by means of empowerment and inspiration.

2009 Sail Trainer of the Year Award Recipient: Meghan Wren Briggs

Meghan Wren Briggs

Meghan Wren Briggs started the Bayshore Discovery Project (then known as The Delaware Bay Schooner Project) in her early twenties. Her dream was to restore an historic vessel representative of her home area and use it to educate people about the environment, history and culture of the Delaware Bay. To that end she obtained a derelict former Oyster Schooner and started recruiting volunteers to help with the stabilization of what was left. At the same time she began raising the money necessary to complete the restoration. Many people thought that the schooner would never sail again. One by one she convinced them that it would.

Starting in 1996 the *A. J. Meerwald* was operating as a working example of the New Jersey Bayshore region's past history. Since then tens of thousands of school children, many of whom had never been on a boat before, have had the experience of sailing on a vessel, helping to raise the sails, and feeling what it is like to sail on the water without an engine pushing you along.

Meghan's determination and dedication to sailing and the environment has been an inspiration to the crew, the volunteers and to the tens of thousands of individuals who have sailed on "New Jersey's Tall Ship" and participated in the programs of the Bayshore Discovery Project.

🚢 Sail Trainer of the Year

2010 Sail Trainer of the Year Award Recipient: Captain Wesley Heerssen

Captain Wesley Heerssen, Mike Rauworth, Bert Rogers (left to right)

Captain Heerssen started sailing almost 25 years ago as a young volunteer in Elissa and has spent his entire career devoted to sailtraining. He has worked his way through the ranks to captain by sailing in many different vessels, learning the art of traditional seamanship and becoming a most dedicated sailtrainer. He has never forgotten what it feels like to be a green kid in a totally new environment, and the difference between those who yelled at him for what he didn't know and those who taught him what he needed to know. He is now an excellent example of the latter.

Wes has a generous soul, and a keen sense for the morale of the ship's company, professional crew and trainees combined. He has a great feel for when a joke is needed, or when a stern safety reminder is needed instead. He genuinely cares about the experience trainees have onboard, and communicates this to them through his teaching and attention to detail. This personal touch sets an example to be emulated by the rest of the professional crew. Wes encourages their professional growth through continued learning, but also sets a tone onboard that encourages the other members of the crew to extend themselves as teachers when working with the trainees. Wes recognizes and practices to the fullest the basic truth that the key to safety is the knowledge, vigilance, and ability of the crew, including the trainees, and that the better they are taught the better off all will be. Wes' quiet and infinitely patient ways serve as an example for stellar leadership and as a sailtrainer.

Sail Training Program of the Year

Awarded to a current Tall Ships America member program, that significantly contributes to the development of seamanship, navigation skills, teamwork, and leadership skills. The program must be offered aboard a USCG (or national equivalent) inspected vessel, must be offered by certified/qualified personnel, must have clear training goals and curriculum which is compatible to the Tall Ships America sail training logbook and must offer students the opportunity to demonstrate knowledge at sea by participating as active trainees in the running of the vessel.

2009 Sail Training Program of the Year
Award Recipient: *Bowdoin*

(left to right) Mike Rauworth, Andy Chase, Billy Sabatini, Bert Rogers, Henry Knott

Through their program, the 80 year old, wooden, two-masted schooner *Bowdoin* makes regular trips to the Arctic Circle with a crew of students from the Maine Maritime Academy's Small Vessel Operations program. Along the way, students learn navigation techniques, underway maintenance, and seamanship.

Since acquiring the schooner *Bowdoin* in 1988, hundreds of MMA students have participated in their USCG and NMC approved training curriculum leading to 200 ton, 500 ton and unlimited tonnage USCG mates licenses as well as a BS in Marine Transportation. Maine Maritime Academy's curriculum includes courses in Auxiliary Sail Operations as well as Traditional and Modern Sail Vessel Technology.

Sail Training Program of the Year

2010 Sail Training Program of the Year
Award Recipient: US Brig *Niagara*

Captain Wesley Heerssen, Claudia Bankert

The summer of 2010 marked the 20th sailing season for *Niagara*. Over the years, her program has produced scores of professional tall ship sailors, who first found interest in sailing through their introduction to it in *Niagara*. More than a thousand individuals have joined *Niagara's* crew as a trainee to live onboard for at least three weeks and learn the way of the ship. The ship carries an 18-member professional crew and up to 24 trainees who live alongside the ordinary seamen, in hammocks on the berth deck, and with only a navy sea bag for stowage of their gear.

In *Niagara*, professional crewmembers, volunteers, and paying trainees all come together (through challenge, routine, quality training, and experience) as shipmates and comrades engaged in a common adventure with common goals. Through their experience onboard, trainees gain self esteem, confidence, and an often transformative life experience.

The ship's rigging is complex, her sails large and heavy, and her berthing accommodations rustic. Whether fresh new recruits or seasoned hands, the challenges they face are the same, and the new recruits look to the seasoned hands for guidance.

The value of sail training in *Niagara* is not simply that one learns the arts and skills of the seaman, but that one learns something of greater value through sailing and through the process of becoming a competent and trusted member of the ship's crew.

Sea Education Program of the Year

Awarded to a program offered by a current Tall Ships America member which significantly contributes to the educational credibility of programs under sail. The program must be offered in conjunction with a school, school system, school group or other recognized educational institution, must have a clear curriculum of educational goals which are compatible with curriculum goals of traditional schools and must have qualified instructors on a certified vessel.

2009 Sea Education Program of the Year Award Recipient: Sultana Projects, Inc.

(left to right) Mike Rauworth, Drew McMullen, Bert Rogers

Since 1997, this non-profit organization headquartered in Chestertown, Maryland, has shown an amazing ability to grow in outreach and impact, while holding true to its original vision of educating future generations to be stewards of America's largest estuary - the Chesapeake Bay.

It all began in 1997 with the building of the 1768 replica schooner *Sultana* by thousands of volunteers, followed by her launch in 2001. Eight years later, 45,000 students and teachers have learned of the history and ecology of the Bay on the Schoolship of the Chesapeake, with a healthy lesson in seamanship thrown in.

Sultana Projects works with the National Park Service to develop and implement the John Smith Trail, including its John Smith Trail Expeditions program which takes some 1,000 students yearly in canoes and kayaks for programs in history and environmental sciences. The organization also has an outreach program in the classroom reaching some 3,000 students annually.

For thirteen years, Sultana Projects has consistently been on mission, fulfilling its vision of reaching hundreds of thousands with experiential education in sailing, maritime exploration, ecology, history and the teamwork and personal development that comes from working on a tall ship.

Sea Education Program of the Year

2010 Sea Education Program of the Year
Award Recipient: Sea Education Association

(left to right) Mike Rauworth, Jan Wagner, Richard Hawkins, Liz Maloney, Bert Rogers

In 1994, the first year that Tall Ships America awarded the Education Program of the Year, Sea Education Association was the proud recipient of this honor.

Today there are over 7,000 SEA Semester alumni and an additional 2,000 alumni of their high school programs and they are increasingly being recognized for their work in ocean-related fields.

SEA's faculty continue to develop new and creative SEA Semesters appealing to a wider variety of today's prospective students and responding to today's ocean-related issues. Two new SEA Semesters will operate this year: Sustainability in Polynesian Island Cultures and Ecosystems will study the dilemma of environmental and cultural sustainability in French Polynesia. Energy and the Ocean Environment will investigate the social, environmental and technical dimensions of energy production and transportation in coastal and open ocean environments.

In addition to SEA Semester, a 17-credit college program, SEA has operated collaborative programs with Stanford University, Boston University Marine Program, Harvard College, University of Chicago, Eckerd College, College of Charleston, and University of Hawaii at Manoa over the past several years. They also work with Williams Mystic and with WHOI/MIT for short at sea programs.

Volunteer of the Year

Awarded to a Tall Ships America individual member who has significantly advanced Tall Ships America's overall mission.

2009 Volunteer of the Year Award Recipient:
Claudia Bankert

(left to right) Mike Rauworth, Claudia Bankert, Bert Rogers

Claudia's professional diplomatic background, impressive language ability, deep devotion to sail training, personal graciousness, and endless hard work have been invaluable in Tall Ships America's ongoing effort to cultivate close relationships to foreign-flag ships and their naval and diplomatic authorities. She has volunteered long hours on the ground in each TALL SHIPS CHALLENGE® port, supporting the visiting ships in countless ways, and ensuring that they are cared for as honored guests of our Nation, and of Tall Ships America.

Through Claudia's efforts, Tall Ships America has achieved excellent relations and an enhanced reputation with the international fleet. Claudia's work benefits the ships who participate in TALL SHIPS CHALLENGE® directly, and all those who benefit indirectly from the way in which the TALL SHIPS CHALLENGE® promotes public awareness for tall ships and sail training.

Claudia's volunteer efforts do not stop with Tall Ships America. She has an active and central role in the brig *Niagara,* sailing on deck every chance she gets, and contributing as a member of the board of directors of the Flagship NIAGARA League.

Claudia Bankert is a great sailor, a diplomat extraordinaire, and a friend to all who follow the sea with their heart and soul.

🚢 Volunteer of the Year

2010 Volunteer of the Year Award Recipients:
Captain Jonathan Boulware and Captain Jonathan Kabak

(left to right) Captain Jonathan Boulware, Captain Deborah Hayes, Captain Jonathan Kabak

Captain Jonathan Boulware and Captain Jonathan Kabak have shown unflagging support of Tall Ships America and the Tall Ships America membership, donating their valuable time and expertise to the Ship Operations and Safety Committee.

Their efforts on behalf of the sail training fleet, dealing with issues including Third Party Rig Inspection Alternatives and the Integration of STCW into US Licensing Rules, has allowed us to provide valuable services and representation to and for our membership which we would be hard stretched to do otherwise. Both are elegant speakers and very thorough in their research. Over the past several years, both have very capably represented Tall Ships America, making room in their already busy schedules to attend regional meetings, conferences, public hearings, and other such events on our behalf.

Special Recognition Award

2010 Allen Agency Insurance and Financial Safety Award

On behalf of Captain Bill Curry and Captain John Beebe-Center, Captain Deborah Hayes accepts the award from (left to right) Rick Bagnall and Gene McKeever of Allen Agency Insurance and Financial

Presented to Captain Bill Curry and Captain John Beebe-Center for their steadfast safety drills and procedures which were instrumental in saving 64 crew, educators and students aboard the *Concordia* tall ship which sank 300 miles off the shore of Brazil in February 2010.

The Perry Bowl

Awarded to the top finishing Tall Ships America member vessel in the TALL SHIPS CHALLENGE® Race Series.

2009 TALL SHIPS® ATLANTIC CHALLENGE
Perry Bowl Recipient: *Europa*

(left to right) Mike Rauworth, Reinoud van der Heijden and Bert Rogers

2010 Great Lakes United TALL SHIPS CHALLENGE®
Perry Bowl Recipient: *Pride of Baltimore II*

Bert Rogers and Linda Christenson

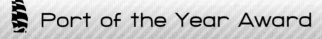

Port of the Year Award

Awarded to the overall highest scoring port in each of four categories: Sail Training and Education ~ Operations, Logistics, Marketing & Promotion ~ Ship & Crew Vote ~ Economic Impact

2009 TALL SHIPS® ATLANTIC CHALLENGE
Boston, Massachusetts

(left to right) Mike Rauworth, David Choate and Bert Rogers

2010 Great Lakes United TALL SHIPS CHALLENGE®
Chicago, Illinois

(left to right) Mike Rauworth, Tony Camarillo, Marilyn Gardner and Bert Rogers

TALL SHIPS CHALLENGE® Port Recognition Awards

2010 Great Lakes United TALL SHIPS CHALLENGE® Port Award Recipients

Presented to the top scoring port in each of four categories:

Sail Training and Education: Cleveland, Ohio

Assesses Port's efforts and success in facilitating youth participation on board TALL SHIPS CHALLENGE® participating vessels in the TALL SHIPS CHALLENGE® Races/Cruises in Company, educational programs offered during the event, and educational outreach to the port community.

Operations, Logistics, Marketing and Promotion: Bay City, Michigan

Assesses Port's efforts and success in promoting and marketing the event, and in execution of delivery. New programs, innovations, expansions of access, etc. are especially considered.

Ship and Crew Vote: Chicago, Illinois

Based on reports from participating vessels and crew, per a standardized questionnaire.

Economic Impact: Toronto, Ontario, Canada

Mathematical calculation based on ratio of reported total expenses/economic impact.

Best New Port Organizer: Toronto, Ontario, Canada

Ports or Port Organizers which are new to the TALL SHIPS CHALLENGE® series are evaluated according to their scores in each of the four categories above. Each category's score is equally weighted.

2010 Port of the Year is awarded to the overall highest scoring port in items one through four above.

The TALL SHIPS CHALLENGE® Series

The TALL SHIPS CHALLENGE® Race Series is a series of sailing races, cruises, crew rallies and maritime festivals organized by Tall Ships America in conjunction with United States and Canadian ports on the Pacific and Atlantic Coasts of North America and in the Great Lakes. Traditionally-rigged sailing vessels from Canada, the United States, and many other countries are crewed by young people (either civilians or cadets), ages 13 - 25, who are engaged in sail training programs under the supervision of captains and professional crewmembers.

TALL SHIPS CHALLENGE® Series

The TALL SHIPS CHALLENGE® Race Series began in 2001 on the Great Lakes. Thirty vessels from six countries, and 1,000 sail trainees and cadets participated in the races, sail training rallies and port festivals in seven United States and Canadian ports. Detroit and Windsor celebrated their 300th Anniversary; additional ports were Kingston and Port Colborne, Ontario; Cleveland, Ohio; and Bay City and Muskegon, Michigan.

The 2002 series was sailed on the Pacific Coast of North America. Sixty vessels from seven countries participated in the series which included port festivals in Richmond, British Columbia; Seattle, Washington; San Francisco and Los Angeles, California. Races were sailed from the mouth of the Strait of Juan de Fuca to San Francisco and then on to Los Angeles. More than 1,200 sail trainees enjoyed the experience.

The 2003 series was again on the Great Lakes. Twenty-seven vessels from India, the Netherlands, British Virgin Islands, United States and Canada participated. Port festivals were held in Cleveland and Toledo, Ohio as part of the Ohio Bicentennial; Chicago, Illinois; Muskegon and Bay City, Michigan; and Sarnia, Ontario. Four races were held between ports and more than 1,000 trainees enjoyed the races and cruises aboard vessels in the fleet. Millions of spectators came to the city waterfronts to see the vessels and talk with their crew/trainees to learn about life under sail and the opportunities to sail on Tall Ships America® member vessels.

The 2004 TALL SHIPS CHALLENGE® Race Series brought vessels together from ten different countries: Belgium, Brazil, Canada, the Cook Islands, Mexico, Poland, Romania, the United Kingdom, the United States, and Uruguay. Across 2,300 nautical miles these traditional sailing vessels tested their crews in

Are you ready...

TALL SHIPS CHALLENGE® Series

friendly competition. The sailors aboard proudly displayed their ships to fascinated crowds in a dozen ports between race segments. Under blistering Florida sunshine and through impenetrable Nova Scotia fog, the ships' crews led their trainees in every aspect of running the vessels. Hand in hand with learning the ropes, the ships promoted team effort, responsibility, and personal development.

The 2005 TALL SHIPS CHALLENGE® Race Series returned to the Pacific Coast. Seven United States and Canadian ports and nearly sixty traditionally-rigged sailing vessels from Canada, the United States, Mexico, New Zealand, Russia and other countries took part. Ports included Victoria, Vancouver and Port Alberni, British Columbia; Tacoma, Washington; Channel Islands Harbor, Oxnard, Los Angeles and San Diego, California.

For the third time, the 2006 TALL SHIPS CHALLENGE® Race Series sailed into the Great Lakes. The fleet started in Cleveland, Ohio, raced to Bay City, Michigan, sailed to Green Bay, Wisconsin and finally were welcomed by over one million people in Chicago, Illinois. Throughout the summer, 22 vessels from the United States, Canada, Cook Islands and British Virgin Islands, took trainees on board to sail and show their competitive spirits in the Great Lakes.

The 2007 TALL SHIPS CHALLENGE® Race Series visited the Atlantic Coast ports of Charleston, South Carolina; Norfolk, Virginia; Newport, Rhode Island and Halifax, Nova Scotia. Participating vessels came from India, Indonesia, the Netherlands, England, Germany, Colombia, Brazil, Uruguay, France, Canada and the US. The ships were gorgeous, the crews enthusiastic and the public showed their support by the thousands.

for the Challenge?

The 2008 TALL SHIPS CHALLENGE® Race Series visited the Pacific Coast ports of Victoria, British Columbia; Tacoma, Washington; Port Alberni, British Columbia; San Francisco, Oxnard, Los Angeles and San Diego, California. Thirty-two vessels, some from as far away as New York, Connecticut, the British Virgin Islands and Colombia participated in the multi-port series which included four races.

Sail training tall ships from around the world participated in the 2009 TALL SHIPS® ATLANTIC CHALLENGE, a spectacular odyssey around the North Atlantic Ocean of more than 7,000 nautical miles. Ships and crew participated in an exciting and competitive series and host ports in Vigo, Spain; Tenerife, Canary Islands; Hamilton, Bermuda; Charleston, South Carolina; Boston, Massachusetts; Halifax, Nova Scotia, Canada and Belfast, Northern Ireland provided a fabulous welcome for the fleet and trainee crews. Billed as "the race of the decade", this trans-Atlantic event was the culmination of years of planning on both sides of the pond. Working with Sail Training International (STI), based in Gosport, United Kingdom, Tall Ships America eagerly welcomed the international fleet, representing Argentina, Russia, Portugal, Romania, Belgium, Brazil, the Netherlands, Uruguay, Bermuda, England, France, Germany, Italy, the United Kingdom, the United States and Canada, to the Eastern shores of the United States

The maritime festivals in each host port give visitors a chance to board the vessels and meet the crew and trainees and learn about the many varied opportunities to sail and travel on Tall Ships America® member vessels.

Racing is one of the most important components of the series. Historically, when two or more sailing vessels are found to be heading in the same direction, an impromptu race almost always ensues. The crews pay closer attention to the other ships and to the trim of their own sails in hopes of outdoing their counterparts.

But how can you compare the racing of a 60-foot sailboat with a 240-foot sailing ship carrying 10 times as much sail area? A special rating system developed in the European tall ships races is used to assign vessels of any size a relative performance factor. This gives all vessels an equal chance of winning if they are sailed well. Before the series starts, six pages of hull, rigging and sail measurements for each vessel are submitted to Sail Training International headquarters in England. They compute Time Correction Factors (TCFs) for each vessel using a program that has been fine-tuned over many years of competition. After each race, the TALL SHIPS CHALLENGE® race team multiplies the time it takes for a vessel to complete the course – its elapsed time – by its TCF in the race to determine the corrected time; corrected times are then compared to determine final standings.

Safety at sea is critical and each participating sailing vessel has been inspected and certified for its intended use either by a national maritime authority (the Coast Guard in the US) or by an internationally-endorsed society. At the beginning of the season, the safety equipment on each vessel is double-checked by the TALL SHIPS CHALLENGE® race team and any discrepancies are remedied prior to the first race.

While underway, racers use VHF or SSB radio to keep in contact once or twice daily with the race communications officer on the escort vessel and often with the TALL SHIPS CHALLENGE® race office by satellite-assisted email.

When the series starts, it is likely that not every trainee berth will have been spoken for and interested youth are encouraged to sail in a race or cruise between host ports. Tall Ships America has a scholarship program for eligible youth. More information is available at www.tallshipsamerica.org. Berths are also available for adults on a number of the participating vessels.

Since the first TALL SHIPS CHALLENGE® Race Series in 2001, Tall Ships America and the host cities have strived to bring the experience of sail training to the North American public. As part of its continuing mission to encourage character building through sail training, both trainees and visitors have an opportunity to learn about life at sea aboard a tall ship. Whether it is learning to sail for the first time or learning about local maritime history, the TALL SHIPS CHALLENGE® Race Series brings to the public the opportunity to see and touch history. In this way, we can further our mission of education under sail through the unique experience that the TALL SHIPS CHALLENGE® Race Series offers to youth of all ages.

Great Lakes United
TALL SHIPS CHALLENGE® 2010

Appledore IV

In 2010 Tall Ships America partnered with Great Lakes United to bring a fleet of international tall ships to the Great Lakes, the world's largest body of fresh surface water. As part of the Great Lakes United TALL SHIPS CHALLENGE® 2010 race series, the tall ships raced through all five Great Lakes making port appearances in cities throughout the US and Canada. Two important initiatives sailed along with the tall ships fleet: water conservation education and youth sail training.

Appledore V

The partnership between Tall Ships America and Great Lakes United was fitting. While Tall Ships America® member vessels and programs train young sailors in the tradition of a rich sailing history, Great Lakes United presses the importance of protecting the waters that these ships, sailors and 40 million people depend on.

The Great Lakes are a fragile ecosystem. Despite their immensity, they are especially vulnerable to degradation. Tall ships represent one of the most sustainable forms of transportation, making this one of the most environmentally friendly races on the planet.

Across six ports, the Great Lakes United TALL SHIPS CHALLENGE® 2010 *"Race to Save the Lakes"* carried the message of freshwater conservation in celebration of waters worth protecting.

Denis Sullivan

Toronto, Ontario: The first port of the 2010 Great Lakes United TALL SHIPS CHALLENGE® Race Series, Red Path Toronto Waterfront Festival hosted twelve tall ships along the waterfront. More than 700,000 people came down to tour the vessels over the course of the Canada Day holiday weekend. Picture perfect weather, clear blue skies and cool days, all weekend long ensured steady crowds. Crew members enjoyed all that a big city like Toronto had to offer. Friendly people, enthusiastic volunteers and organizers, and a crew party with tons of dancing all made a lasting impression. As the Race Team drove out of the city, we passed the end of the Parade of Sail and we could see the fleet slowly making their way to the Welland Canal with hundreds

Europa

of boats swarming around them. Toronto didn't seem to want to let the ships leave just yet.

Cleveland, Ohio: Despite sweltering heat soaring into the upper 90's and thundershowers, over 100,000 people visited the Tall Ships® Cleveland 2010 festival sponsored by Rotary International. Thirteen ships were in port for the three day festival which started with a Parade of Sail into Cleveland.

Friends Good Will

Race One: Monday morning dawned grey and drizzly for race one of the *"Race to Save the Lakes"* series. As the Edgewater Yacht Club volunteers headed to their boats, there was hope that the sun would stop playing around and make an appearance. The Class A start for *Roald Amundsen* and *Europa* was scheduled to begin at 12:00 pm. As *Europa* crossed the line, they sounded their ships horn (which they are very proud of) and were soon little more than tiny square sails on the horizon.

Inland Seas

The Class B, C, D start was scheduled for 12:30 pm. Of the participating tall ships, first across the line was *Lynx* out of California, followed closely by a good looking *Appledore V.* Two minutes later, *Pride of Baltimore II* blasted by the race committee boat. Captain Trost shouting out commands to his hard-working crew. On the other end of the line, *St. Lawrence II* crossed the start a minute and a half later. Six minutes later, *Denis Sullivan* cruised by followed by *Pathfinder.* A few minutes later a conversation between the Baltimore Clippers was heard over the radio when *Lynx* asked *Pride of Baltimore II* to take a picture of their stern. Captain Trost of *Pride II* replied that they were right on top of them. One of the bravo boats came over the radio saying that *Pride* was bearing down on *Lynx* with everything flying but their underwear and boy did they look beautiful!

Lynx

Madeline

Bay City, Michigan: Once again, Bay City, Michigan lived up to their two-time Port of the Year status by treating the ships and crew to a warm and enthusiastic welcome to their city. It is always a pleasure returning to this small city in Michigan because of the overwhelming support the fleet receives. Nothing is overlooked by the extremely competent ship liaison officers and the crews are treated to food, drinks and some wild entertainment, this year in the form of Alice Cooper, who gave an energetic and spectacle-filled live performance. Twelve

Niagara

Pathfinder

Playfair

Pride of Baltimore II

Red Witch

Roald Amundsen

tall ships were the recipients of all this attention and lines for boarding wrapped around Wenonah Park during the Tall Ship® Celebration: Bay City.

Race Two: It was a late but no less exciting start off of Tawas Point, north of Bay City, for the second race of the series to Drummond Island with *Lynx* and *Pride of Baltimore II* both over the line within a minute of the starting cannon being fired. *Lynx* blasted the race committee boat and we were once again close enough to hear the water slapping the hull of "America's Privateer". Unfortunately, *Lynx* couldn't race for long and soon retired from the race and headed back down to Toledo, Ohio for a weekend festival, leaving *Pride of Baltimore II*, *Pathfinder* and *Denis Sullivan* on their own. Earlier that day, *Roald Amundsen* and *Europa* had started the race together though both ships retired early due to weekend commitments. *Pride of Baltimore II* and *Pathfinder* both persevered and finished the race, with *Pride of Baltimore II* crossing the finish line 13 hours ahead of *Pathfinder.*

Duluth, Minnesota: You couldn't have asked for a more perfect summer day - crisp blue skies, light wind and tall ships on the horizon. By the afternoon, thousands of people lined the causeway into Duluth and gave the ships a true Minnesota welcome as the ships paraded into the city.

When four ships visited Duluth in 2008, there were eight hour waits to board. This year, with twice as many ships, the lines were only four hours long. Over 200,000 people came down to the waterfront to see eight tall ships during the weekend of the Tall Ships® Duluth 2010 festival. Returning favorites *Pride of Baltimore II*, *Denis Sullivan* and *Niagara* were joined by *Europa*, *Roald Amundsen*, *HMS Bounty* and *Roseway*.

Race Three: It was blowing a stink for the start of race three and Captain Tiffany of *Denis Sullivan* took full advantage of the wind to be the first across the line, 45 seconds after the cannon blew, followed closely by *Europa*, *Pride of Baltimore II* and *Roseway*. *Niagara* was fifth across the line, followed by *Roald Amundsen*. By all accounts, this was the best sailing of the season and the 300nm race from Duluth to Whitefish Point allowed the ships to stretch out their canvas and the crew to show off their seamanship skills.

Green Bay, Wisconsin: It's tough to compete with the Green Bay Packers, especially in Green Bay. But, despite the fact there was a pre-season game right in the middle of the Bay Lake Bank Tall Ships® Festival, the twelve tall ships made for some family friendly entertainment that did not disappoint. The weather was beautiful and over 50,000 people streamed down to the waterfront to board the ships docked along the Fox River.

Roseway

Race Four: It was the largest race start this season for the final race from Sturgeon Bay Canal north of Green Bay to Wind Point, south of Milwaukee, Wisconsin with *Denis Sullivan, Europa, Fazisi, Friends Good Will, Lynx, Niagara, Pride of Baltimore II* and *Roald Amundsen* competing. As the ships motored to the starting area, you could see crews scurrying aloft and shaking out the sails. Some ships, *Lynx* and *Friends Good Will*, were eager to start and came by to sniff out the line, test the wind and get warmed up. At the 10 minute warning signal, you could see the ships perk up and begin to prepare for the start.

St. Lawrence II

Usually at the start, the ships remain spaced apart and cross the lines within a few minutes of each other. This time, the timekeeper was frantically trying to keep pace as the ships crossed the starting line and the crews threw in everything they had to come out ahead. It was a thrilling start and we couldn't help but cheer our fleet on from the race committee boat.

Unicorn

Chicago, Illinois: A beautiful Parade of Sail into Chicago kicked off the Pepsi® Tall Ships® Chicago festival with the ships arriving to the cheers of thousands of people lined along Navy Pier. Twenty ships were berthed for six days along Navy Pier in downtown Chicago and a record attendance of visitors thronged the festival grounds. Every night culminated in a fireworks display which set off the majesty of the tall ships and was the perfect way to end each day.

Welcome

The Great Lakes United TALL SHIPS CHALLENGE® 2010 exceeded expectations, inspiring many to break out of their comfort zones and join us on the water. Through our partnership with Great Lakes United and their dedication and passion to saving the lakes, thousands of people came away with a clearer understanding of the role they can play in preserving the Great Lakes for future generations.

Windy

2010 Great Lakes United TALL SHIPS CHALLENGE® Race Results

RACE 1: CLEVELAND, OH TO PELEE PASSAGE, ONTARIO

Class A Division
First Place: *Europa*
Second Place: *Roald Amundsen*

Class B,C,D Division
First Place: *St. Lawrence II*
Second Place: *Pride of Baltimore II*
Third Place: *Lynx*

RACE 2: TAWAS BAY, MI TO DRUMMOND ISLAND, MI

Class A Division
Retired: *Europa*
Retired: *Roald Amundsen*

Class B,C,D Division
First Place: *Pride of Baltimore II*
Second Place: *Pathfinder*
Retired: *Lynx*
Retired: *Denis Sullivan*

RACE 3: DULUTH, MN TO WHITEFISH POINT, MI

Class A Division
First Place: *Europa*
Second Place: *Roald Amundsen*
Third Place: *Niagara*

Class B,C,D Division
First Place: *Denis Sullivan*
Retired: *Pride of Baltimore II*

RACE 4: STURGEON BAY CANAL TO WIND POINT, WI

Class A Division
First Place: *Niagara*
Second Place: *Roald Amundsen*
Third Place: *Europa*

Class B,C,D Division
First Place: *Friends Good Will*
Second Place: *Pride of Baltimore II*
Third Place: *Lynx*

2010 Great Lakes United
TALL SHIPS CHALLENGE® Race Results

OVERALL WINNERS

First Place: *Pride of Baltimore II*
Second Place: *Europa*
Third Place: *Roald Amundsen*

SPECIAL RECOGNITION AWARDS

Fleet Award - *Pride of Baltimore II*
Presented in recognition of special service to the fleet and enhancing the safety
and management of the races

Seamanship Award - *US Brig Niagara*
Presented for special service to the fleet, in the true spirit of seamanship
(for providing the assistance of expert divers to sister brig Roald Amundsen)

Seamanship Award - *Appledore IV*
Presented for special service to the fleet, in the true spirit of seamanship
(for her helpfulness in getting all the ships comfortably settled at the docks in Green Bay)

Race results are based on corrected times

TALL SHIPS CHALLENGE® 2011
Oxnard/Channel Islands Tall Ships® Festival

Bright sunny days greeted visitors to the Tall Ships® Festival of Sail in Oxnard, California. June gloom had settled in during the arrival of the ships on the first day but it soon lifted leaving beautiful California coast weather for the duration of the festival.

Saturday afternoon was busy as visitors came down to the waterfront to tour the seven ships in the harbor – *Amazing Grace*, *Curlew, Spirit of Dana Point*, *Californian*, *Patricia Belle*, *Bill of Rights*, and *Irving Johnson*. Twenty thousand people came down to the waterfront of Channel Islands Harbor to see and tour the fleet.

For the third time, Channel Islands Harbor's small community of passionate volunteers and tall ship enthusiasts pulled off a wonderful event that we look forward to repeating in 2014.

Amazing Grace

Bill of Rights

Californian

Curlew

Irving Johnson

Patricia Belle

TALL SHIPS CHALLENGE®
Atlantic Coast 2012

The Bicentennial of the War of 1812 is an important commemoration for the people of the United States and Canada and there will be many public celebrations and maritime festivals up and down the Atlantic Coast. Our itinerary has been carefully designed so that ships can attend many of these exciting events and still be part of the races and the excitement of the TALL SHIPS CHALLENGE® series.

Savannah, Georgia May 3-7, 2012	**Charleston, South Carolina** May 10-14, 2012
Greenport, New York May 24-28, 2012	**Newport, Rhode Island** July 6-9, 2012
Halifax, Nova Scotia July 18-23, 2012	**Nova Scotia Outports** July 24-30, 2012

TALL SHIPS CHALLENGE® races and cruises are held at sea, between ports. Precise race routes and schedules will be announced. This schedule of port events is preliminary and subject to change.

TALL SHIPS CHALLENGE®
Great Lakes 2013

TALL SHIPS CHALLENGE® Great Lakes 2013 will celebrate the 200th anniversary of the major military events of the War of 1812 that took place in the Great Lakes. The series is also dedicated to promoting awareness of the Lakes' ecosystems and fresh water conservation. The series will sail to all five Great Lakes and the St. Lawrence Seaway. There will be point-to-point races, dozens of ships, more than ten ports, wonderful hospitality, and millions of visitors.

Toronto, Ontario
June 18-23, 2013

Bay City, Michigan
July 12-14, 2013

Duluth, Minnesota
July 26-28, 2013

Chicago, Illinois
August 9-11, 2013

Battle of Lake Erie - Put In Bay
August 30 - September 2, 2013

Erie, Pennsylvania
September 6-8, 2013

TALL SHIPS CHALLENGE® races and cruises are held at sea, between ports. Precise race routes and schedules will be announced. This schedule of port events is preliminary and subject to change.

What Did YOU Do On Your Summer Vacation?

From the Logs of the Summer Interns

Each summer during the TALL SHIPS CHALLENGE® Race Series, Tall Ships America offers a team of young people the opportunity to serve as interns with the TALL SHIPS CHALLENGE® Race Team. Throughout the course of the summer series, the interns assist the race director, work in the race office, man the information booths, interact with the participating vessels and their crews and trainees, the port organizers and volunteers, and represent Tall Ships America to the hundreds of thousands of people who come out to see the tall ships. Not to mention, sailing! Long days and hard work are a part of the job - but so are enduring friendships and memories that will last a lifetime. Since the first TALL SHIPS CHALLENGE® Series in the summer of 2001, young people from as far away as Japan and the United Kingdom, as well as Canada and the United States have had the chance to experience the CHALLENGE from this unique perspective.

2010 Summer Intern - Libby Drew

In April, I finished my second year of an undergraduate film and media degree at Queen's University in Kingston, Ontario; the same city as Brigantine Inc.'s Sail Training Vessel, *St Lawrence II*.

The first time I sailed on the *St. Lawrence II*, or on any tall ship for that matter, I was eleven years-old on a day sail with my Mom's work. When I turned 14, I sailed (reluctantly) for a week as a trainee and fell in love. After that, I spent every winter and summer working, sailing, and training on the *St. Lawrence II* and even spent some time on her sister ship, TS *Playfair*.

The one thing that I love most about traditional sail training, is that it has challenged me in ways that are not possible on shore. I've been constantly pushed out of my comfort zone and have had to make decisions keeping in mind the effect they will have on 25 other people. It has shaped me into the person I am today, and I really can't imagine my teenage years without the lakes, my crew and tall ships.

As a sailor who has spent so much time navigating, sailing and exploring the Great Lakes, I could not be happier that this year's TALL SHIPS CHALLENGE® Series will be happening on my home waters. I am so lucky to have experienced tall ship sail training both as a trainee and officer, and am extremely excited that I will be able to support and promote sail training as a Summer Intern. I know that this year's TALL SHIPS CHALLENGE® Series will be incredible. I'm really delighted that I get to be a part of it!

Greetings From the Windy City
August 26, 2010: By Libby Drew

Let me tell you, a lot has happened since Bay City, Michigan where I boarded the STV *Roald Amundsen* hailing from Eckernforde, Germany and I was a little bit nervous about how it would turn out. Although I felt a little bit more behind than usual on a ship because of the language barrier, communication was actually one of the *Roald* crew's strongest qualities. We operated on a fixed watch system, meaning that during the day I would be on from 12-4 PM and at night I stood 12-4 AM the entire time I was aboard from Bay City to Duluth to Green Bay. As you can imagine, standing watch every night with the same people with not too much action can leave a lot of time to talk and get to know each other (and also make dough for bread the next day). Every night our mate would gather watch One to the bridge to give our "personal weather" and talk about our hopes for the night, week, and just in general.

This kind of open communication and understanding between shipmates is surprisingly rare in the tall ships world. This camaraderie was also echoed every change of watch where instead of it either going unnoticed or being a formal military style turnover, was all about thanking the off-going watch.

"Tonight we braced around and trimmed the headsails, did lookout, altered course and watched as the stars came out from behind the clouds. In total we made about 20 nautical miles during our watch."

"Thank-you, watch One for this beautiful sailing vessel and the work you have done for us tonight. Watch Two would like to wish watch one a gute Ruhe (good rest)."

"Thank-you, watch One would like to wish watch Two a gute Wache (good watch)."

The sailing aboard *Roald Amundsen* was also amazing (although a little bit slower than some of the other Class A ships) especially during the race from Duluth over Lake Superior. Even though the fleet was out of sight within the first seven hours of the race, we still ripped. Lake Superior gave us west winds the whole race that only got stronger and following seas that only got bigger as we got closer to White Fish Bay, our finish line. Unfortunately the day the swells were at their worst I had Backschaft, also known as galley duty. One of the advantages of having a ship's galley at deck level is that there is more air flow and light. The downside however is having more movement than you would in a below decks galley. The day I had to cook and clean in the galley, a pickle jar exploded and everything smelled like pickle juice, the sole was slippery, and the glass shards were also a downer. That day in the galley has definitely given me a renewed sense of respect and love for all the ships` cooks in the fleet and pretty much everywhere else. You have to be hard-core to be a sailor, but you have to be way tougher to be a cook onboard a tall ship. That's why the next time you meet a ship's cook, give them a big hug and buy them a drink, they've earned it.

After the race ended in White Fish Bay, *Roald Amundsen* took it easy until we got to Green Bay, Wisconsin, home of the Packers and cheese curds. Along the way, we anchored most nights to swim, relax and have nice dinners together. In Sault Saint Marie, we ended up with the lovely *Denis Sullivan* and *Europa*. Because of the nature of tall ship sailing, restrictive quarters, limited food options, etc, sometimes sailors going ashore can be even more of an exciting adventure than sailing through a storm. I would like to take the time to quickly say thanks to the people of Sault Saint Marie for driving Samara and I around town when we were lost and had no means of transportation, on the afternoon we needed to stock up on shampoo and treats. It was a wild day but we made it back to the *Roald* in one piece. If it weren't for the kindness of people in port, tall ship sailors would be a very sorry bunch.

When we arrived at Green Bay we were all treated to a dinner and dance party as the fleet reunited again. The festival was great and the time came again for me to move on to a new ship and away from the German crew I lived and worked with for almost a month. My new home was the STV *Unicorn* who houses the *Sisters Under Sail* program, a tall ship for girls to develop leadership, seamanship and self-confidence among other qualities. I found myself right at home with the crew and really loved the six girls from Chicago that came on for our trip to Port Washington, Wisconsin then over to Chicago for the festival.

Sailing aboard the *Unicorn*, although very short compared to the other transits aboard *Sullivan* and *Roald,* was really amazing. The crew is very small and they can only take six girls at a time which makes for a very intimate and sweet crew dynamic. We planned to anchor for the night sometimes so during the day we would go all hands and squeeze as much sailing in as possible which I feel really helped gel the girls together as a team. In our society, where girls are encouraged to compete with each other on such absurd levels, it was nice to see a crew of all women working, sailing and living together in the coolest environment imaginable without any problem. I've heard about the work *Sisters Under Sail* have done in the past, but I now understand firsthand how big of an impact sail training can have on young girls in an environment that is safe and comfortable while encouraging them to take risks and try new things. I truly believe that this program is on the right track and I am excited to see more and more professional female sailors in the next ten years at these festivals.

Right now Navy Pier is in full swing and I am super excited to see it all, but also sad to see all of my friends leave, especially those ones that are heading back to Germany and Holland and scattered all across the U.S. I know I have been lucky to have been able to sail with the fleet this summer and can't believe it's almost over. However, before I head back to the real world, I'll be joining Brig *Niagara* back to their hometown of Erie, Pennsylvania… in a hammock. It's probably going to be rough, but I'm looking forward to learning more traditional maintenance and seamanship, and *Niagara* is definitely the place to learn it.

It's All Over Now
August 29, 2010: By Libby Drew

The Great Lakes United TALL SHIPS CHALLENEGE® 2010 Race to Save the Lakes is drawing it's last breath and many of the shipmates I grew to love over the past two months are leaving via plane, train and automobile. Although I myself am moving onto the next port with Brig *Niagara* before school starts, many ships are turning over crew almost entirely, making this a very bittersweet day.

I can remember when I first heard about the TALL SHIPS CHALLENGE® and having a tall ships fleet traveling in company for a summer back when I was a teenager sailing on the STV *St. Lawrence II*. I knew it even then that this is what

I wanted to do even if I had to wait until I was much older (luckily I didn't!). To have been able to sail, race and hang out all summer on tall ships, especially with this fleet, has been beyond amazing. Tall ship sailors are definitely a different breed, and living in close quarters with so many of them these past two months has definitely given me stories to last a lifetime.

What I find amazing about tall ship sailing is how much of a social, emotional and developmental catalyst it can be, not only for the crew members but more so for the trainees that come aboard for a short time. I think for the crew members of these ships, it can be hard to recognize just how much of a difference they make to people every day. I understand from personal experience how long and repetitive a day of deck tours can be, especially considering some of these ships have over 5000 people cross their deck in one day. But what I think a lot of these crew members don't realize is how much being on these ships, talking to crew members and taking pictures can mean to people. This also goes for the trainees. In one summer, a crew member could've taught over 100 people how to sail, tie knots, climb aloft, or just feel more comfortable and confident in their skills. Again, I don't believe that many of the sailors in the fleet recognize how much of a difference they've made because it can get so hectic sometimes with races, festivals and parties happening around them all the time. That's why I'd like to take the time to praise the sailors in the fleet for their hard work, support and endurance this summer. I've seen the difference they've made firsthand and I've also been on the receiving end of their patience, lessons, and friendship. It's definitely what sail training is all about and it sometimes can be easy to forget why we are at these festivals. We want sail training to stay alive and stay strong for generations to come because we believe it builds character, self-reliance and interpersonal skills among other valuable life skills.

Because you are reading this book I assume you have an interest in sailing tall ships. If you have never sailed before and are not sure whether or not it's right for you yet, I would encourage you to do it as soon as possible. I have been so lucky this summer to have been able to sail aboard so many ships and with so many amazing people and I can't imagine anyone wanting to miss an opportunity like this one. The ships are beautiful and sturdy, the crews are eager to teach you what they know.

So even though it's all over now, I know I'll see some of these ships and shipmates again in the future, though maybe not all in one place. The sailing community is surprisingly small and simultaneously infinite and I'm excited to see where I'll go from here.

2010 Summer Intern - Becca Hopkins

Hey y'all! I hail from Charleston, SC. I'm currently working on my undergraduate degree at College of Charleston, and I'm very happy to be sailing with Tall Ships America! As an intern working with the TALL SHIPS CHALLENGE® Series, I'll not only be sailing, but also writing and talking to people about the importance of what Tall Ships America does.

I grew up on the water, sailing sunfish and kayaking. It wasn't until I landed an internship on the Schooner *Virginia* that I became interested in tall ships. On the *Virginia*, I worked as part of a team of talented individuals to maintain the ship and sail her from port to port. The experience and physical labor were grueling at times, but incredibly rewarding. To me, my new calluses represented obstacles overcome.

Though dorm life is a far cry from life at sea, my experience at College of Charleston has also shaped me as an individual. I feel that my major in English has helped me to expand my creative abilities. As an English major, I have worked to hone my writing skills. I have also worked part-time during the school year on a harbor tour boat, the Schooner *Pride*. Aboard *Pride* I have helped to educate guests about sailing, the history of Charleston, and local geography. I have always been happiest on the water. I'm looking forward to being able to travel from port to port, and to meet other people who are just as passionate about sailing as I am.

Ship, Shipmates, Self
July 11, 2010 By Becca Hopkins

I'm listening to my new shipmates, Rebecca and Angela, singing and playing ukulele together. They're sitting on the foredeck of the *Denis Sullivan*, at our dock in Cleveland. We've just come off of a three-day sail from Toronto, and a parade of sail into Cleveland Harbor. The water is just barely rippling, the sun is setting, and my friends' lovely, lilting voices complete the calm scene. It's been a hot, windless passage through the Welland Locks and across Lake Erie.

As sweltering as it was outside, I heard hardly a complaint from the sailors. In fact, complainers are somewhat disdained aboard tall ships. In an environment as contained and cramped as a boat, there isn't room for complaints! Sailors can be incredibly resilient in the face of uncomfortable or difficult situations, and even make light of them. During a gale, with gusts up to 40 knots, I once heard a mate remark that it was "a bit wet out." While the locks were slightly less exciting than a gale, they were long and tiresome, and the crew of the *Sullivan* endured it without a murmur.

Seamanship is not just about line handling, tying knots and setting sail. The ability to endure hardship with grace is a quality that makes a good seaman, because complaining can affect morale aboard a ship. What makes a sailor a "good shipmate" is his ability to not make the lives of his companions more difficult. He pulls his weight and observes certain traditions that have developed from centuries of maritime living. They're mostly common courtesy: don't cause drama, always ask before you board a vessel, etc. But others are less obvious. For example, it is considered impolite to ask the cook what she's making for dinner. If everyone asked, she would have to answer the same question about twenty times (depending on the size of the crew). You never brush your hair below, but on deck, to leeward, in order to keep the boat cleaner. You also never brush your teeth in the sink, because there are a limited number of heads on board and someone might be waiting. The list goes on.

For a beginner, these rules can be overwhelming partly because they are mostly unspoken. Though most of them are easy to follow, the combination of all of them becomes a way of life. And I think most sailors enjoy being surprised at meal times!

August 29, 2010: The Final Blog
By Becca Hopkins

I'm flying home from Chicago, over the Appalachian Mountains. There's haze in the distance, obscuring the curve of the earth. Little puffs of cloud below us are casting shadows on the trees. Wiggly little roads wind around the peaks below. I'm thinking about the beginning of the summer, about flying into Toronto. I knew that the Great Lakes were big, but I didn't imagine a lake large enough to be an ocean--they truly are "inland seas." Ontario was such a bright blue! I wondered if the plane had taken a wrong turn and was landing in Bermuda.

I was a little apprehensive about my internship. I was nervous about being in a new environment, of course, but also as to whether I would be able to handle the challenge ahead. I knew that as an intern for Tall Ships America I wouldn't just be expected to do a little blogging and hand out marketing surveys. Not only would I have to act as a representative for Tall Ships America in port, I would have to change gears completely every few days and become a deckhand. I didn't want to let my shipmates or my Tall Ships America friends down in either role.

I quickly found that my job wasn't easy. I worked long hours underway and ashore; I had very few days off, and was chronically sleep-deprived. And I absolutely loved it. I loved talking to people in port. It was easy to talk to people about sailing, because I had developed a real passion for tall ships. I was especially excited to talk to people who were genuinely interested in getting on a boat. It made me happy to think they might be able to share my passion.

But I lived for being underway. I knew I'd caught the "sailing bug" when I started looking forward to early morning watch, just so I could see the stars and sunrise in the same shift. Off watch, I loved hearing the rush of water against the hull when I lay in my bunk. I loved weaving my way down the deck in lumpy seas. I especially loved setting sail; watching the wind catch the canvas and feeling the ship accelerate beneath my feet. One of my favorite moments was after raising the main on the *Denis Sullivan.* One of my shipmates looked up at the sail and just said, "We did it." And we did. The heavy sail was set. There was no hydraulic lift to raise her, and it was our strength that caused the boat to move. The hum of the engines had stopped. In the background, there was just the sound of the water and wind.

The crew of the *Denis Sullivan* was the most important part of my experience. My shipmates were the ones I worked with, played with, lived with, and trusted absolutely. Underway, I saw how years of experience were reflected in impeccable seamanship. I was never afraid of heavy weather or seas because I knew that I was well taken care of, and that my superiors could handle any situation. I was also inspired by my shipmates' abilities to joke about an uncomfortable situation, while still taking it seriously.

I can't forget the TALL SHIPS CHALLENGE® race team either. Though we didn't sail together, we grew as close as shipmates. If the interns worked hard, I know that Erin, Patti and Brian worked harder and had less time off than we did. The work that they do generates millions of dollars not only for the port cities, but revenue and exposure for the participating ships. They are also shameless recruiters, always trying to shanghai unsuspecting landlubbers into becoming tall ship sailors.

This summer flew by. While I'm happy to be going home, I'm feeling a little melancholy about leaving my friends and the beautiful fleet of tall ships. I'm going to miss the fast-paced cycle of ship, port, ship, port. And I'm especially going to miss early morning watch, with stars setting in the west and the sun rising in the east.

2010 Summer Intern - Samara Haver

I recently graduated from Colorado College with a degree in psychology and studio art. Outside of class I was involved in the outdoor recreation club, student government, and dance workshop.

I was first introduced to tall ship sailing last spring when I spent a semester sailing aboard S.S.V. *Corwith Cramer* in the Caribbean with Sea Education Association. In addition to supporting my love of being on the water, my semester with S.E.A. informed and enriched my long-standing interest in marine biology and ecology.

After returning to the land-locked state of Colorado for my last year of college I am thrilled to join the TALL SHIPS CHALLENGE® race team and spend my summer on the Great Lakes. As an intern for Tall Ships America, I look forward to sharing my passion for sailing, environmental conservation, and experiential education.

Full and By
July 31, 2010: By Samara

In the summer, it doesn't get dark on Lake Superior until nearly 11 pm. This means that at the very end of evening watch the sunlight is still fading and civil twilight lingers until just after turnover. The night before we came into port in Duluth, my watch was on for the evening shift and I was posted as the bow watch. We dropped off the student trainee group that traveled with us from Bay City in Houghton, MI so, for our short transit to Duluth, watches were smaller and we all spent more time completing watch duties. During long stretches on bow watch I needed to constantly remind myself to stay focused on the horizon watching for traffic instead of letting my mind wander to our upcoming arrival in Duluth.

I departed Bay City almost two weeks ago aboard the *Denis Sullivan*. Like my first hours on *Europa*, I once again climbed a steep learning curve to acquaint myself with the crew and pace of a new ship. The day we left Bay City was spent motoring to the starting point of race two. We crossed the startling line in the early evening, setting everything but the two top sails. However, it was not long before the winds died down (as they often do at night on the lakes) and we were forced to retire.

We left Bay City with a group of students from the Michigan Tech summer outreach program. In addition to standing watch and participating in shipboard life, our education director, Joe, also held class every day to teach them about maritime history, lake science, and practical skills such as knot tying and the physics of sailing. Working with high school age students was very different than the guest crew on *Europa* who were mostly all older than me. I enjoyed taking on a leadership position to help the green sailors become adjusted to shipboard life.

The day before we reached Houghton the wind picked up enough for us to fill our sails and we sailed through the afternoon and into the evening. My favorite moment of the trip occured during our watch that afternoon. Captain Loge ordered us to steer full-and-by, which means that we were to steer by the wind and hold the ship at an angle to keep the sails full. Aside from sleeping underway, steering full-and-by is one of my favorite parts of sailing. It is incredible to feel the forces of the wind and water literally in your hands, and I love keeping a course by feeling the wind on my face instead of by monitoring the compass. I was standing on the quarter deck when Carlos, the first mate, had one of the students, Carl, take over the helm. At first Carl struggled to catch his bearings and understand how to steer us in the right direction, but he caught on quickly and within a few minutes was smiling and laughing to himself. When Carlos asked what was up he chuckled again and responded, "I can really feel it…this is awesome!" Moments like that fuel my passion for sail training and experiential education.

Learning how to sail is only a small part of sail training, it is also about teaching stewardship – for others, for oneself, and for our surroundings. Even though Carl only stayed at the helm for a short time, it was long enough to show him power of nature in a way that cannot be explained in words. Even if he forgets the names of the sails, how to tie a bowline, or how to plot our position on a chart – even if he never steps foot on a tall ship again – that moment of realization at the helm will endure in his memory and we, the crew, have done our job.

What I Learned This Summer
August 27, 2010: By Samara Haver

This summer has gone by incredibly quickly. It is almost hard to believe that two months have passed and my internship is just days away from completion. When I stop to reflect on my time with Tall Ships America and the tall ships this summer, it is almost overwhelming to think about the number of new people, places, and experiences I have encountered during my travels in the Great Lakes. Some things have gone well, and others not so much – so before I transition from TALL SHIPS CHALLENGE® intern to *Lynx* crew member on Sunday it seems appropriate to take a moment to reflect.

In the last two months I more than doubled my sailing experience, and vastly improved not only my technical skills but also a few that helped me when I wasn't hauling lines and doing boat checks…

Sailing On Different Ships

This summer I had the opportunity to sail on four tall ships in two months-
Europa, Denis Sullivan, Roald Amundsen, and *Lynx.* I also was invited to
participate in a crew exchange on *Niagara* for one afternoon day sail. It was
hard work to learn the lines and routines of a new ship every couple weeks, but
in retrospect I am very lucky to have had those experiences.

Learning New Names

At the beginning of the summer I was terrible with names. And I am still pretty
bad. However, meeting so many new people (including two international crews)
forced me to improve my short term memory by a long-shot.

Taking Advantage Of My "Crew" Status In Port

Almost all of the ports the tall ships visited this summer went out of their way
to offer activities for crew in their off time. Often, in lieu of sleeping, I chose to
seek out as many of these offers that I could – and at times even try to finagle
my way to additional ones. For example, in Bay City I spent the first days of the
festival lusting after the air-conditioned entertainment at the Planetarium across
the street. I don't know if it was because the employees recognized me from the
breaks I took there every day, or because they knew I was with the festival – but
when I finally got enough free time to go to a show they let me sneak in without
a ticket. Likewise, in Duluth the aquarium staff allowed me to climb up on the
roof to take pictures, and yesterday the Field Museum of Chicago stamped my
hand for entry when all I did was mention that I was with the tall ships.
I have lost track of the number of souvenirs, meals, and experiences that have
been offered me this summer, and I am very grateful for the port's generosity in
showing me and my fellow sailors a good time in their city.

Saying Yes

The advantage of this is two-fold for me. First, when living on a ship it is essential that everyone shares the responsibility of taking care of the ship. So much so, that usually when you feel like you are doing more than your share, you are just barely doing enough. For me, that translates to constantly saying yes. Boat check? Yes. Help me stow/move/haul/clean/fix/prepare (anything)? Yes. Second, it means saying yes to experiences. Working long days underway and in port is very tiring. But if I had elected to stay back at the ship every time that I was tempted to, I would have missed out on a lot of incredible opportunities. A recent example of this comes from our last night in Port Washington, when a small group of sailors including Libby and myself decided to take a break from the standard night-life activities downtown and instead follow Hannah from the *Unicorn* on an adventure. At what felt like three miles into a walk on a road to nowhere, Libby and I almost decided to give up and go home, but we stuck it out and ended up having a blast chasing each other around for two hours at outdoor laser tag.

Making Anywhere Feel Like Home

With each new ship I sailed on, came a new bunk I slept in. Moving around every couple of weeks made it difficult for me to settle into one location, and as Natalie from the *Denis Sullivan* put it when I moved onboard in Bay City, "It must be hard to never really feel like one place is home." And for the first few weeks of the summer I shared that sentiment. But now, after getting to know so many ships and crews I feel at home on almost all of the ships. When the 2010 festivals are over I will be sad to say goodbye not just to the *Lynx*, where I live now, but to all of the ships I have called home this summer.

The S/V *Denis Sullivan* is a 137-ft three-masted re-creation of a 19th century Great Lakes cargo schooner. Celebrating its 10th year of operation in 2010, the *Denis Sullivan* sails the Great Lakes as well as into the Atlantic and Caribbean.

As the flagship of the Great Lakes United TALL SHIPS CHALLENGE® fleet, this majestic vessel is a unique link between the past, present and future of the lakes. The teaching programs run by the knowledgeable crew represent one of the keys to the future of these lakes. Education is essential to the protection of the precious Great Lakes waters, and the *Denis Sullivan* is taking a lead role in this regard.

The ship offers an intensive, adventure-based, academic program designed to provide high school students, as well as college age and older, an opportunity to live and work aboard. Students participate actively in all ship's operations while investigating the different features of the marine environment.

It is also an experiential study of history and culture viewed through the maritime lens. The voyage is a real-world application for the knowledge students have attained, but have yet to apply. Major topics include: introduction to fresh and salt water ecology, nautical science, maritime studies, seamanship and natural resources. Additional topics covered included: team building, personal reflection, journaling and life skills' enhancement.

Sailing on a tall ship provides a rare opportunity for students to live and work as real explorers in the spirit of the 19th century voyagers they otherwise can only read about. They can take aspects from over a century ago and apply them to the 21st century.

The integrity of the Great Lakes and freshwater resources around the globe are threatened by loss and degradation of habitat, urban growth, the invasion of exotic species, and the cycling of toxic chemicals and pollutants. Sailing on the Great Lakes links communities together and fosters the sense of pride that is crucial to overcoming these ecological challenges. The *Denis Sullivan's* journey across the lakes during the Great Lakes United TALL SHIPS CHALLENGE® Series reminds all of us why these lakes are absolutely worth protecting.

2010 Summer Intern - Natalie Joynton

Posts from the *Denis Sullivan*: Setting Sail for the Summer
Jul 12 2010 - 3:17pm: By Natalie Joynton

To speak of my love for the Great Lakes is to tell a tale in reverse. It can only be explained as that: a bottom-up journey, a type of ascent from sand to surface. After working last summer as a fellow for Thunder Bay National Marine Sanctuary, with its massive collection of freshwater shipwrecks, I now find myself living on the ships themselves: schooners, known as tall ships, that are exact replicas of the kinds of vessels that disappeared in the glacial waters off Michigan's shores. It's ironic, like a wreck gone backwards, this return to light from a darker depth.

This summer, sailing on the SV *Denis Sullivan* for two months, I will not learn about the processes of restoring artifacts, not about who/when/what/why/ how of those over-century-old sinkings, not about the survivors or casualties. No—this summer, keeping that shipping history fresh in mind, I get to explore its present—which is really to say I'm exploring the Great Lakes future.

I'll be writing about my adventures on board the S/V *Denis Sullivan*: its mission, its stories, and the way the Great Lakes weave through our daily lives. The decisions that we make as citizens of the Great Lakes region— 42 million of us—have both an immediate and long-term impact on what the lakes become— and in this way, the present contains the future.

And it's the choices we don't even think about: turning off the faucet while we're brushing our teeth, disposing of pharmaceuticals properly, collecting rain water in cisterns to water the garden rather than using the hose: it begins there. It goes without saying that the Great Lakes are immense—but just as in our own bodies, there is a delicate balance at work, there is fragility, there is threat; it is imminent.

I was reminded of this the other day, racing across Cleveland's port in the orange inflatable with Carlos, *Sullivan's* first mate, and Maura, *Sullivan's* second. Someone—a cop? another crew? a visitor? I hadn't seen—had spotted a seagull trapped between one of the other tall ships of our fleet and the dock, caught in fishing line. As we approached the gull, I expected wild wing-flapping as we eased our boat into the tight space—something fighting its death—but instead what we found was a creature so close to death that it was entirely calm: climbing into our hands as we cut it free, its head lying to one side of its short, infant neck.   We took it back to the *Sullivan* and set it in a box, fed it and gave it water, and within a half hour, it was up on its feet.

Great Lakes United is working tirelessly on the regional and national level—but what is this if not the accumulation of the local? The accumulation of us as individuals? Our letters to Congress to close the Lakes off for good from species such as the Asian carp. Our efforts to conserve water within our homes. Real progress—real protection of the Great Lakes—starts with a personal commitment to live with them responsibly. Small, individual change. What a difference it makes.

Posts from the *Denis Sullivan*: The Best Thing You Can Bring Aboard
Jul 15 2010 - 2:07pm: By Natalie Joynton

"The sailing ship life, while rigorous," *Sullivan's* welcome manual reads, "is an engaging one." The same introduction goes on to state that "…a positive attitude is the most important thing you can bring aboard." It's been nearly a week since I joined ship, and I will be with the *Sullivan* until the beginning of September. The learning curve, so far for me, has been nearly vertical.

Those that work the deck of the *Sullivan*—the captain, mates and crew—all have some red in the face: slight sunburn streaking the cheekbones, singed brows. Diligence in reapplying the SPF 70, wearing broad-rimmed hats or baseball caps, and of course sunglasses still means somewhat of a burn, because the hours on deck outweigh even the best protection. But below deck, in the galley where I've been assisting our cook, Angela, the challenge is not the sun. It's the heat.

Our self-lit oven, whose temperature is always only guessable, is turned on an hour or so before meal time and then, one by one, all four stovetops blaze into service to warm what seems to me a gargantuan amount of ground turkey, black beans, rice. By the time those above climb down the companionway to fill their plates, Angela and I are dying to go up on deck, spread our limbs on its white benches, and enjoy the Great Lakes breeze.

It's easy to focus on these challenges—the sun up on deck, the heat below—because as general rule, it's simple and human to complain. But no one here does much of it. A positive attitude is the best thing you can bring aboard.

Besides, spend all your time complaining, and you'd miss out on the stars.

Last night, sailing into the mouth of the Detroit River, I looked up. The galley was cooling off from dinner. As always, a crew was on watch. Angela was somewhere singing "Blue Moon", strumming her ukulele. "You won't see much," Joe, the educational programs director, remarked. "Got too much city glow."

We were nowhere near Detroit itself, but we were near land. Dim lights from the occasional house winked through trees. Still I had never seen so many: the night, in some places, seeming more white than dark. The stars seemed for the first time remarkably different from one another, some brighter, some weak, others barely there— sudden sputter against black. It's more than enough to make me want to stay on.

Long after September.

Posts from the *Denis Sullivan*: When the Wind is High Enough
Jul 28 2010 - 2:16pm: By Natalie Joynton

It's three in the morning and someone is at my bunk, whispering my name. "Natalie." A woman.

"Natalie," Rebecca repeats. "You have thirty minutes until watch. It's cold. Bring your jacket." I resist the urge to pull my comforter over back over my head. I know that the watch before me, who have been on since eleven, won't be released until I am up on deck.

That's the way "watch" works aboard the *Sullivan*: after nine hours off, part of the crew has a four or five hour shift. Each watch we work is at a different time, and we get a full night's sleep every third night. The crew is split evenly into watches, and there is always a crew on watch. Having the 3-8 am shift means I'll go on watch again after dinner, around 6 pm. I pull myself out of my bunk and start searching for my sweater in the dark.

By the time I make it into the lit galley someone has already brewed a fresh pot of coffee. I get in line and squint at the clock. The Northwest wind is more forceful than I'm used to, but the waves are coming straight at the ship and we don't have too much rock. By the time I climb back up on deck, we've assembled into "muster": a small meeting of all the crewmembers on watch that shift, led by one of the mates. My eyes begin to adjust to the night, and I can make out their faces.

Some of the duties while on watch are straightforward, such as standing bow. Standing bow helps ensure that the *Sullivan* doesn't run into anything: radio towers, bouys, lighthouses, and most importantly, other ships. It means scanning the horizon, staring at the water line for your assigned hour and reporting any obstacles within view. It's plain work, especially at night, but requires a high level of attention to detail and part of why those standing bow are relieved after only an hour. You must be totally awake, because the lives of the crew may come down to you spotting something in time to avoid it.

Being at the helm or steering the *Sullivan*, if you can believe it, is less taxing. That said, I've learned it takes practice to stay within five degrees of an ordered course with our finicky helm, a wheel that jerks left or right when the waves hit it. Boat checks are our final duty while on watch, and they are anything but plain. Performed every hour, boat checks are a full scan of the ship's under-deck compartments: the dank bilges, heads (or bathrooms), and a trip into the sweltering engine room to record the oil pressure, voltage and temperature of our dual engines.

Needless to say, being on watch is exhausting. Crewmembers sleep for most of the nine hours that they are not on watch, yet there's not a better job on the ship. I've grown much closer to the crew, as we're often paired off for duties: deep conversation in the dark at the bow just before dawn, or joking our way through a stinky head check.   And since beginning watch, I'm more confident in my role on the *Sullivan*, and feel that I'm finally getting into the routine of sailing life. But most of all, standing watch has taught me to respect the *Sullivan* itself. Because ships, like the Lakes themselves, are large but delicate things, operating on the simple rule that if you respect it, it will respect you back.

Yet it's getting more difficult to think of her as a "thing". In some way, she is alive to me—our Sullivan—with her hissing toilets, creaking masts, diesel scent, and rigging that sings when the wind is high enough.

Posts from the *Denis Sullivan*: The Last Port
Aug 30 2010 - 8:57am: By Natalie Joynton

Last night, 11 pm: the tallest building in Chicago comes into sight as a dim green orb across a calm stretch of Lake Michigan. At first we don't know what it is, the four of us standing on the quarter deck; we spend several minutes staring through the binoculars before identifying it as the Sears Tower.

I am both counting the number of hours until we dock at Navy Pier and dreading it. Something pulls me to shore, some undertow sucks me down and pushes me back out. I count the number of hours until we port—three—because my arrival to Chicago signals the end of this summer, as it's our final stop, the narrowing and then closing of this fraction of my life: two months spent on Erie, Huron, Superior, and Michigan, living, working and writing on the *Denis Sullivan.* "Matchless" is the only word that comes to mind. Arriving in Chicago is a type of graduation, then, because that's what it's been for me on this ship: a 24-hour-a-day education. Instruction through immersion: some new frontier I've come out of more capable than I was before.

But that's true of everyone on *Sullivan*: you can't board this ship for any good amount of time without it transfiguring you at the pit. It's both the way the ship is run, watches and meals and chores and lines, and the fact that you're in a place that humans essentially don't belong: the water. Because it's not our territory, really. Think: as the most dominant species on the globe, we can't survive in over 70% of its available living space. What a bizarre relationship we have with it: our continued existence depending on this element we've yet to figure out and aren't physically equipped to inhabit. Chemically, water is simple: two parts hydrogen, one part oxygen. But the deepest sections of ocean still contain unknowns. When we catch what swims at those depths, they look like they are from other planets. They make us think of outer space, and yet they are here.

When I tell people what I've been doing this summer, they generally have one of two reactions: they stare like I've got screws loose or remark on what a charmed life I lead. It's neither of those. It's not crazy (as there's a peculiar, glad rhythm to ship life) but it's not charming either. It's hard work. Respect the ship and it respects you back. But the Lake? It owes you nothing.

Still I can't help but sense that Lake Michigan knows that this is our last sail. Quiet with 1-2 foot waves and the Eastern winds favorable for *Sullivan's* transit south from Milwaukee. Dawn's cracked the sky and through fog I can make out the Northern segment of Chicago's skyline. We bring down the sails in order: fore, main, mizzen.

What's waiting for me there? "Windy City". "Chitown". "City of the big shoulders". "Paris on the Prairie".

Some old writer friends are travelling up to see me tonight, and on Friday, I'll check into a room downtown that promises "striking views of the Magnificent Mile", but perhaps more notably, free coffee, a hot shower and an air conditioning unit. But these days, I get uncomfortable in air conditioning—too cold, unnatural; I'd rather the breeze and heat. I keep going through this list often, keep hoping to remind myself of what's there, the why of heading home.

Some people are built for life on the water. As Captain Jesse Loge said, "I wasn't born a sailor, but I was born a traveler". Nomad. People who aren't content experiencing life in standstill: same state, same city, same neighborhood, same set of circumstances; the very things that provide most of us with feelings of comfort, home sweet home, make her face long and set off that old itch in the heart. *Go.*

I'm almost 25. Some part of me thinks that if I was built for life on the water, I would have figured it out by now, beyond doubt: two months at sea leaves a lot of time to think. So maybe I'm not nomad enough.

But another part of me wonders if it's something you discover only after being gone from water, off the ship. A few weeks back on land and then the itching starts. You look out your window and the sprouting boxed herb garden, rosemary and basil and cilantro, still isn't enough. Your car seems to go too fast, your days drag out.

How long can I stay away?

How much will I miss the deck, the bunk, the watches, the waves, the people?

Is it over there—that rise of buildings, honking of buses and taxis, painted blues billboards, hot asphalt, railed balconies—is that home? Or is it out here?

Wind. Sun. Warmth. We'll see.

2010 Guest Blogger - Matt Maples

Matt's Back! In the spring of 2007, Matthew Maples began his sailing adventures as an intern with Tall Ships America on the barque *Picton Castle*. His life has not been the same since.

He has sailed on the twin brigantines *Irving Johnson* and *Exy Johnson*, the brig *Niagara*, the schooner *Spirit of Massachusetts* and, most recently, the bark *Europa*.

In a wonderful twist of fortune, Matt was offered a coveted crew position on board *Europa* sailing the West Coast of South America and was onboard as the *Europa* made her way up to the Great Lakes by way of the Panama Canal, Bermuda, Halifax and the St. Lawrence Seaway.

Matthew graduated from Eastern Illinois University in 2007. He is a native of land-locked Bartlett, IL. His internship opportunity with Tall Ships America infected him with a sailing "bug" that to this day persists in ailing him with a chronic-yet-delightful wanderlust over water.

The Races Begin
July 12, 2010: 1540 - 41.35.5 N x 81.55.3 W
By Matthew Maples

"Get ready on the courses! Only two minutes!" says Captain Vos. A flurry of activity follows his commands; canvas crackles as it tumbles from the yard and eager hands haul on lines. The billowing course sails, the lowest and largest square sails on our fore and main masts, are tacked down, their clew corners hauled close to deck. Then, a mighty blast from our foghorn announces the beginning of the first of the Great Lakes United TALL SHIPS CHALLENGE® 2010 races.

Now, hours later, the wind has died down and the ships lazily race for Pelee Island in west Lake Erie – less than thirty miles away. It is a short race, with barely a breeze. This race may instead be quite long as we creep ahead at barely two knots. Ahead of us now is the German brig *Roald Amundsen*, we have closed a lot of distance to her, but have not yet been able to overtake her as we grasp for inches in this race.

Though all plain sail is set there is little wind to work with, so Jay has taken to teaching our new trainees the ropes, "Sheet, clew, bunt, bunt!" I can hear her drilling them about the line location for square sails. No doubt they are confused after an afternoon of fast-paced sail handling as we scrambled to get canvas set aloft as the race began. With little time to explain, we thrust ropes into their hands and said "pull!" The rush is over though and now we will begin to take the time to explain more about just how our ship works – we want them good and trained for tacking and wearing ship since we are, of course, obliged to put the engine to rest and replace it with canvas, muscle and a lucky breeze.

There is plenty of teaching to do! We picked up eighteen more spontaneous souls than we expected in Cleveland, bringing our voyage crew total to twenty-five. The vast majority are green, but refreshingly eager. One of them, Nick, came to give the ship a casual visit yesterday. Now, less than twenty-four hours later he is on board and on watch. A spontaneous decision, but one he feels quite good about. After our afternoon of hauling on braces and halyards, I find him relaxing under one of our canvas towers. He tells me that as soon as he stepped on board he "knew it was awesome" and that he had to do it. I ask him what he is hoping to get out of this experience, and he tells me that he expects "a little food, a little company…and maybe some direction." Then the deep New Zealand accented voice of Sam Swinburn, our chippy (carpenter) pipes in to our conversation; "You gunna find the meanin' of life?" We all laugh. We'll see what happens! A few people claim nearly as much when they leave a ship like ours.

Cleveland now lies about eleven miles off our port – a city that treated us well. Many of us enjoyed our free passes to the Rock and Roll Hall of Fame and the Great Lakes Science Center. Our liason officers and their cadre of volunteers were awesome in getting us supplies and, most importantly, a television to watch the World Cup Final of Spain vs. The Netherlands (a match we will no longer talk about). We also thoroughly enjoyed our well-stocked crew party at Cleveland's Edgewater Yacht Club.

Cleveland now slowly falls into our wake as we make for Bay City. But first, a race!

We Heart our Studding Sails!
July 20, 2010: 2345 - 45.32.7 N x 83.36.6 W
By Matthew Maples

The second Great Lakes United TALL SHIPS CHALLENGE® Race, from Gravely Shoal to Drummond Island has become as much a race against time as against our fellow tall ships. The finish line now lies a mere twenty-two miles ahead of us, yet we have but four hours to cross that distance. The entrance of the St. Mary's River is ahead and we need to be there by 0400 to enter with the current. We may be making five knots now, but if we turn on our engine for speed then we forfeit this race altogether!

This race is relatively short, only about 120 miles in its totality, but light and fickle winds have forced us to fight for ground. All plain sail is set aloft and our studding sails have been exercised vigorously. It would be unfortunate to drop out of the race this late in the game, especially since our competitor in our class, *Roald Amundsen*, has become a small smudge on the horizon beyond our stern. This was not always so. The beginning of the race, on the afternoon of the 19th, saw the *Europa* and *Roald Amundsen* throwing canvas aloft to snatch the barely-present winds, both grasping for ground to push ahead and cut off the wind of the other. Captain Vos tells me that in light winds our two square riggers are fairly evenly matched – I believe it! At one point it looked to me like the *Amundsen* was gaining ground on us…then they tacked, putting themselves windward of us, perhaps in an attempt to block our wind. It was futile however, as our crew was hastily putting up our studding sails, maximizing canvas aloft. With studding sails being set, the *Amundsen* found her speed dragging behind us at half a knot, while the *Europa* slowly accelerated beyond *Amundsen's* reach. Without studding sails herself, the Germans could do nothing but watch us nearly disappear over the horizon in front of them.

Our studding sails are a solid advantage for *Europa* over most of the other ships in these races. With all six of them set we can just about double the canvas area of a mast – allowing us to put up an impressive amount of sail to fill with light winds. If set on both sides of our foremast as we run downwind, they make our ship look as if she has sprouted great wings of white. Positively majestic! With the help of our studding sails, I was able to wake up this morning and had trouble spotting the *Amundsen* far astern. She now trails us by 8.2 miles.

A highlighted aspect of the TALL SHIPS CHALLENGE® races is to push ship crews and trainees to compete against one another in order to build up their teamwork skills. I think our studding sail setting should be the poster child of this goal. The amount of coordinated effort that is involved in setting them (especially when you see another ship gaining on your stern) is considerable! Hands are aloft, shipping out booms, sending down halyards and rigging sheets. Line leads are improvised as we run out of pins to make fast our lines while eager hands unfurl them from their bags. When ready the studding sails are hauled

aloft on one or more halyards, sheets are tensioned to keep the lower boom (an extra wooden spar to provide "framework" for the sail) and sail going aloft steady – like a kite they are hung aloft and held at a trimmed angle by two sheets. It is difficult to describe.

The teamwork involved in setting them is only heightened when they all need to be taken in quickly because of an impending storm – such a situation happened this afternoon, as our once-sunny horizon turned gray and dark. An excellent watch leader, Daniel Baxter, gave good direction as eager, helping hands among our crew and trainees eased halyards and sheets and hauled on clews to bring the corners up, then lines are dis-attached and hands aloft bring in the naked booms left sticking out. All done quickly! We have sent our studding sails up and down several times in the past two days and I can already see our crew getting better with all this practice.

Rain has drenched our deck this afternoon and lightning can be seen on the nearby shore. Yet it seems we have avoided most of that trouble. Now… if only we could be graced with just enough wind to finish the race and hopefully receive some recognition for the hard work of this crew!

Endings and Beginnings
August 16, 2010: 1510 - 44.50.0 N x 87.44.0 W
By Matthew Maples

"First Place" – That's what the burnished gold plaque in our library reads. The announcement of our Class A win was drowned out by roars of jubilation from our crew; who were outright psyched to see their hard work with the studding sails pay off. Captain Robert Vos grinned like a fox. That was the third race, Duluth to Whitefish Point. As I write this, we are on the eve of the fourth and final Great Lakes United TALL SHIPS CHALLENGE® race, spanning the waters near Green Bay to the outskirts of Chicago, a 118 mile race. That is for tomorrow – today we sail from Green Bay to Lake Michigan to get in position for tomorrow's 10:00 start of the race. We will use the time in-between to acquaint our 22 trainees with the ship. Their help will be needed to quickly get canvas aloft at the race's start.

With the conclusion of our hard-hauling race to Whitefish Point, we took it easy with a leisurely sail to Mackinac Island and through the shoals of northern Lake Michigan, before ending in Green Bay. We took a shortcut to Green Bay through the Sturgeon Bay Canal – a narrow canal lined with woodland so close that it created the illusion that we were sailing through a forest.

It is the nature of a world-venturing sailing ship that people are always coming and going. Today, on the quay in Green Bay we left three of our good shipmates; Frank the engineer, Rensje the cook and Captain Robert. We bid them a thunderous farewell with *Europa's* famously mighty foghorn. They are all going on holiday or to other ventures, but will return to us soon. We, of course, won't forget them, and in the case of Frank, can't forget him because he has, undoubtedly, left us a few surprises. Frank's pranks are well-known, and we will keep a sharp eye out for nasty things in strange places.

In their place we have Marius back as engineer, along with Captain Klaas, Marianne and the ship's dog Sirius. They left us in Panama for holiday and have returned to *Europa*. Apparently Sirius enjoyed his carefree holiday among green fields and trees while Klaas caught up on maintenance of his home in Holland. Sirius' return has finally put a timely death to a too-oft repeated joke. Whenever anyone has used the phrase or incredulity, "Are you serious?" someone, (usually Diven) replies "Sirius? He left in Panama!"

Marius's return somehow coincided perfectly with a famous *Europa* braai BBQ – of which Marius is de-facto King of the Braai. That Saturday night (the 14th) saw an overly large *Europa* crew enjoy a huge spread of beef, breads, kabobs and sausages – far more than could be eaten! Perfect! A fine party for ourselves.

We are, of course saddened to part with our shipmates and friends, but it is lessened by the knowledge that we will see them again soon. *Europa* is a good ship, and you can know it by the fact that her crew, trainees and friends keep finding their way back on board to return from all corners of the world

Today has been a noteworthy sail – a steady breeze of up to 20 knots from a favourable direction propels us toward the Sturgeon Bay Canal, where Lake Michigan awaits us. For Tim Valbracht however, it has been much more than that. Ten years ago Tim dreamed of sailing on *Europa* when he visited his cousin, the then-engineer Rob Leering. After years of receiving ship's itineraries, insatiably reading the logbook and visiting her when she was in Canada, Tim finally found time to peel himself away from his aircraft maintenance/engineering job to sail away.

His final incentive to come on board came in a strange form - a random opening of a book. The silhouette of a tall ship on the binder of Pete Brown's "Hops and Glory" caught his attention. Tim opened it up immediately and saw, to his amazement: "Part 4 – *Europa*" – an account of one trainee's time on the ship. "No way!" he thought. "If this isn't a sign." Finally, Tim knew he had to make it happen – today was that day. He says it feels awesome to finally be the one on board, watching the shore fall away, instead of always watching the ship fade away to the horizon. His dream that he had ten years ago is "unfolding with every sail set."

Tim has already been aloft to unfurl the fore topgallant – a fine start. He is using his time on board to make a movie that he began when he filmed the *Europa* leaving Toronto in this year's Parade of Sail (from an airplane!) Perhaps it is a project to inspire others to sail.

"It is always going to be a part of my life, this ship," he told me. I think most of us here on *Europa* understand what he means.

2010 Guest Blogger - Ben Rogers

I was introduced to tall ships on my 14th birthday, when I received as a gift one week aboard the Schooner *Harvey Gamage*. I was hooked, and took a job to pay for the next summer and the next, and all through high school.

I graduated from Southern Nazarene University with my bachelor's in journalism, and along the way participated in the Voyage of Understanding aboard the Brig *Prince William*. Shortly after graduating in 2006 I made my way aboard Barque *Picton Castle* as a volunteer, then a summer as deckhand back aboard *Harvey Gamage*, and most recently I spent two years working and sailing in *Picton Castle* as A.B. and then bosun. I am now currently working on *Niagara* as an A.B

On the Way to Toronto
June 29, 2010: By Ben Rogers

Good morning, Welland Canal. This is our big booger of the summer. It's been circled on the calendar since I arrived in Erie in March. I've been hearing about this Darth Vader of canals for several years now, even aboard the *Picton Castle*, who made a trip through during the TALL SHIPS CHALLENGE® festivals of 2006.

Captain Wes said the Welland is the most difficult canal to navigate in the world, and he's been through a lot of them, so his opinion counts for something. To put it in perspective, Niagara Falls are just to the east of the canal, and run the same route. It's a supremely impressive feat of engineering and seamanship to pilot a ship through the equivalent of those iconic waterfalls that gave even the stout-hearted Superman a tricky go-for.

A huge effort of work goes into getting a square rigger like *Niagara* ready for the canal. She makes regular passages through the canal every year, so some custom rigged canal fenders get lashed to the channels to take the brunt of the banging and grinding against the cement walls of the canal locks as the ship locks up and down. Basically, it's a 6"x 6" spar, that rests against the channels, with a strong epoxied box at the lower end resting against the bulwarks at deck level, all braced together with steel bars. There are eight of them, and we lash them to the ship six ways from Sunday, and smear them with Crisco.

We downrigged our port and starboard boat davits, and shifted *Cutter I* to the stern davits, and then turned our attention to the rig. Niagara's rig is very tall, very wide, and very long. To make the canal passage, she needs shortening. We ran in our flying jibboom, lashed all the loose gear to the catheads, cockbilled the sprityard, mainyard, and foreyard, braced über-sharp the tops'l and t'gallant yards, and lowered the main t'gallant mast six feet. All this was done in a day, en route from Erie to the entrance of the canal at Port Colborne, Ontario.

Then we locked down the canal into Lake Ontario. This took about 9 ½ hours. Locking down is generally easier, but there is a lot of current running up the ship's stern, and the canal has a lot of strange eddies, which makes the ship handling no small trick. We busted a couple fenders, and popped off the horn of one of our open stern chocks, but other than a few grey hairs in the crew, everything went fine.

The next day it was up at 0500 and directly to attending the ship. We hucked all the canal fenders back on deck, put all our sticks back in order, sent up come-alongs to the tops, tuned the rig, and had the lanyards seized-off by the time we arrived in Toronto, 30 miles and a few hours later.

On Board *Niagara* for the Final Race
August 17, 2010: By Ben Rogers

We departed Green Bay yesterday, went alongside at Sturgeon Bay in the afternoon, and set to putting the main t'gallant mast back in order. The main truck is 118 feet high, and our anemometer set up adds another foot or so, which requires us to look hard and close at any bridge we have to cross under. For a lot of ports, this means backing off the backstays and shrouds, housing the main t'gallant mast six feet or so, leaving the t'gallant yard crossed, and lashing the heel tight to the topmast. Once we're past the obstacle, we push the mast back up with the capstan, pop in the fid, and crank home all the stays and reseize the landyards. At first glance it is daunting, but in *Niagara* it becomes a neat routine in the back end of the season, and yesterday it happened during deckwash and below decks clean up.

Today we are racing. We took off at the start with single reefed tops'ls set. As *Pride of Baltimore II* shot past us we put on our t'gallants. When *Denis Sullivan* made a push for us, aloft we went and shook out those reefs, set royals, and soon enough had everyone getting smaller on our starboard quarter. *Pride* is still there stalking, just past dinner time. We are sailing hard and the crew are electric. Hopefully we get some luck from the wind, but it is forecast to back a bit and come more on our nose, which favors the schooners, so we are enjoying the ride and crossing our fingers.

August 18, 2010

Well, the wind went the way they said it would, and we couldn't manage to weather the finish line, so tacking was in order, and we gave up ground to those fore-and-afters. *Pride* finished before us easily, but we gave her a good race most of the way down. She points like a wind-vane, and we point like a brig. A slick brig, but a brig nonetheless. It is only fair, since the race from Duluth was so much to our liking, and the sailing has been a blast in both races for us. Rarely does *Niagara* get to turn loose like she has the past few weeks.

Goodbye From Erie
September 24, 2010: By Ben Rogers

With the dust settling here in Erie after the last Tall Ships® festival of the summer, the *Niagara* crew are uncrossing their dazed eyes and taking some time to focus back on sailing and finishing the season strong. The festival circuit this summer has been wild, as these things always seem to be, with the winds cooperating and lending some action to our lives between port cities. *Niagara* made some of her peak passages since Duluth, keeping the crew energized and in love with their ship.

The Tall Ships® festivals offer an opportunity for ships to do two remarkably unnatural things. One is unhealthy, that is spending a long time in port, and the other is invaluable, offering the public a glimpse of some of human engineering's finest masterpieces. Sailing ships are undeniable exhibitions of beauty and function combined, and the sailors who work in them are specimens in their own right as well. Though the peak age of sailing is past, the relevance of tall ships has not wavered at all thanks to the ingenuity of sail training and modern ship's programming. Sailors are just as weird and baffling to landlubbers as they ever were, maybe even more since we are a bit of an endangered species these days.

These open houses that we put on are, for this sailor at least, a chance to show the public that what we do is as accessible as it has been in three generations, and becoming more so. The sailor's way of life is relevant, beautiful, and hard, and I met many green hands this summer who signed aboard one of the ships here in the Great Lakes between festivals and were quickly becoming hooked.

My friend Chad, who came to visit during the Cleveland festival summed it up best. He said, "I've heard you talk about it, I've seen pictures, but being here and seeing them up close, it's crazy. These are real. It's totally different in person."

It's been a good summer, the ship has been good to us, and we've worked to be faithful to her, and everyone is in one piece and getting ready to put her to bed soon. Then, onwards and upwards, some of us to winter maintenance, some of us to our next job, and some of us to completely new adventures altogether.

Thanks for reading.

Ben Rogers out.

The Sail Training Experience

Tall Ships America® member vessels and programs foster opportunities for intensive personal development -- intensive life experience in order to advance leadership development, an utter reverence for nature, a sense of time and place, an appreciation for history, and teamwork ability. Sail training really teaches the qualities of stewardship, resourcefulness, pride, humility, bravery, strength and grace.
And we learn to sail, too.

The Moral to the Story...

By Meghan Wren Briggs

I grew up in a town that could be described, (and often was), as a tired factory-town going nowhere. As a teen, I was convinced that, as soon as I was old enough to make my own way, I'd want to be as far away from Millville, NJ as I could get. I felt really lucky because my family had a house on the Jersey Shore where I could get out of Millville in the summer. My Dad called me Muck Muck as I explored the mud flats, sand bars and back creeks in my old Keds with the torn tops. After hurricanes and nor'easters, I'd collect the stranded mudhens in a box and deliver them to the marsh across the channel they had been blown across during the storm.

Little did I know I was missing out on learning the cycles, secrets and seasons of my own 'backyard' in Millville, the Delaware Bay.

In 1985, I embarked on a journey to 'find myself' and my 'place'. With my dog, Glory, I packed a 4-season tent, a 10° below sleeping bag, a pile of books (including, of course, Blue Highways) and some favorite tunes into my Chevy Cavalier and hit the road. After a circuitous expedition with adventure and misadventure, I landed on the 'Tall Ship for Texas' sailing to the 1986 100th birthday celebration for Lady Liberty.

I lucked out when I was assigned the 4-8 watch, putting me 'on duty' during the sunrise and the sunset. Each morning I'd be up when the sky was black and starry watching the rosy fingers of dawn creep across the horizon gradually exposing our magnificent ship. The Elissa's authenticity, her textures – wood, line, canvas and iron; smells of tar, linseed oil and salt; sounds of flapping sails, rhythmic waves and creaking blocks, and her aura of quiet power seduced me.

One evening I stood on the end of the bowsprit, my spot, riding the swells on a 200-foot square rigger seeing nothing but water on the horizon in every direction. I felt connected to the sea. I felt connected to all sailors before me. I felt miniscule and huge all at once. The exaggerated rise and fall of the spar I stood on at the extreme end of the ship gave me a just-before-butterflies-in-the-stomach sensation. I looked back to the deck of the ship and saw tranquility in motion; crew members diligently working; the 'off-watch' reading, chatting, dozing or quietly measuring the sun's position above the horizon (practicing their celestial navigation). I was sun burnt with work-weary muscles, skin tight with a salt glaze and my mind was quiet – focused only on the moment. Everywhere I looked were people whose company I enjoyed and with whom I shared months of mutual accomplishments. It sounds corny, but I felt absolute joy. For the first time in my life I could honestly say that there was nowhere on Earth I'd rather be – not a thing needed even a tweak. I had found my passion.

But, it still wasn't tied to a 'place'.

Upon completion of the voyage to NYC and back to Texas, an age-old siren called me back to my Cumberland County roots (a love interest). After my 'Aha' moment at sea, South Jersey was a whole new place to me. I discovered the magic and mystery (and history and ecology and scores of old schooners!) of the Delaware Bay that had been there all along – right under my nose – providing the cultural and economic underpinnings of Millville and its surrounding Bayshore communities. I felt overwhelmed with a sense of having been gypped of a rich legacy since this heritage wasn't celebrated (or even mentioned) in my youth.

Serendipity struck and I had the opportunity to marry my newfound passion for historic sailing ships with my growing appreciation for the Delaware Bay. A dilapidated hulk of a 1928 Delaware Bay oyster schooner became available. I pictured the A.J. Meerwald returned to her former glory and enlisted as the flagship of a 'save the bay' movement for the underappreciated Delaware Bay – making sure that the next crop of young Millvillians and their neighbors were given a chance to connect with this amazing legacy. The schooner would build a persona for Delaware Bay, shifting the local ethos from a collective inferiority complex to one that celebrates pride of place.

The problem? The boat was a wreck. I had no money, no plan, no equipment or supplies, no standing in the community, and I was a 23 year old idealistic 'girl' in a community that didn't much like 'do gooders' and seemed to have missed the women's movement by a few decades. I didn't know it yet, but I needed to raise close to one million dollars - and I had chosen to do it in the poorest county of the state. (Did I mention the boat was a wreck? Seriously.) I started recruiting anyone who'd give me the time of day to help.

One Saturday a Winnebago pulled up. An older guy got out and came aboard. He didn't say much at first but hung around as we lamented the difficulties surrounding removing the steel masts from the surf-clamming rig that added many tons of non-historic weight to the boat. The weight kept her lower in the water and exposed some of her worst seams to the tides, making her more vulnerable to sinking to the bottom of the Maurice River – a place she seemed perpetually to be seeking. We couldn't get a crane close enough and had no budget. Mort finally piped up, "You don't need money. Just get a ladder, a cutting torch, some chain, a shackle and a few strong backs." The next weekend a group of us watched in awe (and did the grunt work) as he cut the mast down, bit by manageable bit. Week after week, year after year, Mort was our guru as we removed over 15 tons of steel from the tired hull, then all other extraneous items, improved her watertight integrity and prepared a shipyard in a barren clamshell covered lot for the rebuilding phase. It wasn't until years later that Mort let us in on the fact that, 30 years earlier, as a welder at Tony's Marine Railway in Cape May, he personally had fabricated and installed that steel clam mast on the *Meerwald*!

The cold misty February day in 1992 when we hired a 275 ton crane to roll into Bivalve to muscle the *Meerwald* out of the River and place her on the bank for her restoration; people flocked to witness the spectacle. A few days later a group of us watched a video of the glorious happening in someone's living room.

A voice in the background yelled what most had been thinking, "She's gonna crack like an egg!" (I'm guessing it was Wayne Robinson - his voice is hard to miss) Miraculously, she held together. Once we started carefully removing her planks, we all wondered how she had made 'the pick'.

The restoration begins...

For several more years it seemed like slim odds that the sorry hulk on the bank would ever sail again. Progress was painfully slow and fundraiser after fundraiser wore out our dedicated gang of volunteers but only chipped away at the huge amount of money needed for the restoration. Gradually, very gradually, we built credibility by not giving up. I couldn't really even say when, but the odds seemed to turn in our favor. We got a major grant from New Jersey Historic Trust, then one from NJ DOT and suddenly the launch was within sight. Four years after the haul-out and eight after I initiated the restoration project, on the *Meerwald*'s return trip to her native element, the crowd was much larger than at the haul-out. The mood had switched from one of 'detached spectators' to 'event participants' – even the sun cooperated, partnering with the wind and sky to make a magical September backdrop for the occasion. An old-timey band put the celebratory mood to music and people jockeyed for positions as players; no one seemed content to be just an onlooker – everyone had helped make it happen – even the old timers who drove by once in a while to heckle.

finishing the deck

What a crazy mix of pride, excitement, gratitude, anxiety, hope and trepidation when the *Meerwald* finally sailed!

At the same time as my seemingly impossible goal was achieved in the face of immeasurable skepticism and hardships; some of the biggest challenges were still around the bend. I had a schooner to run, a program to market, an organization to manage, a growing staff to orchestrate and a bay to save! Commissioning Day sails, all five

of them, were short and sweet. We needed to give lots of folks who had helped a chance to taste the *Meerwald*'s glory. For me, it was another event that needed organizing. My true celebration took place the following October. On the return trip from our debut at the Great Chesapeake Bay Schooner Race we cleared Cape Charles with the sun setting. I climbed out to the bowsprit for which I had ordered the Douglas fir from the west coast; hired the spar maker from Maine; watched take shape from tree to square to octagon back to round; studied historic photos to determine its authentic hardware; and debated its appropriate coating with more experts than I care to think about. From this reminiscent yet oh-so-different vantage point I had a moment of peace and joy. I was 'one' with 'my' schooner and my world but probably never again could feel an inner quiet without the tug of things yet to be done.

Today, the *A.J. Meerwald* sails as New Jersey's Official Tall Ship, her parent organization, the Bayshore Discovery Project, reaches nearly 50,000 people each year and there is a significant increase in public appreciation for all things Delaware Bay. (And I am glad to find myself living just 8 miles away from Millville which is experiencing its own renaissance.)

The moral to this story is that great things can be accomplished little by little with perseverance and teamwork. If the *Meerwald* can sail again, the Delaware Bay can again be a thriving ecosystem and lifesblood of the Bayshore community. And, bit by manageable bit, individuals can turn their situations around, kids with little hope can choose to make a difference in their lives, and people as a species can make a difference in the well-being of the planet - we can reverse climate change, learn to live with respect for each other and be true stewards of this Earth. Most things aren't as overwhelming as they may seem at first glance – the *Meerwald* wasn't rebuilt in a day.

Sail Training at Maine Maritime Academy

By Andy Chase

In this modern age, all maritime schools are spending a great deal of money and time buying and training our students to operate the latest technologies in ship operations and management. Why then would Maine Maritime Academy want to also train them to sail an eighty year old sailing ship?

The answers are many, but first let it be said that we don't require all of our students to sail on our sail training vessel, the 1921 built, wooden, two-masted schooner *Bowdoin*. We require our Small Vessel Operations students (candidates for 200 ton or 500 ton licenses) to do so, and we encourage all others to do so.

The primary reason we encourage all students to take advantage of this training is that we consider it the finest basic training there is for a career at sea. It is training with consequences.

How many mates, standing watch in the enclosed, air conditioned bridge of a container ship or tanker, do you think would be able to answer the question "What direction and strength is the wind at this moment?" without having to look, either out the wheelhouse windows, or worse, at the anemometer? It would be a rare mate on a sailing ship who couldn't tell you immediately, without even glancing at the compass. Most of them could tell you even when they are off watch. And most of them will notice, even when down below having dinner, if the wind shifts by more than a point.

Why? Because such information has consequences on board a sailing ship. It has consequences on board a container ship or a tanker as well, but too many mates are too far removed from their environment to notice such things. A training program on board a sailing ship requires no contrived input from the "trainers" since the environment provides the curriculum. If you simply require the trainees to plan and execute the voyage they will get plenty of training. That is what makes it such a powerful training tool. There need be no lecture on the effects of a wind shift on your planned route. It will be obvious when it occurs, and it will demand a solution immediately. There will be no grade to debate. You will either arrive on time, and without damage, or you will not. It will be quite clear if you have passed the final exam.

The consequence of each and every decision is obvious ... sometimes painfully so. A delayed decision about reefing might be made out of laziness, inattention to the changing conditions or simply out of decision-making paralysis. Regardless of the reason, such a delay may easily require all hands to be called in the middle of the night to tie in a reef (shorten sail) in the midst of a squall, increasing the risk to all. All hands will know who didn't pass that test of seamanship. There are consequences to even the smallest things.

A furled sail incorrectly secured to the spar will find its way out of its lashing in a squall, perhaps causing the loss of the sail. The consequences of that mistake are more than financial. Shipmates on some vessels will have to be put at risk to climb aloft to secure the damaged sail before more harm is done. Then the vessel will have to proceed at reduced speed until a sail repair lesson is completed.

Every aspect of seamanship is revealed in its purest and most demanding form.

Meteorology: You must understand the minutest details of meteorology if you are to take advantage of every slant of wind between departure and arrival. To miss the signs of an approaching storm or squall can have severe consequences.

Marlinspike Seamanship: You will use knots and splices, bends and beckets, deadeyes and lanyards, wire and rope, canvass stitches and patches, and rigging techniques that though old, are still important today. For what is modern cargo gear but a refinement of the old sailing ship rig? It may be nearly unrecognizable now, but the basic principles are exactly the same, and an understanding of the basics will help the mate understand the most modern equipment.

Stability: A sailing ship is a stability model in motion. You see and feel every force. You are engaged in a perpetual inclining experiment. You must constantly monitor the forces of the sails and the seas so as to stay within the safe limits of your dynamic stability curves. While a sailing ship's generous stability may be forgiving, the crew may not be when you cause them to be thrown from their bunks by misreading the approaching wave, or failing to slack a sheet.

Shiphandling: As master of a modern containership, car carrier, or LNG ship you will be carrying more sail area than the largest sailing ship ever built. If you don't understand the effects of wind on a sail you will forever be at a disadvantage when handling your vessel. If, however, you have learned to handle a sailing vessel you will find it intuitive to use the wind as an assisting force whenever possible. Even when not under sail, a sailing ship is a strict teacher of shiphandling, for such vessels are typically underpowered, carry a large amount of windage, and have very delicate projections at each end (bowsprits and boomkins and such).

Cargo Stowage: Given the amount of heel that sailing vessels typically carry when under sail, cargo stowage is arguably more demanding than on any other type of vessel. Imagine being told to stow your cargo for a voyage that will be conducted with an anticipated list of ten degrees, which will alternate every few days from port to starboard. And expect to roll deeply on a regular basis. Your cargo lashings and shoring will be severely tested.

Navigation: Gone is the notion of laying down a trackline in advance and following it for days or weeks on end. Under sail there is no such thing as a rhumb line or a great circle track from departure to destination. Every day is spent going in every direction but the one you desire, hoping to make good,

on average, a track approximately toward your destination. Your navigation is constantly challenged as you carry each tack as close to danger as circumstances and good seamanship permit, in order to take advantage of a good slant of wind.

Merchant Navies of many countries have long recognized the value of a traditional sailing vessel to train men and women to sail on power driven merchant ships. Some of our students will benefit by this training for a merchant marine career. But with all the traditional sailing ships operating in the world today, we are in fact training many of our students to be the mates and masters aboard these sailing vessels. Tall Ships America lists over 200 such vessels in their directory, and all of them need qualified and certified mates and masters. Maine Maritime Academy is the only school in the US where a student can get a college degree, a license, and all the necessary certificates to sail in these positions. We have a number of faculty and staff with extensive experience in this field, and as a result we have assembled a concentration in sail training. This curriculum includes courses dealing with topics such as rigging, sail handling, sailing vessel casualty analysis, and sailing vessel stability.

Forty percent of our incoming mate candidates considered sail training to be a "major" factor in their choice of MMA over other maritime colleges. It is a niche market, and we are proud to be in the lead position in this unique field.

The Doorway Into Personal Excellence

By Ben Rogers

Cosmic certainties are rare in life. When I was 14, I experienced two in a very short span. The first one came soon after I lugged my over-packed duffel bag on board the schooner *Harvey Gamage*. I was struck by the perfect twist of the rope, the strangely familiar tarred and served shrouds and the gentle droop of the ratlines running up and meeting at a point aloft that might as well have been the peak of Everest.

Though all these things are known to me now by name, at the time I recognized them only as faded images from the age of seafaring. Things that existed in an American boy's peripheral vision and lingered at the back of his imagination. But here it was in front of me, in full color and very much in use. I was lined up with the other new trainees and a thick rope was passed down the row. We pulled on it. There was shouting, straining, more shouting, then the job was done and I looked at my palms, appalled at the burning sensation that left my hands frozen halfway between fists and splayed flat.

I looked around again at the hanging ropes – lines, we were corrected – with distinct names and uses. I judged there to be about 5,000 on that schooner, all leading up to the no-man's land aloft where they were connected to mysterious bits of machinery and heavy chunks of wood. I did not recognize it, but I was in the realm of verifiable sacrament, experiencing firsthand a thing that is agreed by all mankind as an unassailable truth: your first time on board a tall ship, you are wholly overwhelmed.

The second moment came shortly after. I can't remember if it was a day, two days or three, but for the first time in my life I found myself out of sight of land, the deck beneath me the closest thing resembling firmament available. It was then I learned that the ocean was bigger and stronger than I could ever imagine myself to be, and there would be no apologies for having my fragility so openly pointed out. Playing on a beach, the sea is less daunting, a backdrop to a vacation, convenient scenery. Surrounded by it, seeing the long slow-rolling swells sent from thousands of miles away, I learned that fear and awe intersect at bona fide humility. Being a 14-year-old, I took this powerful new notion, ignored it, and spent much of the week trying to flirt with girls.

But these revelations are guaranteed to anyone who goes to sea in a ship – the crisis of seeing our own smallness, the eye-crossing learning curve of life on a tall ship – however they are not the final sum of the experience. And they do not come fully formed. They swirl in the back of the green hand's mind like fish fry and often fall victim to some variety of overactive ego. This is the minimum, the starting line, and it is where something truly great can begin. It is the soil from which sailors are conceived.

My first week at sea was an introduction to a life of seamanship, and though I was too distracted to fully appreciate what I was being included in, a seed was planted, and I came away from the week changed. I felt alive, I felt the thrill of leaning over the jibboom and watching the bow surge through the water. I even learned most of the lines.

And I went back, again and again. Summer jobs, birthday money, mowing lawns, begging Mom and Dad, I did whatever I could to go back. I felt something come to life during those weeks I spent in schooners. I could not really explain it, but over time and as I matured I became aware of the satisfaction of being handy on deck, of being confronted with the overwhelming circumstances and doing my best to measure up.

Hard work to overcome adversity is not an uncommon theme in life ashore, but there is an added element in life aboard a ship. The community of a crew is small, and the ties between the members are obvious. Ashore, divisions of political boundaries, geographical distance, family ties or cultural identities separate us from each other.

Of course, personal identities are not simply tossed aside, nor should they be, but they do not divide, as they often do ashore. These types of divisions cannot exist in a ship's crew if it is to be strong. There are divisions of rank, chain of command, but these are based on merit and experience, and everyone in a crew has a job to do. A ship and her crew depend on every sailor to do his or her duty. This is where a crew, as a community, shows its greatest virtue in shaping people to be their best. At times on a ship, the distance afforded by life ashore seem like a luxury, but it can also be a crutch and a burden.

Soren Kierkegaard said, "Whatever is great in the sphere of the universally human must therefore not be communicated as a subject for admiration but as an ethical requirement. In the form of a possibility it becomes a requirement."

This is what a ship requires of her crew as a group, and offers sailors, individually. Green hands and new trainees see the skill and training in the senior deckhands, the mates, the captain. They are real examples of seamanship – seaworthy men and women who do their jobs and do them well – and their examples are meant to be followed. They do not scamper aloft to stow sail in the face of squall simply because they are paid to. They do not do deck wash because God blessed them with an extraordinary knack for scrubbing. They do not fix the toilets because it turns them on. They do it because it simply must be done, because the ship demands it. (Consequently, sailors do not take kindly to the so-called "busy work" that often clogs agendas ashore.)

Sailors are devoted to their ship and devoted to their crew, and they do not want to be admired for that devotion. It is offensive. Sailors are not Olympic long-jumpers, gifted with unnatural ability. A sailor excels because of the frame of mind he or she chooses to maintain at every minute of every day. To stand back and admire that would be ludicrous. Lend a hand! Pitch in! Get in line, and follow the lead. That is the beauty of the heroes at sea. They do not want praise, they do not want sidekicks, they want peers to scurry aloft with them and stow t'gallants – shipmates.

And when you sail in a tall ship, one thing will be communicated over and over: it is your ethical requirement to be a good shipmate. And the deckhands and mates and captains will drive you to meet your requirement. They will teach you, encourage you, correct you, and demonstrate that the level of excellence the ship and the sea demand is possible, as evidenced in them. In that push, you will be welcomed into the fold, because a crew is always accountable to itself and the ship, and is always pushing to improve from within.

This happens naturally aboard a ship, but ashore, it is harder to come by. People who work hard, who persevere, who succeed by their own sweat are elevated by society for the virtue they demonstrate. Society's saints are revered and usually left dusty and alone, or approached only on occasions of convenience. They are pointed to, maybe followed from a safe distance, but they are not emulated, and it is not demanded that they be.

"I can't do that."

"I'm not as good as them."

These thoughts allow us a safe distance from lofty expectations for ourselves. That distance protects us from struggle, from potential failure, the soreness of ambition. Unfortunately, the conversation often stops at this point.

A ship, by nature of the demands put upon sailors, teaches us to say,

"I can't do that, yet."

"I'm not as good as them, yet."

Because sailors must do the jobs we are presented with, we must work astride our shipmates and pull our weight. The whole environment of shipboard life demands this. We are not simply told we are capable of excellence, excellence is the expectation.

But this constant drive toward excellence is more than an individual struggle, it is one that involves the group, the people brought together despite their wide-ranging backgrounds. This is perhaps one of the most beneficial side-effects of seamanship. When a sailor joins a crew, it must be as a sailor first. The ship demands this. National borders, political party lines, religious faith, dietary preferences, country music collections, all of these add to the flavor of a crew but they are no longer boundaries between us. For sailors, the boundary that matters most is the ship's rail.

In my time at sea, I have seen crews unite across gulfs that, ashore, have violently divided us for centuries. We united as shipmates, a glue that sets quickly. The divisions we had inherited – white or black, Christian or Muslim, Israeli or Palestinian, Republican or Democrat – were no longer such catastrophic differences as they were made out to be ashore. What mattered more was working together, looking out for each other, finding common ground with the people to whom we had entrusted our lives and who had entrusted their lives to us. Diversity makes a crew stronger, but divisions are crippling. As shipmates, we are in it together, at sea or ashore. Sailors know this.

We begin to see that much of shipboard life is really the most sensible way to live in any setting. Devotion to the job and to shipmates, perseverance, heartiness and resourcefulness are qualities that mankind values inherently. They are not qualities unique to a sailor, but a sailor is accustomed to living in daily awareness of the keen immediacy of these qualities, and they are qualities that, once instilled, are hard to undo.

It is this doorway into personal excellence that life at sea in a tall ship offers an individual, and it is what tall ships offer to everyone, ashore or afloat.

An Adventure Unlike Anything Else

By Samara Haver

I first found tall ship sailing because I craved adventure. As a junior in college I decided that I wanted to study abroad in an environment that pushed me outside the mental and physical boundaries of campus life in Colorado. My search led me to the Sea Education Association (SEA) and I found exactly what I was looking for aboard the S.S.V. *Corwith Cramer*. Unbeknownst to me, however, my first tall ship would certainly not be my only tall ship.

Fast-forward a year and a half. It is June, just over a month after my college graduation. I am wandering through the Toronto airport having followed my heart back to tall ships as an TALL SHIPS CHALLENGE® summer intern.

Loaded down with luggage and unable to use my cell phone internationally, I am relived to find Becca, another summer intern, climb onto the downtown shuttle and into the seat next to me only minutes after I boarded. We made small talk on the ride, sharing predictions about the summer and our mutual excitement to go sailing again. Looking back three months later it is hard to believe how fast our summer, rich in travel and experience, came and went.

Two months, four ships, and six festivals later I left Chicago, the final port of the Great Lakes United TALL SHIPS CHALLENGE® 2010, aboard the square topsail schooner *Lynx*. At the conclusion of my internship I was not ready to say goodbye to tall ship sailing, so I elected to stay on as a deckhand. Like my shipmates, I was hooked on living the independent and adventurous life of a sailor. It isn't an easy job by any means, the hours are long and the work is hard. With barely any personal space we spend weeks, months, even years away from our life on land braving dangerous, dirty, and unfavorable conditions. It seems almost comical why anyone would want to subject him or herself to it, but the rewards of our job – adventure, exploration, and teaching – far outweigh everything else.

In port, many ships open their decks for the public to come feel what it is like to be onboard. A deck tour is, of course, a far cry from the experience of being underway, but that is not why we open our home to the curious. We get to share our infectious passion for tall ship sailing. People who choose to work onboard tall ships do so because they love it, and as a result the community that develops from sailing together is, in a way, a sort of family.

I remember when I joined the crew of the *Europa,* my first ship of the summer. I felt so ordinary and inexperienced in the company of my shipmates who had stories of sailing all around the world. It had been more than a year since I'd stepped foot on a tall ship, but the permanent crew were patient, helping me re-master skills and learn my way around. On one of my first nights I was assigned to help out with my watch's duty to bake fresh bread for the next day. Holed up in the small galley, in the middle of the night, my shipmate and I listened to our favorite songs, baked eight loaves of fresh bread, and shared stories of tall ship sailing. My two weeks onboard flew by and when it was time for me to leave, I was sad to leave the ship and crew who became my home and family.

The relationships I have developed while sailing tall ships are some of my most valued. Living in close quarters and working towards a common goal brings out the best in people, and I have seen many otherwise unlikely friendships develop among shipmates. In the middle of the ocean (or a lake) we form a different kind of household. It isn't perfect. For example, having only 12 sq. ft. of personal closet/bed/storage space gives a new meaning to "within-reach," but it is home. On a tall ship I am part of an interdependent group. Separated from the distractions and responsibilities of life on land, I am able to learn about my abilities and myself in a unique and valuable way.

Among tall ship sailors there is a saying - hurry up, and wait. Its application is nearly universal to life onboard, and even routine practices do not break from its rule. There are busy times, the "hurry up," in which we rush to change the sail plan, haul back the anchor, or practice safety drills. Then there is the calm, the "wait." In contrast to the excitement of a frenzied rush to climb aloft and furl the fore tops'l in biting rain and storm winds, the in-between, when the sail plan doesn't change for a day or we standby the anchor windlass at dawn waiting for the wind to shift, can seem boring. This summer I began my internship with the same "hurry up" intensity that propelled me through my last semester of college. My senior year was a never-ending frenzy of responsibilities, devoid of any "wait." Before I fully realized it graduation had come and gone and for the first time in nearly two decades I was no longer a student. I arrived in Toronto to begin my internship proud of my alumni status, but it was not until I was away from the festivals in the middle of Lakes Ontario, Erie, Huron, Michigan, and Superior, sometimes out of sight of land and disconnected from everything except my intimate boat family, the beautiful ship I called home, and our journey together, that I was finally able to slow down and appreciate how far I had come.

Sailing the Great Lakes on the *Europa*, the *Denis Sullivan*, the *Roald Amundsen*, and the *Lynx*, I improved my skills as a sailor, pushed beyond what I believed to be the limit of my physical abilities, and re-discovered the transformative value of relationships among shipmates that I first found through SEA. I am a more confident, able, and aware person now than I was in June when I arrived in Toronto.

The most valuable part of sail training is not learning the technical details of how to sail tall ships, it is learning from that process. Above all sail training teaches stewardship – for others, the environment, and oneself. This summer I spoke to thousands of people about my experiences sailing on tall ships, urging each of them to try it themselves. To visit a tall ship in port, to walk around the deck and speak to the people who work aboard is inspiring, but to actually go sailing is an extraordinary adventure unlike anything else.

The Life and Legacy of Captain and Mrs. Arthur Kimberly and the Brigantine *Romance*

By Deirdre O'Regan, Captain Daniel D. Moreland, and Captain Bert Rogers

Captain Arthur Kimberly passed away on 17 September 2011. Gloria Kimberly passed away in 2006. Captain Kimberly received the Lifetime Achievement Award of the American Sail Training Association in 1996. Captain Kimberly, Gloria Kimberly, and the brigantine *Romance* were awarded the Karl Kortum American Ship Trust award in 2008 by the National Maritime Historical Society.

This article is excerpted from a two-part series originally published by the National Maritime Historical Society in 2008 in Sea History Magazine issues #123 and #124, and reprinted here with permission. We wish to thank NMHS and Sea History Editor Deirdre O'Regan for their support and cooperation in reprinting this article.

It began with a pony ride in Boston Garden. As a grammar school student in Worcester, Massachusetts, "Zeke" Kimberly entered a contest and won a pony. After his victory lap in the saddle during the rodeo at the Garden, his pediatrician father had him hand back the reins of the animal and accept a check instead. With the money, they purchased a small catboat, which the lad started sailing on a nearby lake in Webster, MA.

One summer between high school semesters, he shipped aboard an old Maine coaster, the *George Gress*. He developed an affection for this ship (as he did for just about every ship he sailed in), despite the grasses growing in the foc's'le— she was wrecked the day after he disembarked. In 1939, he joined a club in Boston that gave him many opportunities to crew on some fine yachts during summer breaks, including the 72-ft. schooner yacht *Nordlys* with Chester Bowles, making coastal passages between New York, Boston, and Maine. Yachts were fast and beautiful, but Arthur Kimberly preferred working ships.

During the 1920s and 30s, while he was growing up in Massachusetts, the last of the square-riggers were disappearing from the seas. One of the last to carry cargo under square rig often called at Boston, the Swedish four-masted barque, *Abraham Rydberg*, and Kimberly was there to see her each time she cleared in. From the pier he memorized every line in her rigging; at home, he learned their names in Swedish. He tried repeatedly to get a berth aboard and was turned away just as often. But finally, one night in 1941, just before she was to sail for Brazil, he got word that a berth was available. The next morning tide carried the 2,345-ton ship to sea, this time with a nineteen-year old Arthur Kimberly scampering aloft to loose the topsails. Shipping aboard this hold-out from another age would be a defining moment in his life.

The merchant marine was losing thousands of tons—and men—in the spring of 1942 to German U-boats and was desperately in need of ships' officers. Experienced mariners could apply for the accelerated program at the US Merchant Marine Academy. Kimberly received his commission with the first graduating class at Kings Point. He spent the war as an officer on oil tankers—one of the most hazardous jobs in the already dangerous wartime merchant marine.

As soon as the war ended, Kimberly went back to sailing vessels. He found his first berth on the three-masted schooner *Guinevere*. She was a steel schooner that had been used in anti-sub patrol service during the war but was put back into service as a trading vessel, sailing to the Mediterranean carrying sugar and a little contraband (mostly cigarettes). Arthur Kimberly, as usual, was very fond of the ship. But he had no stomach for smuggling. He signed off in the Mediterranean. Over the next several years, he shipped aboard T-2 tankers as an officer and sailed all over the globe.

In 1956, seeking to learn everything he could about ships and the business of shipping, he took a year off from sailing to learn about the boatbuilding

business and spent another year working in Ted Hood's sail loft in Marblehead, Massachusetts—back when Ted Hood worked in the loft himself.

Now a master mariner, licensed to ship as master in both steam and sail, Kimberly embarked on a voyage that would take him to sea, sailing what he considered the perfect rig, a brigantine. In January 1960, he signed aboard the brigantine *Yankee*, made famous by Irving and Exy Johnson, under its new owner Reed Whitney. This ship would have lasting ramifications in Arthur Kimberly's life. The concept of the world voyage with paying crew or trainees would prove a useful model when he eventually got a ship of his own. The sail configuration for this sort of passage-making was ideal. A brigantine would allow a relatively small crew the opportunity to cruise under square rig, just right for following the trade winds and for mastering the seamanship required to maintain and operate them.

It was aboard *Yankee* in May of 1961, during one of her bread-and-butter Caribbean cruises, that her new master met his soul mate and soon-to-be permanent shipmate, Gloria Cloutier. A photographer from Detroit, Ms. Cloutier took a short vacation sailing aboard *Yankee*. Not long afterwards, she was back aboard for a round-the-world voyage. By Tahiti, they were married.

The Kimberlys (known to those who sailed with them as "Skipper" and "Mrs. K"), stayed at sea aboard sailing vessels for the next three decades. In time, they acquired their own ship, the brigantine *Romance*—a ship with its own interesting history. Movie studio MGM had hired Alan Villiers to purchase, re-rig, and sail the little ship from Denmark to Hawaii to use in the epic movie "Hawaii." After the film wrapped, the producers had no more use for it and were looking to unload it "cheap." The Kimberlys took it off their hands in 1966. They gave her the name *Romance*, partly from their love of the sea and partly hearkening back to a clipper ship, *Romance of the Seas.*

From 1966 to 1989, the Kimberlys sailed their beloved, beautiful, salty, and seaworthy brigantine with young men and women for crew—some paid, some paying. They sailed on many trips to the Galapagos and the South Pacific, two epic voyages around the world and countless eight-day trips in the Virgin Islands and the Lesser Antilles. No GPS, no Loran, no RDF, no Radar, no single side-band radio, no program directors, no office ashore—just their ship, a sextant, a lead-line, Skipper's knowledge, Mrs. K's dedication, and a whole lot of will power.

Romance was Skipper and Mrs. K's ship, their home, their passion, their mission in life. Skipper's "marineros," what they called their *Romance* crew, were the prime beneficiaries of their dedication and commitment to ships and the sea. John Masefield once said that "we will not see such ships again." He was right, but he should have added that we will not see such seamen as well. The offshore voyages were as good as it gets for blue-water seafaring. Weeks and weeks of uninterrupted passages gave fortunate *Romance* sailors the opportunity to feel the satisfying rhythm of standing watch. To sail on *Romance* was to be prepared to roll out at—or before—"all hands" was called; to grow to understand the benefits of a daily fare of hard work for the ship between-watch. There was always work to do: sewing sails, maintaining the rig, endless paint and soogee, and as always, fixing what was broken with materials at hand. A deep-sea voyage in *Romance* was a direct connection to seafaring life as it is so often described, but so seldom experienced.

In *Romance*, marinero "self improvement" was always self-directed and self-motivated. There was no curriculum, no reading list. Skipper's formal lessons were reserved for training his crew for the job at hand: wire splicing and seizing when part of the standing rig needed to be renewed; sailmaking when a new sail was ready for second layout; caulking and ship's carpentry when the ship was hauled for maintenance. Studying celestial navigation, meteorology, fancy work, ship lore, and maintaining one's kit filled the quiet hours between watch and sleep. A new crewman was ill advised to brandish a sextant for stars or meridian passage until he or she had first shown that he knew the way of the ship. Once that threshold was passed, though, Skipper became a great resource for advanced knowledge. To be asked by Skipper to take a noon sight for the ship was a de facto, if unofficial, rite of passage.

Romance's ocean passages were great for their distance, deep water, and long-term exposure to seafaring life, but the shorter trips in the Caribbean taught her crew just as much, and in some ways more. While on a trade-wind passage under stuns'ls across the South Pacific, the crew might not touch the braces for days at a time. Sailing amongst the close islands of the Virgins with a much reduced crew, however, was an intensified experience in sail- and ship-handling. In the Virgin Islands, three or four crewmembers would wake up to the sound of the galley water-pump, wash down the decks, scarf breakfast (which Skipper made while listening to VI radio), loose sail, heave up the anchor, set sail, tack up Sir Francis Drake Channel, sail in close-hauled to the Bitter End (Virgin Gorda, BVI), sail out again the next day, end up at Foxy's (Jost Van Dyke), run boats all night after helping out as stand-in bartender while Foxy played his Calypso, heave up the anchor again, paint, tar, varnish, set sail again, tack and wear, furl sails late in the evening and do it all again in the morning.

The Caribbean seasons were *Romance's* bread-and-butter, but the lure of the world voyages was always strong with the Kimberlys. *Romance's* two circumnavigations and subsequent voyages to the South Pacific provided long deep-sea passages, often under stuns'ls, following the explorers, whale ships, and South Seas traders of the age of sail to Grenada, San Blas, Panama, Galapagos, Pitcairn, the Marquesas, the Tuamotus, Tahiti, Huahine, Raiatea, Bora Bora, Rarotonga, Palmerston, Samoa, the Tokelaus, Fiji, New Hebrides, the Solomons, Borneo, Singapore, Java, Bali, Cocos Keeling, the Seychelles, the Commoroes, Durban and Cape Town, Rio de Janeiro, Fernando de Noronha and more.

The places *Romance* sailed were awesome, but the ship herself was the thing. The ship came first, and that was deepest lesson to learn. That, and the commitment to the "properly way"—the way that Skipper taught, lived, and sailed the world—the way of the ship.

Skipper and Mrs. K sold *Romance* in 1989. Sadly, she was lost in 1995, after almost sixty years of remarkable service. The stout Danish trader and world voyager had her back broken beyond repair in a devastating hurricane while close to the end of a complete rebuild at West End, Tortola. The damage was extensive; there was no reasonable choice but to give her up. Then, as she was

being towed out to sea, she got away from her tug and now rests in the waters off the British Virgin Islands, but we do not know exactly where.

In *Romance*, hundreds of young men and women experienced the rare opportunity to serve under a true master of square rig. The legacy of Skipper, Mrs. K, and the brigantine *Romance* is carried on in the contemporary world of tall ships and sail training. Many of the marineros of *Romance* have gone on to command their own ships and to found sail training organizations. Some work as sailmakers, riggers, and shipwrights; others as teachers, writers, and marine environmentalists. *Romance* marineros and even her marinero "descendents" are at the heart of some of today's most active sail-training organizations, including the barque *Picton Castle*; the brig *Niagara*; the schooner *A. J. Meerwald;* the schooners of the Ocean Classroom Foundation, *Harvey Gamage*, *Spirit of Massachusetts*, and *Westward*; the former American Sail Training Association (now Tall Ships America), and Sea History magazine—just to name a few examples. The marineros have taken the lessons from *Romance* and expressed them again to their own crews and colleagues, maintaining the unbroken commitment to seamanship and the properly way that is the core of the *Romance* legacy.

The following excerpt from Gloria Kimberly's memoir (unpublished), perhaps sums up the mission and the meaning of *Romance* best:

"For decades, there were no sailing square-riggers in the world, save only Irving Johnson's famous Brigantine *Yankee*, now gone, and the sail training ships open only to naval and merchant cadets.

An era was done. All that remained were the legends and pictures. Few men would ever again stand spread-legged on a wooden deck and look up into that maze of wire rope, hemp, and soaring spars, to wind-swollen canvas overhead. Few would hear again the windsong in the high rigging, or smell the clean tang of spray, oakum, and tar. Surely we need sailing ships today, as much as we ever did. It is far too good a life to be lost forever. It tests the mettle of a man's soul, yet rewards him with freedom, peace, and beauty, which those who are bound to the land will never know. There is a further need for square rig today, a chance for a young man or young woman to go to sea. Even a small ship will do, as long as she is the real thing, and sailed by a seaman."

Such a ship was the brigantine *Romance*. Such a seaman was Arthur Kimberly. And such a soul was Mrs. K.

Photo credits:

From the personal collection of Arthur Kimberly
Pg. 92 - Captain and Mrs. Kimberly aboard the brigantine *Romance*
Pg. 94 - Wedding day aboard the *Yankee*
Pg. 97 - Brigantine *Romance*

Courtesy of Mike Dodge
Pgs. 98 - 99 - Aboard the brigantine *Romance*

All photos provided courtesy of National Maritime Historical Society:Sea History Magazine

The Epic Adventure

By James Abrams - Henry H. Anderson Jr. Sail Training Scholarship Recipient

As I walked down a hill, past seventeen other teenagers going in the opposite direction, I said to these strangers, "I think I'm going the wrong way, guys." Some of them laughed. Awkwardness surrounded us. We were the first eighteen students to arrive on the SEA campus grounds. We didn't know how to say hello, or at least I didn't. Then someone suggested that we play Ninja. The game involves quick reflexes, agility, and is also really fun and silly. We played for at least fifteen minutes, but in that time, we welcomed more students who were just arriving. We looked ridiculous in front of each other and, by the time orientation began, the awkwardness was gone and I had made twenty-three new friends.

These weren't just friends, though. They were intelligent, witty, talented people with so much to offer me. I grew to love all of them. We became comfortable with each other fast. I was never afraid to ask a stupid question in class which helped me get the most out of my academic experience. I learned a lot from my classes and homework assignments. If I didn't understand something, I had twenty-three other people willing to help. We also had three residential advisors and three stellar professors ready to help at any time.

In class, we were taught about marine life, the bathymetry of the ocean, and how to navigate a ship on the sea. We learned about man's personal connection with the ocean. We examined this relationship by reading essays and short stories, like the *Catching of the Cod*, and the first chapter of *Moby Dick*.

When we all got aboard the *Corwith Cramer,* I was psyched. Ready to take on the world from this tiny sailing vessel! As our voyage began, the ship began to feel even smaller. We were cooped up in tiny bunks where we kept all of our stuff and ourselves. We had very tight watch schedules with a proportion of six hours of work to five hours of sleep, which was sometimes only achieved by skipping meals. Yet, even with all of these hardships, we stayed a family. In fact, we became a stronger one because now we really had to depend on each other. This made us truly open our eyes and accept each other.

Life on the boat itself was an amazing experience. We lowered scientific instruments into the ocean and pulled up awesome sea creatures like shrimp, magalobs, puffer fish, salps and copepods. I did a science report on the diversity of phytoplankton along the course we traveled. In a 100-count comparison, Dinoflagellate phytoplankton were found in a larger population closer to the coast than Diatom phytoplankton. This is because Dinoflagellates like to feed off run-off nutrients from land and prefer more turbulent waters than Diatoms, which prefer more open waters. I thought this was an interesting thing to notice from our data.

My seasickness passed after one day and after that the *Corwith Cramer's* movement didn't bother me. Below deck, it was like we were back at the SEA campus. We moved about doing homework and socializing, oblivious to the fact that we were on a boat one hundred and fifty miles off the coastline. I could eat, ignoring the gimbaled tables that went up and down, and then go to bed. But, if someone called me, I would climb the ladder to the deck and leave the lab or doghouse (chart room) to find that I was on a 100-foot by 20-foot brigantine sailing vessel surrounded by water everywhere I looked.

White caps of froth erupted from the sea and knocked against the side of the *Corwith Cramer* dispersing bubbles in every direction. Fog crept in, surrounding the boat, and limited all visual bearings. As lookout, my job of spotting buoys and lobster traps became that much more serious. The sun appeared but the fog would remain. The sun turned orange as it set, turning the sky around it into a rainbow. Dolphins swam by at night, disturbing the waters and causing bioluminescent bacteria to glow. Sometimes the stars shone very clearly, with no disturbances. Mars glowed bright red.

About James Abrams
Tall Ships America©
2011 Henry H. Anderson Jr.
Sail Training Scholarship
Recipient

My name is James Abrams. I am going on fifteen years old and my friends call me Jamie. I am currently a freshman at Burr and Burton Academy in Manchester, Vermont. I lived in New York City for the first eleven years of my life and my best memories from there were when my family and I visited museums and the New York Aquarium at Coney Island. I draw all of the time and I love to sculpt and paint. I enjoy writing, creating my own stories and characters, and playing the piano. I enjoy ancient history, music and Shakespeare, but science is my real passion. As long as I can remember, I have enjoyed aquatic ecosystems, from streams and ponds to the vast blue ocean.

When I was six, I decided I was going to be a marine biologist. Now, I consider it a serious pursuit. I find the most enjoyment being around and learning about sea life. Coral reefs especially fascinate me. I like finding the answers to, "Why?" Why is the earth round? Why did we evolve? Why did sharks never really evolve? I view the ocean as an answer to many of my questions. All life came from water. All life needs water. Water makes up 70% of our planets surface. Water is important. I want to have as much knowledge in the field of marine biology as I can before applying to a college, including real-life, practical familiarity with the sea itself.

My favorite watch was the twilight watch which started at 7 PM and ended at 11 PM. It was the best watch to have because you worked during the last hours of daylight and watched the sun set. After that the watch was the same as any of the other watches which usually consisted of either working in the lab or setting and striking sails until you got off duty. When the twilight watch was over you were able to sleep a full seven hours, as opposed to any other watch where you would be lucky to get five hours of rest. Sleep was very important on the boat.

I steered the boat! It's the coolest thing - knowing that you are in control of the ship. It requires constant vigilance to make sure that you stay on the proper heading. You have to keep your eyes on the compass at all times. I also learned all of the lines and their functions with the proper sail.

To see and experience these kinds of things as a teenager is really great. Being on a boat for eight days really puts things in perspective by reminding you how insignificant you are, yet at the same time that you are ever so important in the world. You can hear about this amazing experience. You can see pictures and say, "Wow, that's really cool," but you can never really fully understand what it feels like until you're there, saying to yourself, "Where did the land go?"

My experience at SEA deepened my passion for sea life and made me really want to become a marine biologist, but for me the best part of my SEA experience are the friends that I made and will never forget. I learned so much from my friends, teachers and crew. I think that everyone should have the same chance to experience something so amazing!

Jibe Ho: How Sailing Changed My Self Perspective

By Heidi Stinson - Henry H. Anderson Jr. Sail Training Scholarship Recipient

When summer camps are mentioned, one thinks of campfires and friendship bracelets, not scientists and sea captains, but that is what my summer camp involved. One of the most influential experiences of my life was attending a marine biology and sailing camp this summer, sponsored by Sea Education Association (SEA).

When I first found the camp website, I was unsure how my family could afford the camp. I wasn't interested in marine biology as a career, but as I looked into the camp more, it seemed like a once in a lifetime opportunity. Scholarships were available, so I decided to apply.

I was accepted and received scholarships from both SEA and Tall Ships America.

I was slightly anxious when I received the liability forms: Can you function under stress? Can you perform demanding tasks while sleep-deprived? These were some of the questions on the release forms. I was worried. What was this camp going to be like? The class list showed that almost all of the students attended private schools in exclusive areas. Would I even fit in?

I needn't have worried. Although I come from different circumstances, I fit in with the other students well. We all shared a passion for learning. The camp was divided into two portions: ten days on land and ten days at sea on a sailing ship crewed by the campers. This camp wasn't for "slackers or sissies". I fit in wonderfully.

During our time on land we had three lectures, two labs and one field activity each day. We had four hours of free time and then a two-hour study hall. We felt overwhelmed trying to keep up with the demands of two college level classes. Our free time and study halls were spent working. Every morning we awoke feeling as if we had two hours of sleep rather than seven - and we all wondered what would happen on the ship. We knew that we might have as little as two hours of sleep for every 24 hours of wakefulness, and this seemed impossible.

The first day on the ship I was terrified. I was sure I would fail somehow - and when one is steering a ship, or standing watch, an error affects not just oneself but the entire crew.

Thankfully, I did fine. After the first 24 hours of sleep-deprived misery, my body and brain learned a new biorhythm. Four hours of sleep seemed enough. I felt fine. I realized at one point that in 48 hours, I'd had less than five hours of sleep and I was still functioning coherently and working well.

I loved life at sea and I learned as much as I possibly could about sailing. My watch was assigned the first mate, a wonderful woman who made sure that each of us got as much out of the experience as we could. I learned to tack and jibe

and even got to have the con for one practice maneuver. I spent hours in the lab titrating oxygen or "winkling". I learned how to set and strike sails all by myself.

The ten days I spent on the ship were some of the most formative days of my life. I came to understand the true meaning of teamwork - that when I fail to show up for my watch on time or neglect to complete an engine room check - I am not just failing myself but every other person on the ship.

This experience helped me to understand the aspect of teamwork that demands that I be the best person I can be all the time, even when I feel totally incapable of it. I realized that while working with teammates, I always have to be aware that completing my job is up to me and me alone.

About Heidi Stinson
Tall Ships America®
2010 Henry H. Anderson Jr.
Sail Training Scholarship
Recipient

My name is Heidi Elizabeth Stinson. I am 17 years old. I live in a rural town in western Colorado. All of my life I have camped, hiked, backpacked and otherwise enjoyed the mountains and canyons of Colorado, Utah and New Mexico. Each year my family camps and goes on river trips. I would like to get to know the ocean as well as I do the deserts of Colorado.

I am an active member of my community. I volunteer in the local food bank, my church and other community events. I am enrolled in several college credit and advanced level classes and I am ranked first in my class as well as being an honor roll student. I am a member of the Colorado All-State Academic First Team, an active member of my high school track, cross country and swim teams and I am the captain of the cross-country team.

I have been homeschooled for most of my life and have a strong sense of self and am very motivated. I can identify what I want and take the steps necessary to achieve it. I never back off from a chore, no matter how tedious or menial, until the job is done.

I enjoy science and am excited to learn sailing, which would be a new skill for me. I enjoy the outdoors and have always wanted to learn how to sail.

Thaddeus J. Koza
1940 - 2010

A native Rhode Islander, Thad Koza photographed tall ships for over three decades.

He was a graduate of the University of Michigan at Ann Arbor completing his BA in English Honors (1963) and held a MA in English from Northwestern University (1965).

Thad began his professional life as a college English teacher at the University of Missouri in Columbia, MO. But days spent in classrooms and libraries proved to be too passive a life for this lover of travel and the outdoors. Photography and travel were his passion, and in his thirties, he began taking pictures of sailing ships. Soon his photographs were being published in leading tall ships journals.

His photographic credits include the *New York Times*, the *Boston Globe*, *Op Sail '92*, *Eurosail '93*, *Sail Toronto '94*, *Windjammer* and *Discovery Magazine* of Cathay Pacific Airlines, as well as postage stamps issued by Ireland and Chile. His articles and essays have been published in *Cruising World*, *Sea History*, *Classic Boat*, and *Traditional Boats & Tall Ships*. He was the official photographer for the American Sail Training Association (now Tall Ships America) for over twenty years and his work was regularly featured in *Sail Tall Ships! A Directory of Sail Training and Adventure At Sea*.

Thad's most engaging project was the completion of the manuscript text and photograph selection of a book on 151 tall ships, *Tall Ships: An International Guide* first published in 1997 and now in its fifth edition.

Thad's annual calendars and several books established him as one of the leading authorities on tall ships. He traveled the world on such sailing vessels as *Pogoria*, *Zawisza Czarny*, *Dar Mlodziezy*, *Libertad*, *Christian Radich*, *Alexandria*, *Tole Mour*, *Bill of Rights*, *Concordia*, *Mir*, and the *Stad Amsterdam* to name a few, as well as photographing and lecturing on the cruise ships *QE2*, *Crystal Symphony*, *Crystal Serenity* and *Silver Cloud*.

Everywhere he traveled he had friends who remember his charm, his wit, his smile, and his fast walk. He was a man of refined taste in literature, art, music and culinary pleasures and a friend to many people around the globe and of all walks of life, treating everyone with honor and dignity. He never failed to share his experience, strength and hope with all those who became a part of his world and he will be deeply missed by all those who knew him.

In His Own Words:
"Just Plain Luck?" A Professional's Perspective

By Thad Koza

I am often asked by audiences and individuals, "How did you get that shot?" My usual reply is the clichéd response, "Location, location, location." But location is only the beginning of the tale. Another relevant factor is just plain luck. Too often the photographs you see are not as interesting as those not seen.

Take the time I was swamped in an open motor boat, having just shot exciting shots of the *Pride of Baltimore II* and *Highlander Sea*, in a pitched sailing duel at the Great Chesapeake Bay Schooner Race, and lost all of the film. I am not sure that Captain Thomas has accepted my apologies yet.

A photograph of the schooner *Bill of Rights* was easy - after three or four days of waiting for a wind shift to the SW to return the *Bill* from a routine cruise to Block Island. In the mid-70s the *Bill of Rights* had no auxiliary engine and photographers and guests were subject to the whims of nature. Not only had I waited days for her return, but I had also enjoyed the lag time aboard her on a Block Island run when northerly winds delayed her return to Narragansett Bay for 36 or 48 hours.

Cooperation with the vessels and their captains is also essential to a successful shoot. One needs the right sails set and the correct side of the vessel in the sun to get a successful shot. I can think of two instances of photographs where the captains and their ships were essential to the success of the finished product.

The shot of *Stad Amsterdam* and the skyline of lower Manhattan is an example. *Stad Amsterdam* made a visit to New York in May 2001. After an afternoon on board with Captain Robin Snouck-Hurgronje and Cess Rosman, we were unable to identify a vessel to utilize as a chase boat on *Stad's* departure. There was no way a dinghy would work since the *Stad* would set and depart with full sails.

As the afternoon waned, I spoke with Captain Robin and indicated that one way I could get a shot would be to board the Staten Island Ferry for a round-trip, and coordinate the passing with him. It would be a one shot deal, but we might get something interesting. I told him if he left the dock at the 5 PM departure time, I would ride the 5:30 PM ferry back to Manhattan, and we would have one pass. He would have to navigate to the eastern end of the harbor, toward Governor's Island, and away from the Statue of Liberty to get the shot. If he and the *Stad* went by the Lady in the harbor, I would be directing the camera into the setting sun, and the exposure would be fouled. Captain Robin agreed and voila!, the shot of *Stad Amsterdam* with the twin towers of the World Trade Center in the background was created.

Another choice opportunity came aboard the *Crystal Symphony*. I was on the bridge, giving commentary on the start of a tall ships race off Lerwick, Shetland Islands. As the fleet started and dispersed over the line, Captain Reidulf Maalen asked me which vessel I was trying to get a shot of. I replied that I needed a shot of *Christian Radich* under sail. She was out in the middle of the fleet with all sails set. Captain Maalen then put the 990-foot *Crystal Symphony* into a 180 degree turn and came up so close on the *Christian Radich* that I could not get the full ship into my 50mm lens. He had to back off, and I succeeded in getting the shot

of the *Christian Radich* under full sail. I asked the captain why he had pulled off that maneuver and he said simply, "Forty years ago, at the age of 17, I received my first sail training aboard *Christian Radich*. I wanted you to get a nice shot of her."

There is a tale with every photograph. Sometimes, one is not so lucky. At the launch of the *Robert C. Seamans*, I was aboard a restored tugboat that was moving about lower Puget Sound to take photographs of the new brigantine on her launch day. On board was ASTA board member, Chuck Fowler, who had arranged the platform for photographing the *Seamans*. The *Joe*, a 1942 tug built by Foss Boats of Tacoma, was brought into the service. At the helm was Rob Paterson, president of the International Retired Tugboat Association. After a couple of hours of taking shots of the *Seamans* we headed back to the Port of Tacoma when I suddenly had an opportunity for an interesting shot of *Seamans* as she came upon us dead to stern. As we approached I asked the tug captain, Rob Paterson, for a "head-on" bow shot as the *Seamans* bore down on us. As I stabilized and focused the shot I became aware of something above me. I looked up and saw that we were under the bowsprit of the *Seamans*. More unnerving was the fact that the tugboat captain was standing next to me enjoying the view - with no one at the helm! Luckily he reacted quickly when he realized we were less than ten feet from the bow stem and about to be run over.

Finally, there is the series of dramatic shots of the *Dar Mlodziezy* at the start of the tall ships race off of Bergen, Norway in 2001. All the vessels were ready for a full out spring to Ebsjerg, Denmark. At the starting line, the *Dar's* well-disciplined crew set all of her sails quickly. A sharp gust of wind and a cross-current led to a difficult position for the *Dar* as she began to heel with the wind shift. I was on the starboard side and witnessed the *Dar* in her heel, exposing most of her keel. It

was a dramatic moment. As the *Crystal Symphony* passed under her stern, I was able to get a shot of her with rails in the water, a 45-degree heel on her port side. I later asked the purser on board the *Dar,* Michal, how many dishes were lost from the ungimbaled shelves. He responded cryptically, "I'm not allowed to say."

Photo by Thad Koza

Photo by Thad Koza

Photo by Thad Koza

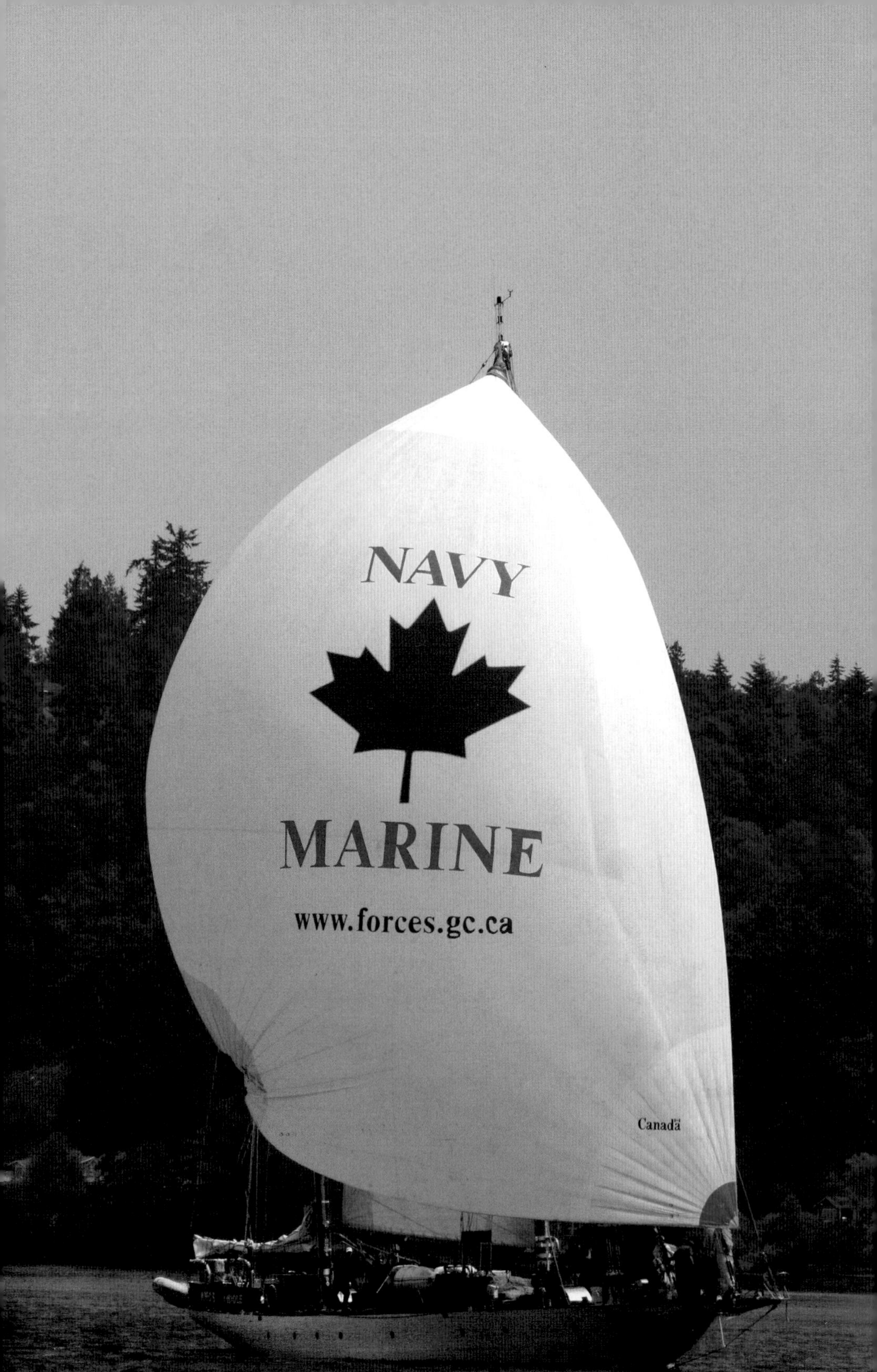
NAVY
MARINE
www.forces.gc.ca
Canada
Photo by Thad Koza

Photo by Thad Koza

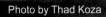
Photo by Thad Koza

Photo by Thad Koza

Photo by Thad Koza

About Sail Training

Adventure and Education Under Sail!®

Take Responsibility For Your Adventure!

One of the most important products of sail training is the development of a sense of judgment about what and whom you can rely on, and to what degree. This applies to: the compass, the weather forecast, your shipmates, the depths on the chart, the strength of the anchor cable, the vigilance of the lookout on the other ship, and many other things. Sail training also builds a reasoned sense of self-reliance. All of this starts from the moment you begin to think about a voyage. Use the information in this Directory to begin to evaluate and decide what might be the best sail training experience for you.

Recognize who you are dealing with and what is included. When you book a sail training trip, you are dealing with the vessel owner or its representatives— Tall Ships America is not involved. You must evaluate whether the financial and business arrangements make sense for you. If there is connecting travel involved, for example, find out if you must make the arrangements, or if it is somehow tied into those you make with the vessel. What happens if you miss your ship because your plane is delayed, or vice versa? Do you need trip insurance? Have you confirmed with the vessel owner any possible customs or immigration issues? Will you need a passport or a pre-purchased air ticket? You must seek out the answers to these questions.

Make informed, responsible decisions about risk and safety, level of challenge, physical suitability and other important issues. One of the important reasons to embark on a sail training trip is to engage the world in a different, stimulating, and challenging way—if you want to stay warm and dry, you should stay at home by the fireplace. Much of the point is to come face-to-face with the elements. At the very least, this probably means that you will find yourself wet, chilled, or tired at some point in a challenging voyage. But everyone's threshold for this is different, and you need to find out what you are likely to be experiencing in order to find out if it is well matched for you.

Since the beginning of time, going to sea has been recognized as carrying an element of risk. These days, we more commonly think about risk in connection with highway travel or aviation, but the idea is the same: you get a pre-flight safety brief on an airliner, you get a lifeboat drill on a cruise ship. Part of the value of sail training is addressing these issues head on. You need to decide whether you are comfortable with the combination of risks and safety measures connected with your proposed sail training trip.

For example, will you be able to go aloft? Will trips in smaller craft be involved? Will you be expected to stand watch at night? Do the demands of the ship match your physical and health capabilities? Are you on medication that will (or may) become necessary during the voyage, or do you have a condition (for example, hemophilia or epilepsy) that may require special access to medical attention; if so, is the vessel operator aware of this? Will you be able to get up and down the ladders, in and out of your berth, and along a heeled-over deck? If there is an emergency, will you be needed to handle safety equipment or to help operate the vessel?

Remember that sail training is often not intended to be like a vacation. Some vessels, on the other hand, may offer leisurely voyages, where very little will be asked of you. You should arrive at a clear understanding of these issues prior to setting sail.

In short, you must satisfy yourself that the trip you are looking into is the right thing for you to do, considering safety, risk, suitability, challenge, comfort, convenience, educational value, cost, and any other factors you consider important.

> In short, you must satisfy yourself that the trip you are looking into is the right thing for you to do, considering safety, risk, suitability, challenge, comfort, convenience, educational value, cost, and any other factors you consider important.

Does Tall Ships America have a hand in any of this? In a word—no! Tall Ships America is your "bulletin board" to introduce you to opportunities. However, Tall Ships America does not operate any vessels, and has no ability or authority to inspect, approve, or even recommend vessels or programs because programs are constantly evolving and changing.

Tall Ships America is a nonprofit organization with a limited staff. It serves as a forum for the sail training community, but it has no authority over what programs are offered, or how vessels are operated. The information in this Directory is supplied by the vessel operators, and Tall Ships America can not possibly verify all the information, nor visit all the ships in order to evaluate programs. For these reasons, you must take the information in this Directory as a starting point only, subject to change and correction, and proceed directly with the vessel operator. Tall Ships America is not an agent or business partner for the vessel operators, and is not a travel agent.

Tall Ships America believes in the value of sail training as a concept, but remember, from the moment you step beyond looking at this book, the decision and the resulting experiences rest with you.

Choosing A Sail Training Program

There are as many sail training programs as there are ships, and choosing the right one depends a great deal on your personal needs and desires. Sail training differs from going on a cruise ship, in that you are expected to take part in the running of the ship by handling sails and lines and standing watch, as well as working in the galley (the ship's kitchen) or performing routine cleaning or maintenance duties. To what degree depends on the sail training program you select.

Do you want a program that specializes in marine biology or adventure travel? Would you like to ship out for a day, a week, a school semester—or, for as long as it takes to circumnavigate the world? Are you interested in maritime history? In celestial navigation? Whales? Do you want the unique challenge of climbing aloft in a square-rigger? A race across the Atlantic? Maine lobster dinners aboard classic windjammers? Exotic ports of call? Will you be bringing your wheelchair? Would you like to receive academic credit?

The answers to the above questions provide a profile for just some of the options available to you. As to what sail training programs require of you—beyond an eager willingness to get the most out of your voyage—the requirements are few:

SAFETY FIRST!
Take a close look at the vessel's credentials. In the US, check to see if the vessel operates under United States Coast Guard regulations. Does the vessel currently hold a USCG-issued Certificate of Inspection (see pg 102 "Regulations for Vessels") or comparable certification from the authorities of the country in which it is registered? If it is a non-US vessel you should ensure that the vessel operates in accordance with the maritime safety rules of that country. In most cases this is supervised by a government agency similar to the US Coast Guard.

Talk to the program provider! Ask questions! Read the organization or company's literature, check out their website and, most importantly, visit the ship if you can. Get a sense of the professionalism of the operation and the quality of its program. Find out about the experience level of the captain and officers. How long have they served the ship you are looking into? If you will be joining the vessel in a distant port, or if it does not hold a current USCG Certificate of Inspection, be especially diligent in your research. Ask the program operator for the names of past trainees or clients and give them a call and ask about their experience. The amazingly diverse range of sail training opportunities featured in this book provides each of us with a variety of options.

EXPERIENCE

With very few exceptions, no prior sailing experience is required of trainees. Some programs do accept non-paying volunteers as crewmembers, but typically require experience in similar vessels or a long-term commitment—or both. Paying positions typically require a license—"Able-bodied Seaman" papers document a minimum of 180 days spent underway and successfully passing an exam administered by the US Coast Guard. Licenses are awarded to crew based on additional time underway, the tonnage of vessels served in, waters sailed, technical training, and additional testing. Trainees are encouraged to have the ability to feel comfortable in and around the water; however, many programs have no formal swimming requirements.

AGE

Most voyages are planned with a specific age group in mind. This varies from program to program, but many sail training programs start accepting unaccompanied trainees from the age of 14 (ninth grade). Ask what the composition of the ship's complement will be and, if you plan to send a young person on an extended voyage, what the in-port supervisory arrangements will be. Day sails and dockside education programs are readily available for elementary school students and overnight trips can be arranged for older school groups as well. There are a tremendous variety of adventure programs for adults of all ages, including "Elderhostel" voyages for seniors.

ACADEMIC CREDIT

Some vessels are tied directly to academic institutions that grant credit to trainees who successfully complete sail training programs as part of a course of study or project in a wide range of subjects. Some educational institutions will also grant credit for on-board independent study.

CO-EDUCATION

Just about every sail training vessel in the US sails with both male and female professional crew and programs are typically co-ed. Others are designed specifically for groups such as the Girl Scouts or in conjunction with a single-gender school or affiliated program.

COST

Prices vary considerably depending on the nature and the duration of the program and the type of vessel. Some vessels have limited financial assistance available, and some trainees, Scouting, and school groups have successfully sought private, business, and/or community support . Check with the sail training program you are interested in to see what opportunities may be available. Tall Ships America offers sail training scholarships and criteria and applications can be found on the Tall Ships America® Website (www.tallshipsamerica.org), or by calling the office of Tall Ships America.

Regulation of Vessels

Virtually all vessels are subject to some form of regulation by the national maritime authority of their "flag state"—the country in which they are registered. In the United States, these regulations are written and enforced by the United States Coast Guard, pursuant to laws enacted by Congress. Under the Safety of Life at Sea (SOLAS) Convention, administered by the International Maritime Organization (IMO), vessels of any nation signatory to the convention and over a certain size, or carrying more than 12 passengers and operating internationally, must comply with the requirements of the Convention with regard to construction, safety equipment, manning, crew training, etc. Compliance is documented in a "SOLAS Certificate" issued by the ship's national maritime authority.

US-registered vessels listed in this directory will generally fall into one of the following categories: Small Passenger Vessel, Sailing School Vessel, Oceanographic Research Vessel, and Uninspected Vessel. For each category there is a comprehensive set of regulatory requirements governing construction and arrangement, watertight integrity and stability, lifesaving and firefighting equipment, machinery and electrical systems, vessel control and equipment, and operations.

With the exception of Uninspected Vessels, all categories of US-registered vessel are subject to Coast Guard inspection on an annual basis. Upon satisfactory completion of the inspection, a Certificate of Inspection (COI) is issued, and must be permanently displayed on board the vessel. The COI spells out what waters the vessel may operate in (its authorized route), how many passengers or sailing school students may be carried, how many crew must be carried and what qualifications the master and crew must have, the requirement for and location of lifesaving and firefighting equipment, and so forth. Although not inspected annually, Uninspected Vessels (which are generally vessels less than 65 feet in length and carrying six or fewer passengers for hire) must still comply with requirements for safety equipment and a licensed skipper. The type of COI to be issued to inspected vessels is determined by both the size and construction of the vessel and the operating intentions of the owner. Some vessels carry dual certification.

The Coast Guard also prescribes the qualifications for the officers and crew of inspected vessels, and requires both that they have certain minimum levels of experience and training, and that they be examined and issued licenses or documents before they can lawfully serve on board. The following page gives a brief description of the various types of certifications governing the operation of US-flagged vessels.

Sailing School Vessels (SSV) are inspected under Title 46, Subchapter R of the Code of Federal Regulations (CFR). An SSV is a vessel of less than 500 gross tons carrying six or more sailing school students or instructors, principally propelled by sail, and operated by a nonprofit educational organization exclusively for the purpose of sailing education. Sailing School Vessels are required to pass regular inspection by the USCG in order to maintain their certification.

Passenger Vessels are certified according to size and number of passengers (not engaged in educational activities or in the operation of the vessel) carried under Title 46 of the CFR:

Subchapter C – Uninspected vessels which operate with no more than six passengers.

Subchapter T – Small passenger vessels of under 100 gross tons that carry more than six passengers and are required to pass regular USCG inspection of the ship and all onboard equipment.

Subchapter K – Small passenger vessels of under 100 gross tons that carry more than 150 passengers and are required to pass regular USCG inspection of the ship and all onboard equipment.

Subchapter H – Passenger vessels more than 100 gross tons that carry passengers for hire and are required to pass regular USCG inspection of the ship and all onboard equipment.

Attraction Vessel certification is required whenever a vessel is open to public boarding or conducts dockside programs. The vessel may be permanently moored to a pier, or it may also be certified under one or more of the above subchapters, but the Attraction Vessel COI (ATCOI) certifies its safety for dockside programs and visitation only. Oceanographic Research Vessels (ORV) are certified under Subchapter U of Title 46 of the CFR. An ORV is a vessel employed exclusively in either oceanographic (saltwater) or limnologic (freshwater) instruction and/or research, and is not necessarily equipped for passengers or other non-professionals. For more information, contact the United States Coast Guard or the Government Printing Office for the above listed sections of the Code of Federal Regulations.

Shipping Out

While often similar, each sail training vessel has its own list of suggested items so be sure to ask for it. The list shown on the following page is intended as an example of what you might be expected to bring. This list is from the schooner *Adventuress* and can be found on the Sound Experience Website at www.soundexp.org

Sound Experience is a Puget Sound-based environmental and youth leadership organzation that uniquely delivers its programs aboard the 133' historic wooden schooner *Adventuress*. A nonprofit 501(c)(3) organization since 1989, Sound Experience reaches more than 3,000 young people and adults each year, inspiring in them a greater understanding of the complexity of our marine ecological systems and stronger commitment to the stewardship of our waters. Aboard *Adventuress*, on day or overnight programs, participants experience the majesty and vulnerability of Puget Sound - and why the future of our marine environment matters to all of us.

Overnight Gear List

This checklist is for your comfort and safety. As you are packing, keep in mind that the weather on Puget Sound can be very unpredictable, even in the summer. Be prepared for cool, wet weather as well as hot, sunny weather. You may want to bring less than you think. Afterwards, most people feel they brought too much clothing for the trip. Pack thoughtfully. Layers of warm-when-wet fabrics like wool, polypropylene and synthetic fleece will help you keep up with the changes in conditions. Expect to get dirty and wet; don't bring anything too elegant, but focus on functional clothing. Please use a soft pack or duffel bag. You will be stowing your bag every day.

What to bring:
♦ Warm coat or jacket
♦ Waterproof rain jacket and pants
♦ 1-2 wool or fleece sweaters
♦ 1-2 long-sleeved shirts
♦ 1-3 t-shirts
♦ 1-2 pairs of long pants
♦ Plenty of wool or synthetic socks (wicking is best– not cotton)
♦ Underwear
♦ One set of long underwear/sweats (tops & bottoms- also function as pajamas)
♦ 1-2 pair of shoes (Closed-toed shoes must be worn while underway and during tide-walks. Closed-toed sport sandals such as Keen's are acceptable, but must have a heel strap. No flip-flops while underway!)
♦ Sleeping bag (outdoor weight)
♦ Small pillow
♦ Toiletries (there are no showers aboard)
♦ Wool hat/beanie (covers ears)
♦ Securable sunhat (for sun protection)
♦ Water bottle with your name on it
♦ Medicine/Devices (to be stored and locked when youth are aboard)

The following items may be nice but are optional:
♦ 1-2 bags for dirty laundry and wet clothes
♦ Gloves for warmth
♦ Personal/Nature Journal, paper and pencils
♦ Camera and binoculars (an inexpensive one is best)
♦ Day pack
♦ Cloth napkin (we don't have paper napkins on board)
♦ Poems or other readings/music to share

Please DO NOT Bring the following items:
♦ Personal music, digital game or web devices
♦ Personal communication device
♦ Drugs or alcohol
♦ Weapons
♦ Cigarettes: Smoking is not permitted on the vessel
♦ Personal food or candy/gum: It inevitably ends up on the deck or in the bilge and is very difficult to remove and can cause serious damage to the ship
♦ Any electrical devices such as hair dryers

What is a Tall Ship?

Full-Rigged Ship

A tall ship is not a strictly defined type of sailing vessel. Most of us use the term to mean a large traditionally rigged sailing vessel, whether or not it is technically a "ship". The United States Coast Guard's training ship *Eagle*, for example, is technically a "barque". A tall ship can also be a schooner, ketch, sloop, brigantine, barquentine, or a full-rigged ship depending on the number of masts and the cut of the sails.

For the purposes of classification and race rating, Tall Ships America adheres to the descriptions found in the Racing and Sailing Rules and Special Regulations established by Sail Training International.

CLASS A
All square-rigged vessels and all other vessels over 40m (131 feet) length overall (LOA)

CLASS B
Traditional-rigged vessels with a LOA of less than 40m (131 feet) and with a waterline length (LWL) of at least 9.14m (30 feet).

CLASS C
Modern-rigged vessels with a LOA of less than 40m (131 feet) and with a LWL of at least 9.14m (30 feet), not carrying spinnaker-like sails.

CLASS D
Modern-rigged vessels with a LOA of less than 40m (131 feet) and with a LWL of at least 9.14m (30 feet), carrying spinnaker-like sails.

Ship Shapes

Sail training vessels are as varied as the programs operated onboard them. Below are examples of the different rig configurations used by Tall Ships America's Member Vessels. On the following page you will find a diagram of the different sails carried by a full-rigged ship as well as a glossary of terms commonly used in this book.

Two-Masted Schooner

Topsail Schooner

Three-Masted Schooner

Brigantine

Brig

Barquentine

Barque

Ship Rigging Identification

1. Bowsprit	12. Fore upper topsail	22. Main lower topgallant sail	32. Mizzen upper topgallant sail
2. Martingale	13. Fore lower topsail	23. Main upper topsail	33. Mizzen lower topgallant sail
3. Figurehead	14. Foresail, Fore course	24. Main lower topsail	34. Mizzen upper topsail
4. Flying Jib	15. Main royal staysail	25. Mainsail, Main course	35. Mizzen lower topsail
5. Outer jib	16. Main topgallant staysail	26. Mizzen royal staysail	36. Crossjack, Mizzen course
6. Inner jib	17. Main middle staysail	27. Mizzen topgallant staysail	37. Jigger topgallant staysail
7. Fore topmast staysail	18. Main topmast staysail	28. Mizzen middle staysail	38. Jigger topmast staysail
8. Foremast	19. Mainmast	29. Mizzen topmast staysail	39. Jigger staysail
9. Fore royal	20. Main royal	30. Mizzen mast	40. Jigger mast
10. Fore upper topgallant sail	21. Main upper topgallant sail	31. Mizzen royal	41. Gaff topsail
11. Fore lower topgallant sail			42. Spanker

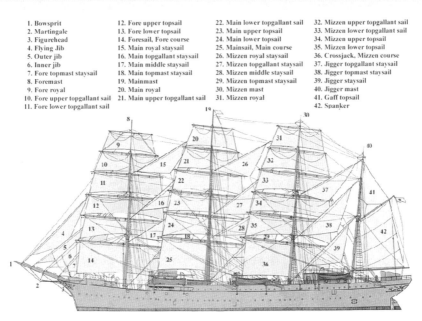

Sparred length - The length between the extremities of any spars that overhang the bow or the stern of a vessel, such as a bowsprit or a boomkin.

LOA - Length overall. The length between the forwardmost and the aftermost points on the hull of a vessel.

LOD - Length on deck. The length between the forwardmost and the aftermost points on a specified deck measured along the deck, excluding sheer.

Sheer - The fore-and-aft curvature of a vessel's main deck from bow to stern.

LWL - Length on the waterline. The length between the forwardmost and the after most points on a vessel's waterline.

DRAFT - The depth of water required to float a vessel.

BEAM - Width of a vessel at its widest part.

RIG HEIGHT - Maximum height of rig above waterline.

FREEBOARD - The vertical distance from the waterline to the freeboard deck, usually measured amidships.

FREEBOARD DECK - The uppermost deck that is designed to be watertight.

GRT - Gross registered tonnage. The volume, expressed in units of 100 cubic feet to the ton, of a vessel's total enclosed spaces below the weather deck and enclosed spaces above the deck including the bridge and accommodations.

Tall Ships America®
Member Vessels

Adventure and Education Under Sail!®

SPECIFICATIONS

Flag: USA
Rig: Gaff schooner
Homeport: New York, New York
Normal cruising waters:
New York Harbor
Sparred length: 80'
LOA: 65'
LOD: 64' 6"
LWL: 58'
Draft: 8'
Beam: 16'
Rig height: 62'
Freeboard: 3' 4"
Sail area: 1,850 square feet
Tons: 41 GRT
Power: twin 65 HP diesels
Hull: wood

ADIRONDACK

The schooner *Adirondack* is the third of seven schooners to come out of the Scarano Boat Building yard, beginning with the 59-foot schooner *Madeline* and the 61-foot *Woodwind* in 1991, followed by the 105-foot schooner *America* in 1995, and sister ships, *Adirondack II*, and *Adirondack III*, launched in 1999 and lastly their newest vessel the *America 2.0*. *Adirondack* combines the virtues of turn-of-the century schooner yachts with the latest in laminated wood technology. Offering an enviable combination of stability and speed, *Adirondack* fulfills the builder and owner's ambition of providing a quality sail for people of all ages and experience.

Who sails: School groups from elementary through college, private and corporate charters, families, and individuals of all ages
Program type: Sail training with paying trainees, passenger day sails
Built: 1994: Albany, NY, Scarano Boat
Coast Guard certification: Passenger Vessel (Subchapter T)
Crew: 3 **Trainees-passengers**: 49 daysails
Contact: Classic Harbor Line, Chelsea Piers, Pier 62, Suite 103, New York, NY 10011 USA
Tel: 212-827-1825 **Fax:** 646-349-5963
E-mail: info@Sail-NYC.com
Website: www.Sail-NYC.com

SPECIFICATIONS

Flag: USA
Rig: Gaff schooner
Homeport: Newport, Rhode Island
Normal cruising waters:
Narragansett Bay
Sparred length: 80'
LOA: 65'
LOD: 64' 6"
LWL: 58'
Draft: 8'
Beam: 16'
Rig height: 62'
Freeboard: 3' 4"
Sail area: 1,850 square feet
Tons: 41 GRT
Power: twin 60 HP diesels
Hull: wood

ADIRONDACK II

Who sails: Private charters, families, and individuals of all ages
Program type: Sail training with paying trainees, passenger day sails
Built: 1999: Albany, NY, Scarano Boat
Coast Guard certification: Passenger Vessel (Subchapter T)
Crew: 3 **Trainees-passengers:** 65 daysails
Contact: Sailing Excursions, Inc., Bowens Wharf, PO Box 1155, Newport, RI 02840 USA
Tel: 401-862-8441; 401-847-0000
Fax: 518-463-3403
E-mail: info@Sail-Newport.com
Website: www.Sail-Newport.com

The schooner *Adirondack II* was launched in August of 1999. The near-sister ship of the *Adirondack* joins the fleet of schooners known for their performance-oriented design/construction, combined with classic traditional aesthetics. With its wide-open cockpit, *Adirondack II* can comfortably accommodate groups of up to 65 trainees/passengers. While dockside, spacious cockpit doghouses double as serving space for food and beverages or classroom navigation paperwork. *Adirondack II* affirms that modern wood composite construction and 19th century elegance blend seamlessly to the benefit of all.

SPECIFICATIONS

Flag: USA
Rig: Gaff schooner
Homeport: New York, New York
Normal cruising waters:
New York Harbor
Sparred length: 80'
LOA: 65'
LOD: 64' 6"
LWL: 58'
Draft: 8'
Beam: 16'
Rig height: 62'
Freeboard: 3' 4"
Sail area: 1,850 square feet
Tons: 41 GRT
Power: twin 55 HP diesels
Hull: wood

ADIRONDACK III

The schooner *Adirondack III* was launched in 1997. She is the sixth of a series of series of schooners designed and built by Scarano Boat in the 1990s. Although dimensionally very similar to the other four vessels, she has an interior layout more suitable for sail training and can accommodate up to 14 trainees and crew for extended sailing adventures.

Who sails: School groups from elementary through college, private and corporate charters, families, and individuals of all ages
Program type: Sail training with paying trainees, passenger day sails
Built: 1997; Albany, NY, Scarano Boat
Coast Guard certification: Passenger Vessel (Subchapter T)
Crew: 3 **Trainees-passengers**: 49 daysails, 14 overnight
Contact: Classic Harbor Line, Chelsea Piers, Pier 62, Suite 103, New York, NY 10011 USA
Tel: 212-827-1825 **Fax:** 646-349-5963
E-mail: info@Sail-NYC.com
Website: www.Sail-NYC.com

SPECIFICATIONS

Flag: USA
Rig: Gaff topsail schooner
Homeport:
Port Townsend, Washington
Normal cruising waters:
Puget Sound and San Juan
Islands
Sparred length: 133'
LOD: 101'
LWL: 71'
Draft: 12'
Beam: 21'
Rig height: 110'
Sail area: 5,478 square feet
Tons: 82 GRT
Power: 250 HP diesel
Hull: wood

Photo by Zach Simonson-Bond

ADVENTURESS

Who sails: Schools and other groups from elementary through college, individuals and families
Program type: Sea education in marine science, maritime history, ecology and adult leadership; passenger day and overnight sails; dockside interpretation during port visits
Season: March - October
Designer: B. B. Crowninshield
Built: 1913: East Boothbay, ME, Rice Brothers
Coast Guard certification: Passenger Vessel (Subchapter T)
Crew: 4-5, with an additional 8-10 instructors
Trainees-passengers: 45 daysails, 25 overnight
Contact: Catherine Collins, Executive Director, Sound Experience, PO Box 1390, Port Townsend, WA 98368 USA
Tel: 360-379-0438 **Fax:** 360-379-0439
E-mail: mail@soundexp.org
Website: www.soundexp.org

The 1913 schooner *Adventuress* sails to increase awareness of the majesty and vulnerability of Puget Sound. Founded in 1989, the non-profit environmental education organization, Sound Experience, provides hands-on education aboard *Adventuress* to thousands of young people annually and partners with youth-serving organizations to reach Puget Sound area at-risk teenagers. Volunteer and paid crew receive environmental and sail training. The ship's apprentice program for youth ages 14 – 18 and month-long internships for adult sailor/educators also feature extensive sail training. The non-competitive environment fosters cooperation, teamwork, and leadership skills. A National Historic Landmark and a Puget Sound treasure, the *Adventuress* is truly a boat for the people, providing empowering, life-changing experiences to more than 3,500 youth and adults each year.

SPECIFICATIONS

Flag: USA
Rig: Schooner
Homeport: Bivalve, New Jersey
Normal Cruising waters:
Delaware Bay, Delaware River, New Jersey Coastal Waters
Sparred length: 115'
LOA: 85'
LOD: 81' 7"
LWL: 78' 3"
Draft: 6'
Beam: 22' 1"
Rig height: 67' 8"
Freeboard: 3' 6"
Sail area: 3,560 square feet
Tons: 57 GRT
Power: 225 HP diesel
Hull: wood

A. J. MEERWALD

The Bayshore Discovery Project operates the schooner *A. J. Meerwald*, New Jersey's official tall ship, as an experiential classroom. This authentically restored ,1928 Delaware Bay oyster schooner sails from her homeport of Bivalve, New Jersey as well as annual visits to cities and coastal towns throughout New Jersey, Pennsylvania, Delaware, and occasional special trips into the Chesapeake and the Northeast Atlantic Seaboard. Students range from 4th graders to senior citizens. Subject matter ranges from the history of Delaware Bay oystering to present water quality issues. Motivating people to take care of the environment, the history and the culture of New Jersey's Bayshore region are the primary goals of all activities on the *A. J. Meerwald*, regardless of their target audience, length of program, and/or port of origin. The Bayshore Discovery Project also conducts shore-based programs, lecture series, hosts Delaware Bay Days (the second weekend in June), and provides leadership on watershed issues throughout the Delaware Estuary. Members and volunteers are the lifeblood of the organization and are always welcome.

Who sails: School groups 4th grade through college, private and corporate charters, individuals of all ages
Program type: Sail training for professional crew, volunteers, paying trainees; 3-hour educational sails, summer camp, family sails, teacher workshops, overnight programs, team building, theme sails; sea education in marine science, maritime history, ecology, and watershed awareness
Season: April 1 - November 1
Designer: Charles H. Stowman & Sons
Built: 1928: Dorchester, NJ, Charles H. Stowman & Sons
Coast Guard certification: Passenger Vessel (Subchapter T)
Crew: 11 **Trainees-passengers:** 45 daysails, 12 overnight
Contact: Meghan E. Wren, Executive Director, Bayshore Discovery Project, 2800 High Street-Bivalve, Port Norris, NJ 08349 USA
Tel: 856-785-2060 **Fax:** 856-785-2893
E-mail: info@bayshorediscoveryproject.org
Website: www.bayshorediscoveryproject.org

SPECIFICATIONS

Flag: USA
Rig: Gaff schooner
Homeport: Vineyard Haven, Massachusetts
Normal cruising waters: Southern New England
Sparred length: 126'
LOA: 90'
LOD: 85'
LWL: 78'
Draft: 12' 6"
Beam: 21'
Rig height: 94'
Freeboard: 5'
Sail area: 5,000 square feet
Tons: 85 GRT
Power: twin diesels
Hull: wood

ALABAMA

Who sails: School groups elementary through college, private and corporate charters, and individuals of all ages
Program type: Sail training for paying trainees ages 9 - 16; private charters and public day sails
Designer: Thomas F. McManus
Built: 1926: Pensacola, FL, Pensacola Shipbuilding Company
Coast Guard certification: Passenger Vessel (Subchapter T)
Crew: 6 **Trainees-passengers:** 49 daysails, 27 overnight
Contact: Coastwise Packet Co., dba The Black Dog Tall Ships, PO Box 429, Vineyard Haven, MA 02568 USA
Tel: 508-693-1699 **Fax:** 508-693-1881
E-mail: office@theblackdogtallships.com
Website: www.theblackdogtallships.com

The ex-pilot schooner *Alabama* is an authentic example of a typical Gloucester fishing schooner of the early 1900s. She was built for the Mobile Bar Pilot Association in Pensacola, Florida in 1926 and designed by the greatest New England designer of Gloucester schooners, Thomas F. McManus. After a major three year reconstruction, the summer of 1998 marked her first year sailing the waters of southern New England joining the *Shenandoah* in The Black Dog Tall Ships fleet of Martha's Vineyard. The *Alabama* runs six-day sailing trips for youth ages 9 to 16 from late June through late August and is available for day and sunset sails and private charter each year from Memorial Day through Columbus Day.

SPECIFICATIONS

Flag: USA
Rig: 3-masted gaff topsail schooner
Homeport: Yorktown, Virginia
Normal cruising waters: Chesapeake Bay (summer), Caribbean (winter)
Sparred length: 105'
LOA: 105'
LOD: 80'
LWL: 65'
Draft: 8'
Beam: 20'
Rig height: 63'
Freeboard: 5'
Sail area: 2,778 square feet
Tons: 85 GRT
Power: 130 HP John Deere
Hull: steel

ALLIANCE

Alliance was built in Florida in 1995 by Treworgy Yachts as the *Kathryn B.* for the windjammer charter trade. She sailed the waters of Penobscot Bay, Maine and the Caribbean Islands with weekly charter guests. In 2005, Yorktown Sailing Charters purchased her and started a public day sail business in Yorktown, Virginia, renaming her *Alliance* in honor of the French and American alliance that won the battle for independence in 1781. She sails in Virginia from May through October carrying up to 49 passengers on two and three hour cruises. In the winter, *Alliance* offers weekly charters in the Caribbean Islands. During the spring and fall, she offers overnight charters on the Chesapeake Bay. Throughout the year *Alliance* works with the Mid Atlantic Maritime Academy (MAMA) offering training cruises that meet the academic requirements for USCG 6-pack and 100 ton masters license. She can accommodate up to 12 guests for overnight cruises with a crew of four.

Who sails: Groups and individuals of all ages
Program type: Daysails and weekly charters
Designer: Tom Colvin
Built: 1995: Palm Coast, Florida, Treworgy Yachts
Coast Guard certification: Passenger Vessel (Subchapter T)
Crew: 4 **Trainees-passengers:** 49 daysails, 12 overnight
Contact: Laura Lohse, Yorktown Sailing Charters, P.O. Box 238, Yorktown, VA 23690 USA
Tel: 757-639-1213
E-mail: info@schooneralliance.com
Website: www.schooneralliance.com

SPECIFICATIONS

Flag: USA
Rig: Schooner, 2-masted
Homeport: San Francisco, California
Normal cruising waters:
San Francisco Bay
Sparred length: 88'
LOA: 62'
LOD: 61' 4"
LWL: 59' 5"
Draft: 3' 6"
Beam: 23' 6"
Rig height: 76'
Freeboard: 4'
Sail area: 2,684 square feet
Tons: 47 GRT
Power: twin diesels
Hull: wood

ALMA

Who sails: Park visitors, school groups, scout groups, families and individuals of all ages
Program type: A science and sailing based curriculum for students in grades 4-8, sail training, ranger-led interpretive programs under sail. Affiliated groups include the SF Maritime National Park Association, San Francisco Maritime National Historical Park, and the National Park Service.
Built: 1891: San Francisco, CA, Fred Siemers
Designer: Fred Siemers
Crew: 5 **Trainees-passengers:** 80 daysails
Contact: Jason Rucker, Executive Director, San Francisco Maritime National Historical Park, Building E, Fort Mason Center, San Francisco, CA 94123 USA
Tel: 415-561-7006 **Fax:** 415-556-1624
E-mail: Jason_Rucker@nps.gov
Website: www.maritime.org

The last of approximately 400 scow schooners that carried cargo in the San Francisco Bay area at the turn of the century, *Alma* was built at Hunter's Point in San Francisco Bay in 1891. Today she is owned and operated by the San Francisco Maritime National Historical Park and docked at Hyde Street Pier near Fisherman's Wharf. From March to November, the *Alma* sails with a part volunteer/part professional crew on board, representing and interpreting a time when commerce moved by boat around the Bay. The volunteer program enables trainees to learn about traditional sailing and wooden boat maintenance. No fees are required as all crew volunteer to sail and maintain the *Alma* and other park vessels. The Park offers ranger-led interpretive sails on Thursdays and Saturdays from March to November.

SPECIFICATIONS

Flag: Republic of Vanuatu
Rig: Main topsail schooner
Homeport: Port Vila, Republic of Vanuatu
Normal cruising waters: Tropical waters worldwide
Sparred length: 126'
LOA: 92'
LWL: 87'
Draft: 10'
Beam: 19'
Rig height: 85'
Freeboard: 2' 6"
Sail area: 5,700 square feet
Tons: 87 GRT
Power: Wichmann 2-cycle diesel 160 HP
Hull: riveted steel

ALVEI

Underway since 1995, *Alvei* makes both long Trade Wind passages using the old sailing ship routes and shorter passages among the islands of the South Pacific. From December through April, *Alvei* sails coastal waters of Australia or New Zealand. From April to December, there is a long, deep-sea passage north to the tropics, followed by inter-island passages among the islands between Tahiti and New Guinea. *Alvei* works with Project MARC, (Medical Aid to Remote Communities). From June to October she carries doctors, medical supplies, technicians and materials to Islands in Vanuatu. *Alvei* operates as a non-profit sailing co-operative. Everyone contributes both work and money toward the operation of the vessel. There are no paid positions. Duties include steering, lookout, standing watch, sail handling, anchoring and docking, along with maintenance projects such as painting, tarring, sewing, cooking and rigging. Lessons on seamanship, boat handling and navigation are provided.

Who sails: Adults 18 and over
Program type: Sail training for volunteers and paying trainees; sea education based on informal in-house participation; coastal and offshore passages
Season: Year-round
Designer: Hull unknown, accommodations and rigging, Evan Logan
Built: 1920: Montrose, Scotland
Certification: Vanuatu Maritime Authority, Charter Vessel (pending final topsides inspection)
Crew: 6 volunteer crew and 12 paying trainees
Trainees-passengers: 36 daysails, 18 overnight
Contact: Evan Logan, Owner/Operator, Alvei Sail Training Cooperative, PO Box 415, Nelson, New Zealand
Tel: 6421-111-8501 **Fax:** 643-546-8505
E-mail: alvei@yahoo.com
Website: www.alvei.com or www.alvei.de

SPECIFICATIONS

Flag: USA
Rig: Gaff schooner
Homeport: New York, New York
Normal cruising waters: New York City and Key West, Florida
Sparred length: 105'
LOD: 84'
LWL: 76'
Draft: 8' 7"
Beam: 20'
Rig height: 83'
Freeboard: 4'
Sail area: 3,600 square feet
Tons: 68 GRT
Power: phase 1: single 200 HP diesel; phase 2: electric grid/ generator
Hull: wood

AMERICA 2.0

Who sails: Students, individuals, groups and families
Program type: Public daysails and private charters
Season: May - October (NYC), November - April (Key West)
Designer: Scarano Boat Building
Built: 2011: Albany, New York
Coast Guard certification: Passenger Vessel (Subchapter T)
Crew: 4 **Trainees-passengers:** 75 daysails
Contact: Scarano Boat Building, Chelsea Piers, Pier 62, New York, New York 10011 USA
Tel: 212-627-1825 **Fax:** 646-349-5963
E-mail: info@sail-nyc.com
Website: www.sail-nyc.com

Scarano Boat Building took sailboat design to the next level by combining more than 35 years of naval architecture and marine engineering experience, plus the latest technologies and materials, and putting them all into *America 2.0*. She features shroudless carbon fiber spars, a two part hull with a removable, aluminum deadwood section for water and fuel tanks and will soon also feature electric motors for propulsion. Her hull is constructed out of an end-grain balsa core, sandwiched between two layers of Port Orford Cedar over wooden laminated frames, an aluminum cabin structure with integrated mast supports, and bullwarks and cabin soles constructed out of plascore, an aluminum honey comb material, for improved strength and additional weight savings.

SPECIFICATIONS

Flag: USA
Rig: Schooner, 3-masted
Homeport: Long Beach, California
Normal cruising waters:
Southern California
Sparred length: 129'
LOA: 105'
LOD: 101'
LWL: 92'
Draft: 10'
Beam: 22'
Rig height: 98'
Freeboard: 6'
Sail area: 4,900 square feet
Tons: 203 GRT
Power: diesel
Hull: wood

AMERICAN PRIDE

The graceful, 3-masted schooner *American Pride* was built in 1941, as a 2-masted "schooner-dragger" and launched as the *Virginia*. She spent over forty years commercially fishing the Grand Banks and George's Banks. Her career spanned the New England ports of New Bedford and Gloucester, Massachusetts and Rockland, Maine. She was a working fishing boat, spending weeks at sea in search of cod, haddock, flounder, and ocean perch. In 1986, she was completely rebuilt in Thomaston, Maine, and certified by the US Coast Guard. The restoration included adding a third mast, watertight bulkheads, new deck, bulwarks, interior, rigging and machinery. She was renamed the *Natalie Todd* and operated as a charter boat out of Bar Harbor, Maine. In October of 1996, she was purchased by the Children's Maritime Foundation, and began her historic 7,500 mile sail through the Panama Canal to her new home in Rainbow Harbor, Long Beach, California. The once successful fishing schooner now majestically sails the waters of Southern California.

Who sails: School groups elementary through college, private and corporate charters, and individuals of all ages
Program type: Scientific or living history educational programs, sail training, team building, sailing adventures
Season: Year-round
Built: 1941: Brooklyn, NY, Muller Boatworks
Coast Guard certification: Passenger Vessel (Subchapter T)
Crew: 6 (paid and volunteer) **Trainees-passengers:** 100 daysails, 48 overnight
Contact: Helen H. Clinton, Director, Children's Maritime Foundation, 4676 Lakeview Ave #109-E, Yorba Linda, CA 92886 USA
Tel: 714-970-8800 **Fax:** 714-970-8474
E-mail: theamericanpride@aol.com
Website: www.americanpride.org

SPECIFICATIONS

Flag: Italy
Rig: Full-rigged ship
Homeport: La Spezia, Italy
Normal cruising waters:
Worldwide
Sparred length: 330'
Draft: 23' 6"
Beam: 50' 9"
Hull: steel

Photo by Thad Koza

AMERIGO VESPUCCI

Who sails: Junior officers of the Italian Navy
Program type: Sail training
Season: Year-round
Built: 1931
Contact: Embassy of Italy, 3000 Whitehaven Street, NW, Washington DC 20008 USA
Tel: 202-612-4400 **Fax:** 202-518-2151
Website: www.ambwashingtondc.esteri.it/ ambasciata_washington

The pride of the Italian Navy, *Amerigo Vespucci* conjures up memories of men-of-war from two centuries ago. Riding high in the water, with triple decks indicated by painted stripes, *Amerigo Vespucci* is a gracious 20th century goodwill ambassador, as well as a symbol of Italy's global maritime heritage and tradition. Named for the great explorer and cartographer of the 17th century, this elegant, full-rigged ship is a grand visitor to many ceremonial parades of sail. Since her launch, *Amerigo Vespucci* has been used to train junior officers of the Italian Navy.

Flag: USA
Rig: Topsail schooner
Homeport: Bay City, Michigan
Normal cruising waters:
Saginaw Bay and Lake Huron
Sparred length: 85'
LOD: 65'
LWL: 53'
Draft: 8' 6"
Beam: 18' 5"
Rig height: 76'
Freeboard: 6'
Sail area: 3,560 square feet
Tons: 48 GRT
Power: 135 HP diesel
Hull: steel

APPLEDORE IV

The schooner *Appledore IV* is owned and operated by BaySail, a 501(C)3 non-profit corporation. Tall ship adventures aboard the *Appledore IV* further BaySail's mission: "To foster environmental stewardship of the Saginaw Bay watershed and the Great Lakes ecosystem and to provide personal development opportunities for learners of all ages through shipboard and land based educational experiences." BaySail's environmental education program, Science Under Sail, begins and ends in the classroom with materials designed to prepare students for their sailing experience and reinforce the lessons learned while on board the *Appledore IV*. During the three-and-a-half-hour excursion, trained volunteer teachers lead small groups of students through hands-on activities including collecting and analyzing water, sediment, and plankton samples. Land use, maritime history, navigation, and weather observation are also discussed. To date over 30,000 K-12 students have taken part in BaySail's award winning education programs.

Who sails: School groups elementary through college and individuals of all ages.
Program type: Half-day K-12 marine science and ecology education; public sails and private charters. **Affiliated institutions include:** Saginaw Valley State University, Delta College, and the Boy's and Girl's Clubs of Michigan.
Season: April – October
Designer: Bud McIntosh
Built: 1989: Palm Coast, FL, Treworgy Yachts
Coast Guard certification: Passenger Vessel (Subchapter T)
Crew: 4 **Trainees-passengers:** 48 daysails, 18 overnight
Contact: Roger Nugent, Executive Director, BaySail, 107 Fifth Street, Bay City, MI 48708 USA
Tel: 989-895-5193 **Fax:** 989-460-1472
E-mail: info@baysailbaycity.org
Website: www.baysailbaycity.org

SPECIFICATIONS

Flag: USA
Rig: Gaff topsail schooner,
Homeport: Bay City, Michigan
Normal cruising waters:
Great Lakes
Sparred length: 65'
LOD: 58'
LWL: 49'
Draft: 7' 6"
Beam: 14'
Rig height: 63' 6"
Freeboard: 4'
Tons: 34 GRT
Power: 90 HP diesel
Hull: steel

APPLEDORE V

Who sails: Youth ages 12 – 18.
Program type: Youth Sail Training. Affiliated with Boy's and Girl's Clubs of Michigan.
Season: April to October
Designer: Bud McIntosh
Built: 1992: Palm Coast, FL, Treworgy Yachts
Coast Guard certification: Passenger Vessel (Subchapter T)
Crew: 2 **Youth Officers:** 2 **Passengers:** 29 daysails, 9 overnight.
Contact: Roger C. Nugent, Executive Director, BaySail, 107 Fifth Street, Bay City, MI 48708 USA
Tel: 989-895-5193 **Fax:** 989-460-1472
E-mail: info@baysailbaycity.org
Website: www.baysailbaycity.org

The *Appledore V* delivers BaySail's youth sail training program "Windward Bound". During the 5 to 10-day Windward Bound voyages, *Appledore V* is sailed by a professional captain and mate, two youth officers, and nine youth trainees. On their regular watches trainees are involved in every aspect of running the ship, from navigating and steering, to galley duty and manning the oars in *Appledore's* tender on trips ashore. Selected Windward Bound voyages also include a freshwater science curriculum which combines traditional sailing with study of Great Lakes habitats, aquatic species, shoreline geology, water quality, and nautical science. Trainees who successfully complete a summer training voyage become eligible to join the year-round program and train to qualify as youth officers. In the fall, the *Appledore V* sails Lake Huron's beautiful Cheneaux Islands and the North Channel on 3 to 5 day training voyages for adults. The *Appledore V* is owned and operated by BaySail, a 501(C)3 non-profit corporation.

SPECIFICATIONS

Flag: USA
Rig: Schooner
Homeport: Newport, Rhode Island
Normal cruising waters:
Narragansett Bay
Sparred length: 80'
LOD: 63'
LWL: 52'
Draft: 6' 6"
Beam: 17'
Rig height: 63'
Freeboard: 4' 6"
Sail area: 2,000 square feet
Power: diesel
Hull: steel

Photo by Thad Koza

AQUIDNECK

The Schooner *Aquidneck* (Ah-quid-neck) is a traditional, gaff rigged, topsail schooner. *Aquidneck* is named after Aquidneck Island, the island where Newport is located and is an Indian name meaning 'Isle of Peace'. With a length of 80-feet and a beam of 17-feet, the Schooner *Aquidneck* is our largest boat and one of the largest daysail schooners in New England. She is US Coast Guard inspected for up to 49 guests. Reminiscent of coasting schooners that were built to carry freight and passengers at the turn of the century, the Schooner *Aquidneck* was designed specifically to carry guests in comfort and safety. Her cabin tops are the perfect height for comfortable seating. Her large beam provides stability and allows guests plenty of room to move about with ease. She offers a terrific, tall ship style sailing experience.

Who sails: Individuals of all ages.
Program type: Passenger day sails, private charters
Season: April – October
Designer: Charles Wittholtz
Built: 2004: Long Island, New York
Coast Guard certification: Passenger Vessel (Subchapter T)
Crew: 3 **Trainees-passengers:** 49 daysails
Contact: John Hirschler, Sightsailing, Inc., 32 Bowen's Wharf, Newport, RI 02840 USA
Tel: 800-709-7245 or 401-849-3333
E-mail: info@sightsailing.com
Website: www.sightsailing.com

SPECIFICATIONS

Flag: USA
Rig: Gaff topsail schooner
Homeport: Mystic, Connecticut
Normal cruising waters:
Fishers Island, Block Island and Long
Island Sounds
Sparred length: 81'
LOD: 56'
LWL: 48'
Draft: 7' 6"
Beam: 20'
Rig height: 75'
Freeboard: 5'
Sail area: 1,800 square feet
Tons: 20 GRT
Power: 100 HP diesel
Hull: Honduran mahogany
on white oak frames

ARGIA

Who sails: All ages
Program type: Sail training for paying trainees and passengers; sea education in marine science, maritime history, and ecology in cooperation with accredited institutions and other groups; passenger day sails
Season: May – October
Designer: Frank Fulchiero
Built: 1986: Reedville, VA and Mystic, CT, Frank Fulchiero and Jennings Boat Yard
Coast Guard certification: Passenger Vessel (Subchapter T) Inland
Crew: 5 **Trainees-passengers:** 49 daysails
Contact: Molly Arps, Argia Cruises, 15 Holmes Street, Schooner Wharf, Mystic, CT 06355 USA
Tel: 860-572-1407 **Fax:** 860-536-0000
E-mail: molly.arps@yahoo.com
Website: www.sailawaynewengland.com

Argia Cruises operates the *Argia* out of Mystic, Connecticut during the months of May through October. She is a replica of a 19th century schooner, designed and built by Captain Frank Fulchiero for the day passenger trade. She carries 49 passengers on the waters of Block Island and Long Island Sounds for two to three hour day sails, charters, and marine science/coastal ecology programs. The Coastal Ecology Program utilizes various sampling and testing techniques to provide students with a better understanding of marine and coastal ecosystems. Volunteer and intern positions are available for this program which runs in spring and fall. Paid crew positions include: deckhand, 1st and 2nd mate, licensed captain, educator and assistant educator.

SPECIFICATIONS

Flag: United Kingdom
Rig: Schooner, 2-masted
Homeport: Road Harbour, British Virgin Islands
Normal cruising waters: Worldwide
Sparred length: 112'
LOA: 101'
LOD: 94'
LWL: 71'
Draft: 10'
Beam: 25'
Rig height: 102'
Freeboard: 6'
Sail area: 4,700 square feet
Tons: 130 GRT
Power: 425 HP diesel
Hull: Steel

ARGO

S/Y *Argo* is a 2-masted staysail schooner that measures 112-feet overall and accommodates 26 students and seven professional crew on ocean voyages around the globe. *Argo* is certified and inspected by the British Maritime and Coast Guard Agency as a Category 0 vessel, allowing her unrestricted operation in the world's oceans. Sailing under the Sea|mester flag, *Argo* circumnavigates the globe offering students the chance to cross oceans while furthering their educational and personal goals in a highly experiential college-level academic environment. Sea|mester offers 40 and 90-day voyages aboard *Argo* during the fall, spring, and summer terms. Under the guidance of professional staff, students learn through interaction and involvement with a focus on oceanography, marine science, leadership, and professional mariner training. Students earn certificates in sailing and scuba diving from IYT (International Yachtmaster Training) and PADI (Professional Association of Diving Instructors). No experience is necessary. Programs are available to high school seniors, graduates, and college students.

Who sails: High school graduates and college age students (fall, spring, and summer)
Program type: Experiential education semesters for high school graduates and college students; accredited academics with sail and scuba training and adventure travel; service projects and adventure travel
Season: Year-round
Designer: Langan Design Associates
Built: 2006: Marsun Shipyard, Thailand
Certification: MCA (UK) inspected Small Commercial Vessel up to 24 meters LWL, Catergory 0 unrestricted ocean service
Crew: 7 **Trainees:** 26
Contact: Sea|mester, P.O. Box 5477, Sarasota, FL 34277 USA
Tel: 941-924-6789 or 800-317-6789
Fax: 941-924-6075
E-mail: info@seamester.com
Website: www.seamester.com

Flag: Indonesia
Rig: Schooner
Homeport: Jakarta, Indonesia
Normal cruising waters:
Worldwide
Sparred length: 129'
Draft: 9'
Beam: 22'
Hull: steel

Photo by Thad Koza

ARUNG SAMUDERA

Program type: Sail training vessel of the Indonesian Navy
Built: 1991
Contact: Embassy of the Republic of Indonesia, 2020 Massachusetts Avenue, NW, Washington DC 20036 USA
Tel: 202-775-5200 **Fax:** 202-775-5365
Website: www.embassyofindonesia.org

In 1995, the Indonesian government celebrated their golden anniversary of independence by hosting a conference, heralded the Arung Samudera '95, to draw attention to the archipelago nation. At the conclusion of the conference, a 129-foot staysail schooner purchased in New Zealand was commissioned as Indonesia's first sail training ship. Known originally as *Adventurer*, the schooner was built in 1991 to serve as a sail training vessel based in Auckland, New Zealand. She was renamed Kri *Arung Samudera* to reflect her new home and service. The honorific "kri" is used just as "HMS" is used in Britain to designate a ship in service of the Royal Navy. Together the words "arung" and "samudera" in this context mean "cruise the ocean" a fitting goal for this adventurous schooner. *Arung Samudera* embarked on a circumnavigation of the globe as her first assignment.

SPECIFICATIONS

Flag: USA
Rig: Gaff rigged schooner
Homeport: Portland, Maine
Normal Cruising Waters:
Casco Bay
Sparred length: 72'
LOA: 55' 6"
LOD: 54'
LWL: 44'
Draft: 7' 6"
Beam: 14' 6"
Rig height: 65'
Freeboard: 4'
Tons: 21 GRT
Power: 72 HP diesel
Hull: wood

BAGHEERA

The schooner *Bagheera* was designed by John G. Alden and built in 1924 in East Boothbay, Maine. Shortly after launching, she sailed in the Bermuda Race, and then spent the next 50 years sailing in the Great Lakes. *Bagheera* was entered in the Chicago Mackinac Race numerous times, winning in 1930. The vessel was sailed to the Caribbean in the 1970s, eventually finding her way to the Galapagos Islands. She was converted to the passenger trade in the 1980s. She then sailed out of Los Angeles, San Diego and San Francisco before being shipped to Maine in 2002 to serve Portland Schooner Co., her current stewards. Today, *Bagheera* sails Memorial Day through Columbus Day from the Old Port in Portland, Maine, offering a variety of educational courses, public sails, and private charters.

Who sails: Schools, camps, organizations, families and individuals of all ages
Program type: Sea education based on in-house programming
Season: Memorial Day through Columbus Day
Designer: John G. Alden
Built: 1924: East Boothbay, ME, Rice Brothers
Coast Guard certification: Passenger Vessel (Subchapter T)
Crew: 2 **Trainees-passengers:** 48 daysails
Contact: Scott Reischmann, Portland Schooner Company, Box 111, Pears Island, Portland, ME 04108 USA
Tel: 207-766-2500 or (toll free) 1-87-SCHOONER
Fax: 866-319-5736
E-mail: scott@portlandschooner.com
Website: www.portlandschooner.com

SPECIFICATIONS

Flag: USA
Rig: Full-rigged ship
Homeport:
San Francisco, California
Sparred length: 301'
LOD: 256'
Draft: 22' 7"
Beam: 38' 6"
Rig height: 145'
Tons: 1,689 GRT
Hull: steel

BALCLUTHA

Program type: Dockside sea education in maritime history
Designer: Charles Connell
Built: 1886: Scotland, Charles
Contact: Jason Rucker, Executive Director, San Francisco Maritime National Historical Park, Building E, Fort Mason Center, San Francisco, CA 94123 USA
Tel: 415-561-7006 **Fax:** 415-556-1624
E-mail: Jason_Rucker@nps.gov
Website: www.maritime.org

The 3-masted, riveted steel ship *Balclutha* was built in Glasgow, Scotland, in 1886 "to the highest class in Lloyd's Registry." As a deepwaterman, *Balclutha* and a 26-man crew rounded Cape Horn with grain for Great Britain, and later ran Pacific Coast lumber to Australia. Each year as a salmon packet, the vessel carried hundreds of men (with boats and supplies) to the salmon fishing grounds of Alaska. She was rescued from decay by the San Francisco Bay Area community in 1954, and has been restored as a memorial to the men and times of the grand days of sail. Today the vessel hosts a slate of unique school education programs presented by the San Francisco Maritime National Park Association and is open to the public as part of the San Francisco Maritime National Historical Park.

SPECIFICATIONS

Flag: USA
Rig: Gaff topsail schooner, 2-masted
Homeport: Oxnard, California
Normal cruising waters: Coastal California and other offshore islands
Sparred length: 136'
LOA: 129'
LOD: 94'
LWL: 85'
Draft: 10'
Beam: 23'
Rig height: 100'
Freeboard: 5' 8"
Sail area: 6,300 square feet
Tons: 95 GRT
Power: 210 HP diesel
Hull: wood

BILL OF RIGHTS

The *Bill of Rights* is operated by the non-profit American Tall Ship Institute in her new homeport of Oxnard, California. The American Tall Ship Institute provides positive youth development programs, as well as educational and sailing opportunities to local schools, youth groups, and non-profits in Ventura County. The *Bill of Rights* is a fully certified passenger vessel under USCG Subchapter T.

Who sails: Primarily youth
Program type: Educational
Season: Year-round
Designer: McCurdy, Rhodes & Bates
Built: 1971: South Bristol, ME, Harvey F. Gamage Shipyard
Coast Guard certification: Passenger Vessel (Subchapter T)
Crew: 5 (day), 8 (overnight), 4 instructors
Trainees-passengers: 83 daysails, 32 overnight
Contact: Captain Stephen Taylor, American Tall Ship Institute, 3600 S. Harbor Boulevard #56, Oxnard, CA 93035
Tel: 805-436-7805
E-mail: Stephen@americantallship.org
Website: www.americantallship.org

SPECIFICATIONS

Flag: Canada
Rig: Brigantine
Homeport: Ottawa, Ontario, Canada
Normal Cruising Waters: Upper Ottawa River
Sparred length: 90'
LOA: 87'
LOD: 68'
LWL: 57'
Draft: 6'
Beam: 15'
Rig height: 60'
Freeboard: 3'
Sail area: 2,300 square feet
Tons: 40 GRT
Power: 235 HP diesel
Hull: steel

Photo by Cal Vandergeest

BLACK JACK

Who sails: Middle school 12 – 15 year olds
Program type: Sail training for paying trainees; Island Adventure Camp; overnight voyages; bursary programs available
Season: Summer and fall
Built: 1904: Scotland
Certification: Sailing School Vessel, Inland/Minor Waters
Crew: 4 high school and university students
Trainees-passengers: 15 daysails; 12 overnight
Contact: Bytown Brigantine, 2700 Queensview Drive, Ottawa, Ontario K2B 8H6 Canada
Tel: 613-596-6258 **Fax:** 613-596-4335
E-mail: info@tallshipsadventure.org
Website: www.tallshipsadventure.org

On May 2, 1904, *G. B. Pattee II*, a steam tugboat, was launched in Quyon, Quebec, Canada. She worked the logging industry for 50 years on the Upper Ottawa River. In 1952 the hull was purchased by the late Captain Thomas G. Fuller and converted into a tall ship brigantine, *Black Jack*, for a family yacht. On May 2, 2004, after a major refit, *Black Jack* was re-christened and launched at Britannia Yacht Club by Her Excellency, the Right Honorable Adrienne Clarkson, Canada's Governor General. At the same time, the vessel was designated Ottawa's Signature Vessel by the City of Ottawa. Bytown Brigantine was founded by the Thomas G. Fuller Family as a charitable foundation to provide opportunities for youth to experience adventure in the time honored traditions inherent in square rigged sailing. *Black Jack* is now the centerpiece of the Black Jack Island Adventure Camp, a 10-day program where youth 12-15 sail this tall ship or one of our 27-foot navy whalers as well as participating in other various camp activities.

SPECIFICATIONS

Flag: Canada
Rig: Gaff topsail schooner
Homeport: Lunenburg, Nova Scotia, Canada
Normal Cruising Waters: East Coast of Canada and the United States
Sparred length: 181'
LOD: 143'
LWL: 112'
Draft: 16'
Beam: 27'
Rig height: 132'
Sail area: 11,139 square feet
Tons: 191 GRT
Power: 250 HP twin diesels
Hull: wood

BLUENOSE II

The original *Bluenose*, launched on March 26, 1921, was a typical Nova Scotia Grand Banks fishing schooner. Built at Lunenburg both for fishing and for the International Fishermen's Trophy series of races between Canada and the United States, *Bluenose* was undefeated under her legendary master, Captain Angus J. Walters of Lunenburg. Her likeness became a national emblem and is depicted on stamps and the ten-cent coin of Canada. Launched on July 24, 1963, *Bluenose II* was built from the same plans at the same yard and by some of the same men. The only difference lies in the accommodations for the coed crew of 18 and the modern navigation and communication instruments. She serves as a goodwill ambassador for the Provence of Nova Scotia, participating in tall ship events throughout the Western Hemisphere. Her 12 deckhands receive instructions from her officers in all matters of seamanship. Today she sails in the best *Bluenose* tradition, and all officers and deckhands are encouraged to enhance their skills and certifications.

Who sails: Individuals and groups
Program type: Sail training for crew; passenger day sails; dockside interpretation
Season: April through September
Designer: William J. Roue, Halifax, Nova Scotia, Canada
Built: 1963: Lunenburg, Nova Scotia, Canada, Smith & Rhuland Shipyards
Certification: Canadian Coast Guard certified
Crew: 18
Contact: Director of Operations, Lunenburg Marine Museum Society, PO Box 1363, Lunenburg, Nova Scotia B0J 2C0 Canada
Tel: 866-579-4909 or 902-634-4794
Fax: 902-634-8052
E-mail: bluenose@gov.ns.ca
Website: www.schoonerbluenose2.ca

SPECIFICATIONS

Flag: USA
Rig: Full rigged ship
Homeport: Greenport, Long Island, New York
Normal cruising waters: East Coast US, Canada, Florida and Europe (upon request)
Sparred length: 180'
LOD: 120'
Draft: 13'
Beam: 30'
Rig height: 115'
Freeboard: 12'
Sail area: 10,000 square feet
Tons: 412 GRT
Power: (2) twin 375 John Deere diesel
Hull: wood

BOUNTY

Who sails: Students, individuals, and groups of all ages
Program type: Sail passages, dockside interpretations, school groups
Season: Year-round
Designer: British Admiralty
Built: 1960: Lunenburg, Nova Scotia, Smith & Rhuland
Coast Guard certification: Moored Attraction Vessel
Crew: 18 **Trainees-passengers:** 12
Contact: Tracie Simonin, Director, HMS Bounty Organization, LLC, 20 Cedar Lane, Setauket, NY 11733 USA
Tel: 631-584-7900 **Fax:** 631-471-2913
E-mail: Tsimonin@tallshipbounty.org
Website: www.tallshipbounty.org

HMS *Bounty* was built for the 1962 movie "Mutiny on the Bounty" by MGM Studios in Lunenburg, Nova Scotia to tell the story of the famous maritime mutiny that occurred in the South Pacific in 1789. Now owned and operated by the HMS Bounty Organization LLC, she makes Greenport, Long Island, NY her homeport. The ship carries 18 full-time paid crewmembers working side by side with our sail trainees and passengers. When docked in port, the *Bounty* is open for dockside tours, private functions and educational programs. She offers day sails for individuals and groups, sail passages, and corporate sail training and is available for private functions, film production, commercials and documentaries. Strongly dedicated to the educational development of today's youth, *Bounty* works closely with universities and other non-profit organizations to provide leadership learning and youth education-at-sea programs. The mission of the *Bounty* is to preserve the skills of square rigged sailing in conjunction with youth education and sail training.

SPECIFICATIONS

Flag: USA
Rig: Schooner
Homeport: Castine, Maine
Sparred length: 100'
LOA: 88'
LOD: 83'
LWL: 72'
Draft: 10'
Beam: 20'
Rig height: 70'
Freeboard: 4'
Sail area: 2,000 square feet
Tons: 66 GRT
Power: 190 HP diesel
Hull: wood

Photo by Captain Wendell Corey

BOWDOIN

The schooner *Bowdoin* is the flaghip of Maine Maritime Academy (MMA) sail training fleet, and the official sailing vessel of the state of Maine. Built in 1921 for exploring the Arctic waters, she is one of the strongest wooden vessels ever constructed. Between 1921 and 1954 she made 26 voyages above the Arctic Circle under the command of explorer Donald B. MacMillian. Today, *Bowdoin* serves the students of MMA, the state of Maine, and New England. She is the flagship of MMA's Sail Training Curriculum in which students learn to sail and manage traditional and modern sailing vessels. *Bowdoin's* sailing grounds include New England, Nova Scotia, Newfoundland, Labrador, and Greenland. Training afloat is performed on the Academy's fleet of over 100 vessels, including a 500-foot training ship, a 35-foot schooner, a Tugboat, five Colgate 26's, and numerous other sailing and power vessels from 15 to 50 feet. In 2008, *Bowdoin* made a return to the Arctic with Maine Maritime Academy students and continues in the tradition of Admiral MacMillan in carrying young people to the northern latitudes.

Who sails: Students of the Maine Maritime Academy
Program type: Sail training
Season: June to October
Designer: William Hand
Built: 1921, East Boothbay, ME, Hodgdon Brothers Shipyard
Coast Guard certification: Sailing School Vessel (Subchapter R), Passenger Vessel (Subchapter T), Ocean
Crew: 6 **Trainees-passengers:** 40 daysails, 11 overnight
Contact: Marine Operations Manager, Castine, ME, 04421 USA
Tel: 207-326-2364 **Fax:** 207-326-2377
E-mail: eric.jergenson@mma.edu
Website: www.mma.edu

SPECIFICATIONS

Flag: USA
Rig: Gaff schooner, 2-masted
Homeport: Mystic Seaport, Mystic, Connecticut
Normal cruising waters: New England
Sparred length: 74'
LOD: 61' 6"
LWL: 49'
Draft: 9'
Beam: 14' 8"
Rig height: 81'
Tons: 30 GRT
Power: 97 HP diesel
Hull: wood

BRILLIANT

Who sails: Teens ages 15–19 and adults 20+; participants must be physically fit, agile, and competent swimmers; affiliated institution is Mystic Seaport
Program type: Sail training with paying trainees; sea education in cooperation with individuals and organized groups such as Scouts and schools.
Season: May through October
Designer: Sparkman & Stephens
Built: 1932: City Island, New York, Henry B. Nevins
Coast Guard certification: Sailing School Vessel (Subchapter R), Passenger Vessel (Subchapter T)
Crew: 2-3 **Trainees-passengers:** 10 daysails, 9 overnight
Contact: Mystic Seaport, Brilliant Program, PO Box 6000, Mystic, CT 06355-0990 USA
Tel: 860-572-5323 **Fax:** 860-572-5355
Website: www.mysticseaport.org/brilliant

The *Brilliant* educational sailing program introduces teens and adults to life aboard a classic schooner while sailing the New England coast. On programs ranging from 2-day trips to 10-day voyages, teenagers and adults become full participants in the sailing of *Brilliant*: steering the vessel, raising the sails, standing watch and learning navigation. Participants are not passengers but are instead crew aboard our 61- foot wooden schooner. As the oldest sail education program in the country, *Brilliant* has taught teamwork, leadership, stewardship, and traditional seamanship for over 55 years to more than 9,000 teenagers and adults. Participants learn under the guidance of a professional crew and a Coast Guard licensed Captain.

SPECIFICATIONS

Flag: USA
Rig: Schooner, 3-masted
Homeport: San Francisco, California
Sparred length: 219'
LOD: 156'
Draft: 11' 3"
Beam: 36'
Rig height: 105'
Tons: 453 GRT
Hull: wood

Photo by Steve Danford

C. A. THAYER

Built in 1895, the *C. A. Thayer* was part of a mighty Pacific Coast fleet of sailing schooners that carried lumber to San Francisco from Washington, Oregon and the California Redwood Coast. Later, the vessel supplied the Alaskan salt-salmon canneries, anchoring out during the summer and returning in September with the season's catch packed in her hold. From 1925 to 1950, *C. A. Thayer* carried men north to the Bering Sea cod fishing grounds. She was purchased by the State of California in 1957, and transferred to the National Park Service in 1977. Now a National Historic Landmark, the *C. A.Thayer* is a rare survivor from the days when strong canvas sails billowed over tall deckloads of freshly milled fir and redwood. Today, the *Thayer* is open to the public daily as a part of the San Francisco Maritime National Historical Park.

Program type: Dockside sea education programs in maritime history
Designer: Hans Bendixsen
Built: 1895: Fairhaven, CA, Hans Bendixsen
Contact: Jason Rucker, Executive Director, San Francisco Maritime National Historical Park, Building E, Fort Mason Center, San Francisco, CA 94123 USA
Tel: 415-561-7006 **Fax:** 415-556-1624
E-mail: Jason_Rucker@nps.gov
Website: www.maritime.org

SPECIFICATIONS

Flag: USA
Rig: Topsail schooner
Homeport: San Diego, California
Normal cruising waters:
Southern California and the
California Coast
Sparred length: 145'
LOA: 93' 4"
LWL: 84'
Draft: 9' 5"
Beam: 24'
Rig height: 95'
Freeboard: 6'
Sail area: 7,000 square feet
Tons: 130 GRT
Power: 140 HP diesel
Hull: wood

CALIFORNIAN

Who sails: Groups and individuals of all ages
Program type: At sea and dockside education programs in maritime history and programs for at-risk youth in cooperation with area schools and social services agencies, passenger day sails and overnight passages
Season: Year-round
Designer: Melbourne Smith
Built: 1984: San Diego, CA, Nautical Heritage Society
Trainees-passengers: 60 daysails
Contact: Scott Baldwin, San Diego Maritime Museum, 1492 N. Harbor Drive, San Diego, CA 92101 USA
Tel: 619 234 9153 x 120
E-mail: sbaldwin@sdmaritime.org
Website: www.sdmaritime.org

Californian was launched in celebration of the 1984 Summer Olympics in Los Angeles. In 2003, *Californian* was designated the official tall ship of the State of California. She is the only ship to carry this prestigious title. A 145-foot topsail schooner, *Californian* is a replica of a mid-19th century revenue cutter. She has played host to thousands of adventure travelers, sailing enthusiasts, students and history buffs during her career. In 2003, she underwent an extensive refit including a haul out, re-stepping the masts, replacing the standing rigging, new sails and mechanical systems and a re-design and refurbishing of the areas below deck. The Maritime Museum of San Diego uses her for a variety of educational programs and public adventure sails. Her annual coastal tour offers residents and visitors an opportunity to enjoy the state of California's official tall ship.

SPECIFICATIONS

Flag: Uruguay
Rig: Staysail schooner
Homeport: Montevideo, Uruguay
Normal cruising waters: Worldwide
Sparred length: 205'
LOA: 198'
LOD: 172'
LWL: 147' 5"
Draft: 12'
Beam: 27'
Hull: steel

Photo by Thad Koza

CAPITAN MIRANDA

Built in 1930 in the Matagorda Shipyard and factory located in Cadiz, Spain, the *Capitan Miranda* originally served as a hydrographic vessel. As such, she carried out an outstanding and extensive career, performing countless cartographical surveys which were, and still are, highly useful to seamen. The ship honors the memory of Captain Francisco P. Miranda (1869 – 1925), who was not only a bright professional but also an exceptional teacher, particularly remembered for his research in sea subjects. In 1977, the vessel underwent a major refit and in 1978 was rededicated as a sail training vessel for the Uruguayan navy teaching newly graduated midshipmen to apply the knowledge acquired at the Naval Academy.

Who sails: Midshipmen, civilian students, foreign guests
Program type: Sail training vessel of the Uruguayan Navy.
Built: 1930: Cadiz, Spain, Astiueros Matagorda
Crew: 12 officers, 39 enlisted
Trainees-passengers: 35
Contact: Embassy of Uruguay, 1913 I Street, NW, Suite 419, Washington, DC 20006 USA
Tel: 202-331-1313 **Fax:** 202-331-8142
E-mail: navyofuruguay@yahoo.com
Website: www.armada.mil.uy

SPECIFICATIONS

Flag: USA
Rig: Gaff-rigged cutter
Homeport: Traverse City, Michigan
Normal cruising waters: Great Lakes
Sparred length: 53'
LOA: 39'
LWL: 35'
Draft: 4' 6" board up, 7' board down
Beam: 12'
Rig height: 68'
Freeboard: 3' 2"
Sail area: 1,460 square feet
Tons: 18 GRT
Hull: wood (plank on frame)

CHAMPION

Who sails: MHA members, guests, and at-risk youth throughout Northern Michigan
Program type: Sail training, maritime history, and experiential education
Designer: Fenwick Williams
Built: 1968: Concordia Yachts, Massachusetts
Coast Guard certification: Uninspected Passenger Vessel
Crew: 3 **Trainees:** 5
Contact: Maritime Heritage Alliance, 13268 S. West Bayshore, Traverse City, Michigan 49684 USA
Tel: 231-946-2647
E-mail: info@maritimeheritagealliance.org
Website: www.maritimeheritagealliance.org

Champion is a beautifully maintained, 1968 Concordia-built, Great Lakes cutter donated to the Maritime Heritage Alliance in 2008 by Mr. Henry Barkhausen of Harbor Springs, Michigan. She is utilized in a sailing program for at-risk youth in Northern Michigan. Qualifying youth spend four days aboard, learning to sail the boat and work together as a team, while building responsibility and self-esteem at the same time. The boat and program allows the MHA to further its mission of preserving, interpreting and sharing the maritime heritage of the Great Lakes.

In addition, she will is made available for limited private charters and corporate outings on West Grand Traverse Bay, an arm of Lake Michigan. *Champion* also attends local festivals to promote the MHA and the at-risk youth sailing program, and is available for passengers.

SPECIFICATIONS

Flag: Norway
Rig: Full-rigged ship
Homeport: Oslo, Norway
Sparred Length: 205'
Draft: 15'
Beam: 36'
Hull: steel

Photo by Thad Koza

CHRISTIAN RADICH

Christian Radich was a successful businessman and shipowner of Danish descent who died childless in 1889. He stipulated in his will that 50,000 kroner should be donated for the purpose of building a sail training ship for the youth of Norway. The funds were to be released only after the death of his wife, who lived on for 27 years. by that time, the initial endowment had grown to 106,000 kroner, an amount large enough to provide much of the capital of the entire building fund. When the ship was finally christened in 1937, it was appropriate that it bear the name of its prescient donor, Christian Radich. The *Christian Radich* is owned and administered by Ostlandets Skoleskib, the East Coast Training Ship, although Norway's Ministry of Education is responsible for its operating expenses. For the past decade sail training has been integrated into the official Norwegian school system. Its basic curriculum is a full ten months of education for 50 cadets ranging in ages from 18 - 24; in addition, 18 cooks become part of the training class.

Who sails: Individuals ages 16 and older
Program type: Sail training for paying trainees
Built: 1937: Framnæs Mekaniske Værksted
Crew: 18 Trainees-passengers: 88
Contact: Stiftelsen Christian Radich, Box 666 Sentrum N - 0106 Oslo, Norway
Tel: +47 22 47 82 70 **Fax:** +47 22 47 82 71
E-mail: postmaster@radich.no
Website: http://radich.no/en/front-page/

SPECIFICATIONS

Flag: Brazil
Rig: Full-rigged ship
Homeport: Rio de Janeiro, Brazil
Normal Cruising Waters: Worldwide
Sparred Length: 254'
LOA: 249'
LOD: 205'
LWL: 183'
Draft: 15' 9"
Beam: 34' 6"
Rig Height: 152'
Freeboard: 5' 3"
Sail Area: 23,627 square feet
Tons: 703 GRT
Power: 1001 HP diesel
Hull: steel

Photo by Thad Koza

CISNE BRANCO

Who sails: Sail Training for Officers and Cadets from Brazilian Navy, Academy of Merchant Marine and other Naval schools.
Program type: Sail training, goodwill ship and representation for Brazilian Navy
Season: Year-round
Designer: Gerard Djikstra
Built: 2000: Amsterdam, Holland, Damen shipyards
Certification: Brazilian Naval Vessel
Crew: 52 **Trainees-passengers:** 31
Contact: Embassy of Brazil, 3006 Massachusetts Ave NW, Washington, DC USA
Tel: 202-238-2805 **Fax:** 202-238-2827
Website: www.brasilemb.org

The *Cisne Branco* (White Swan) is a Brazilian navy tall ship which was built in Amsterdam, Netherlands, by Damen Shipyard. The keel was laid on November 9th, 1998 and the ship launched and christened on August 4th, 1999. She was delivered to the Brazilian Navy on February 4th, 2000 and commissioned as a Brazilian Naval vessel on March 9th, 2000. *Cisne Branco* made its maiden voyage across the Atlantic Ocean to Brazil, celebrating the 500th anniversary of the discovery of Brazil by the Portuguese Admiral Pedro Alvares Cabral. The ship's project is inspired in the design of the 19th century clippers. The *Cisne Branco* is normally used in national and international activities as a representative of the Brazilian Navy and for Brazilian culture. Also, it is used as an instructional sailing ship to the cadets of the Brazilian Naval Academy, Academy of Merchant Marine and other naval schools.

CLEARWATER

The *Clearwater* is the only full-sized replica of the 18th and 19th century merchant vessels known as Hudson River sloops. Owned and operated by the Hudson River Sloop Clearwater, Inc., a non-profit membership organization dedicated to defending and restoring the Hudson River and related waterways, the *Clearwater* has served as both a plat-form for hands-on environmental education and as a symbol for grassroots action, since 1969. She sails seven days a week, carrying as many as 50 passengers for three- to five-hour educational programs. Adults and children take part in a range of activities involving water life, water chemistry, sail raising, steering, piloting and more. A USCG licensed captain is in charge, and an education specialist directs the program. The permanent crew is composed of apprentices, ages 16 and older, an education assistant, and volunteers.

Who sails: Students of all ages, individuals, families, and groups
Program type: Sail training for crew and apprentices; sea education in marine science, maritime history, and ecology; passenger day sails; dockside interpretation during port visits
Season: April through November
Designer: Cy Hamlin
Built: 1969: South Bristol, ME, Harvey Gamage Shipyard
Coast Guard certification: Passenger Vessel (Subchapter T)
Crew: 6 **Trainees-passengers:** 50
Contact: Captain, Hudson River Sloop Clearwater, Inc., 724 Wolcott Ave., Beacon, NY 12508 USA
Tel: 845-265-8080
E-mail: office@clearwater.org
Website: www.clearwater.org

SPECIFICATIONS

Flag: USA
Rig: Full-rigged ship
Homeport:
Baltimore, Maryland
Sparred length: 282'
LOA: 200'
LOD: 179'
LWL: 176'
Draft: 21'
Beam: 42'
Rig height: 165'
Freeboard: 16'
Sail area: 20,000 square feet
Tons: 398 GRT
Hull: wood

USS CONSTELLATION

Program type: Dockside interpretation, overnight and day education programming
Designer: John Lenthall
Built: 1854: Gosport Naval Shipyard, Portsmouth, VA, US Navy
Contact: Historic Ships in Baltimore, Pier 1, 301 East Pratt Street, Baltimore, MD 21202 USA
Tel: 410-539-1797 **Fax:** 410-539-6238
E-mail: administration@historicships.org
Website: www.historicships.org

The last all-sail warship built by the US Navy, USS *Constellation* served her country for nearly 100 years in both military and non-military roles. From 1859-1861, she was the flagship of the US African Squadron charged with the mission of intercepting vessels engaged in the illegal slave trade along the coast of West Africa. During the Civil War, *Constellation* saw duty in the Mediterranean Sea protecting American interests, and later was reassigned to the US as part of the Gulf Coast Blockading Squadron. During her later years, she sailed as a training ship for the US Naval Academy and then as a stationary training ship at the Naval War College in Newport, Rhode Island. She was last under sail in 1893. Her final role as a commissioned vessel came during World War II when she served as flagship of the US Atlantic Fleet. In 1955, *Constellation* was brought to Baltimore to be preserved as a national shrine. The ship underwent a massive restoration (1996-1999) to return her to her original 1854 configuration. She is now open for public tours, offering a wide array of living history and educational programs under the management of the Living Classrooms Foundation.

159

SPECIFICATIONS

Flag: USA
Rig: Full-rigged ship
Homeport: Charlestown, Massachusetts
Normal cruising waters: Boston Harbor
Sparred length: 306'
LOA: 204'
LOD: 174' 10" (gun deck)
LWL: 175'
Draft: 22'
Beam: 43' 6"
Rig height: 189' 2"
Freeboard: 15'
Sail area: 42,710 square feet
Tons: 2,200 GRT
Hull: wood

USS CONSTITUTION

"Old Ironsides" is the oldest commissioned warship afloat in the world. One of six ships ordered by President George Washington to protect America's growing maritime interests in the 1790s, *Constitution* earned widespread renown for her ability to punish French privateers in the Caribbean and thwart Barbary pirates of the Mediterranean. The ship's greatest glory came during the War of 1812 when she defeated four British frigates. During her first engagement against HMS *Guerriére* in 1812, seamen nicknamed her "Old Ironsides" when they saw British cannonballs glance off her 21-inch thick oak hull. In the 1830s, the ship was going to be to be disassembled, but the public outcry, sparked by the publication of an Oliver Wendell Holmes poem, saved her. Over the following century, the ship undertook many military assignments and served as a barracks and as a training ship. She was restored in 1927, and after a coast-to-coast tour, *Constitution* was moored in the Charlestown Navy yard in 1934 where she is now open year-round to the public for free tours.

Program type: Dockside interpretation
Built: 1797: Boston, MA, US Navy, Edmond Hartt Shipyard
Certification: Commissioned Naval Vessel
Crew: 75
Contact: Commanding Officer, USS Constitution, Charlestown Navy Yard, Charlestown, MA 02129-1797 USA
Tel: 617-242-5670 **Fax:** 617-242-2308
Website: www.ussconstitution.navy.mil

SPECIFICATIONS

Flag: USA
Rig: Brigantine
Homeport: Woods Hole, Massachusetts
Normal cruising waters: North Atlantic Ocean and Caribbean Sea
Sparred length: 134'
LOD: 98'
LWL: 87' 6"
Draft: 12' 6"
Beam: 26'
Rig height: 110'
Sail area: 7,500 square feet
Tons: 158 GRT
Power: Cummins KTA19, 500 HP
Hull: steel

CORWITH CRAMER

Who sails: College students admitted by competitive selection from over 150 colleges and universities worldwide. Also high school students participating in summer seminar programs.
Program type: SEA programs combine 6 weeks of academic study on campus in Woods Hole, MA with 6 weeks of oceanographic research at sea. Courses on shore include oceanography, nautical science, and maritime studies. Program offerings include SEA Semester (college level, 12 weeks, 17-18 credits), SEA Summer Session (college level, 8 weeks, 12 credits), and SEA seminars for high school students.
Designer: Woodin & Marean, Inc., Wiscasset, ME
Built: 1987
Coast Guard certification: Sailing School Vessel (Subchapter R) for Ocean service
Crew: 6 professional mariners and 4 scientists
Trainees-passengers: 24-25
Contact: Sea Education Association (SEA), PO Box 6, Woods Hole, MA 02543 USA
Tel: 508-540-3954 OR 800-552-3633
Fax: 508-540-0558
E-mail: admissions@sea.edu
Website: www.sea.edu

Along with the SSV *Robert C. Seamans*, the SSV *Corwith Cramer* is owned and operated by the Sea Education Association (SEA) of Woods Hole, Massachusetts. Built in 1987 and named for SEA's founder, the 134-foot steel brigantine was the first vessel built to the stringent safety requirements of the Sailing School Vessels Act. She is outfitted with an oceanographic laboratory, classroom, library, and computer laboratory. SEA Semester students investigate and study the ocean from multiple perspectives. Our 12-week SEA Semester programs are tailored to meet a wide variety of undergraduate majors and interests. Every SEA Semester begins with a shore component in Woods Hole, Massachusetts followed by an open ocean research cruise aboard the SSV *Corwith Cramer* or the SSV *Robert C. Seamans*. Each program combines elements of oceanography, maritime history and culture, environmental studies, public policy, and nautical science. SEA Semester programs offer 17-18 credits from Boston University; the Summer Session and Trimester Program offer 12.

161

SPECIFICATIONS

Flag: Portugal
Rig: Schooner, 4-masted
Homeport: Lisbon, Portugal
Normal cruising waters:
Worldwide
Sparred length: 221'
Draft: 15' 6"
Beam: 32' 6"
Hull: steel

Photo by Thad Koza

CREOULA

Creoula is a 4-masted, steel-hulled schooner built in 1937 in a record 62 workdays. She was constructed for a Portuguese fishing company, Parceria Geral de Pescarias, and until her last trip in 1973, *Creoula* had wooden topmasts, booms, and gaffs. The standing rigging has always been steel, and the running rigging was originally made from sisal rope. Until 1973, this 4-masted schooner spent 37 consecutive years working the cold waters off Grand Banks, Newfoundland. The ship typically set sail from Lisbon in April for Nova Scotia, where she remained until the end of May. After renewing supplies in Sydney, Nova Scotia, or St. John's, Newfoundland, *Creoula* would sail to Greenland, where she fished until mid-September. In 1979, she was purchased from the Portuguese Department of Fisheries with the intention of converting her to a museum of fishery. A survey showed her hull to be in impeccable condition, however, and a decision was made to restore her as a sail training vessel. She is now owned by the Portuguese navy but carries only civilian cadets and trainees.

Program type: Sail training vessel
Season: Year-round
Built: 1937
Contact: Naval Attache of Portugal, Embassy of Portugal, 2010 Massachusetts Ave., NW Washington, DC 20008
Tel: 202-232-7632

SPECIFICATIONS

Flag: Mexico
Rig: Barque
Homeport: Puerto de Acapulco, Mexico
Normal cruising waters: Worldwide
Sparred length: 270'
LWL: 220' 4"
Draft: 17' 1"
Beam: 39' 4"
Sail area: 25,489 square feet
Power: 1,125 HP engine
Hull: steel

Photo by Thad Koza

CUAUHTEMOC

Who sails: Captains, officers, cadets, and sailors of the Mexican Navy
Program type: Sail training vessel
Season: Year-round
Built: 1982: Bilbao, Spain, Celaya Shipyards
Crew: 123 (officers and sailors)
Contact: Naval Attache of Mexico, Embassy of Mexico, 1911 Pennsylvania Avenue, NW, Washington, DC 20006 USA
Tel: 202-728-1760
E-mail: navalmx@msn.com or buquetemoc@hotmail.com

The sail training ship *Cuauhtemoc*, "tireless navigator", has covered 378,725 nautical miles and trained officers of the Mexican Navy for nearly 20 years. Through almost two decades, it's accomplishments have been acknowledged and praised by other navies in the world. The ship has participated in important regattas like the Colón Regatta, the Cutty Sark Tall Ship Races, and the Centenary of Osaka Port Modernization Regatta, among others. The sail training ship *Cuauhtemoc* is undoubtedly a living symbol of the sailor spirit that characterizes the personnel of the Mexican Navy, who are always ready to serve their country.

SPECIFICATIONS

Flag: USA
Rig: Gaff ketch
Homeport: Coupeville, Washington
Sparred length: 55'
LOA: 52'
LOD: 40'
LWL: 33' 4"
Draft: 6' 6"
Beam: 13' 6"
Rig height: 55'
Freeboard: 3' 6"
Sail area: 1,100 square feet
Tons: 19 GRT
Power: 225 HP diesel
Hull: wood

CUTTY SARK

Captain John Colby Stone is a world sailor and maintains the 52-foot classic ketch, *Cutty Sark*. In the summer you will commonly see the boat on the water in Penn Cove taking passengers on sailing tours. The *Cutty Sark* was built of teak by American Marine in Hong Kong in 1960. The first of 10 sister ships of the Mayflower class designed by Hugh Angleman and Charlie Davies, she wears the number 1 proudly on her mains'l. She is broad of beam, providing stable sailing and plenty of room for comfortable deck lounging. Her pilot house offers an alternate steering station and comfortable sitting area. She has a full galley with hot and cold pressure water, a propane stove and oven. You can charter this beautiful vessel for scenic sails throughout the waters surrounding Whidbey Island and the San Juan Islands. Relax. Let the wind pull the sails ahead, and Captain John Colby Stone assures you of a wonderful time.

Who sails: Families and individuals of all ages
Program type: Private charters
Designer: Hugh Angleman/Charlie Davies
Built: 1960: Hong Kong, American Marine
Contact: Captain John Colby Stone, Æolian Ventures, Inc, 2440 West Libbey Road, Coupeville, WA 98239 USA
Tel: 360-678-5567
E-mail: captjohn@whidbey.net
Website: www.svcuttysark.com

SPECIFICATIONS

Flag: Poland
Rig: Full-rigged ship
Homeport: Gdynia, Poland
Normal cruising waters:
Worldwide
Sparred length: 360'
LOD: 311'
Draft: 20' 7"
Beam: 45' 9"
Rig height: 162'
Sail area: 32,453 square feet
Tons: 2,385 GRT
Power: Cegielski - Sulzer type 8
AL 20/24, 2 * 750 PS (552 kW)
Hull: steel

Photo by Thad Koza

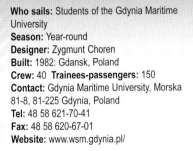

DAR MLODZIEZY

Who sails: Students of the Gdynia Maritime University
Season: Year-round
Designer: Zygmunt Choren
Built: 1982: Gdansk, Poland
Crew: 40 **Trainees-passengers:** 150
Contact: Gdynia Maritime University, Morska 81-8, 81-225 Gdynia, Poland
Tel: 48 58 621-70-41
Fax: 48 58 620-67-01
Website: www.wsm.gdynia.pl/

Dar Mlodziezy, "gift of the children", is a full-rigged ship designed by the distinguished Polish Naval architect Zygmunt Choren and is the flagship of the Merchant Marine Academy in Gdynia, Poland. *Dar Mlodziezy* was funded in part by contributions of elementary school children during the 1960s and 1970s. Commissioned in 1982, she replaced the venerable *Dar Pomorza,* "gift of Pomoraze" (a reference to the coastal region of Poland), which served Poland for more than six decades before her retirement. *Dar Mlodziezy*'s distinctive design served as the prototype for a class of vessels (five in all) built in Gdansk for the Russian confederation of the 1980's. Four of the five vessels – *Mir, Druzhba, Pallada,* and *Nasheba* – now fly the Russian flag, while *Khersones* flies the flag of Ukraine. These are true sister ships and vary only slightly in dimensions and configuration.

165

SPECIFICATIONS

Flag: USA
Rig: Schooner, 3-masted
Homeport: Milwaukee, Wisconsin
Normal cruising waters:
Great Lakes, Florida, Bahamas
Sparred length: 137'
LOA: 99'
LOD: 98'
LWL: 88' 4"
Draft: 8' 9"
Beam: 24'
Rig height: 95'
Sail area: 5,916 square feet
Tons: 99 GRT
Power: twin 180 HP diesels
Hull: wood

DENIS SULLIVAN

The S/V *Denis Sullivan*, owned and operated by Discovery World Ltd., was completed by over 900 volunteers in 2000. This replica of a Great Lakes schooner, and Flagship of Wisconsin, operates as a floating classroom and goodwill ambassador for the State of Wisconsin. From her homeport in Milwaukee on Lake Michigan, the schooner offers educational day sails and private charters for people of all ages from May through September and is committed to re-establishing the historical, cultural and environmental bonds between the community and one of its most valuable resources, the Great Lakes. She winters in Florida, the Bahamas and Caribbean. Three hour LakeWatch Expeditions and Dockside Discovery educational programs are offered for 5th through 12th graders. High school and college students can partake in five to fourteen day Science Under Sail ™ programs in the Great Lakes, Bahamas and Caribbean.

Who sails: Students and the general public
Program type: Sail training for crew, volunteers, and paying trainees; sea education in maritime history, ecology, and marine science; professional development for educators; "themed" sails and passenger day sails; dockside interpretation while in port
Season: Year-round
Designer: Timothy Graul
Built: 2000: Milwaukee, WI, Rob Stevens
Coast Guard certification: Passenger Vessel (Subchapter T), Sailing School Vessel (Subchapter R)
Crew: 10 **Trainees-passengers:** 50 daysails, 16 overnight
Contact: Jeff Phillips, Marine Operations Manager, Discovery World, 500 North Harbor Drive, Milwaukee, WI 53202 USA
Tel: 414-765-8641 **Fax:** 414-765-0311
E-mail: JPhillips@discoveryworld.org
Website: www.discoveryworld.org

SPECIFICATIONS

Flag: Indonesia
Rig: Barquentine
Homeport: Surabaya, Indonesia
Normal cruising waters:
Indonesian waters, Indian Ocean,
Pacific Ocean
Sparred length: 191'
LOA: 165'
LOD: 163' 1"
LWL: 138' 4"
Draft: 13'
Beam: 31'
Rig height: 119' 7"
Freeboard: 15' 1"
Sail area: 11,738 square feet
Tons: 847 GRT
Power: 986 HP diesel
Hull: steel

Photo by Benson Lee

DEWARUCI

Who sails: Cadets of the Indonesian Naval Academy
Program type: Sail training and sea education for Indonesian Naval cadets
Season: Year-round
Built: 1952: Hamburg, Germany, H.C. Stulchen & Sohn
Crew: 70   **Trainees-passengers:** 80
Contact: Indonesian Naval Attaché, Defense Attaché Office, 2020 Massachusetts Avenue NW, Washington, DC 20036 USA

KRI *Dewaruci*, the beautiful barquentine flying the red and white Indonesian flag, is the largest tall ship in the Indonesian Navy. She was built in 1952 by H. C. Stulchen and Son of Hamburg, Germany and launched in 1953. Since then, the ship has served the Indonesian Navy as a sail training vessel and as a successful ambassador of goodwill for the people of Indonesia. *Dewaruci's* name and figurehead represent the mythological Indonesian god of truth and courage.

SPECIFICATIONS

Flag: USA
Rig: Barque, 3-masted
Homeport: New London, Connecticut
Normal cruising waters: US East Coast, Caribbean, Europe
Sparred length: 295'
LOA: 266' 8"
LWL: 231'
Draft: 17'
Beam: 39'
Rig height: 147' 3"
Freeboard: 9' 1"
Sail area: 22,300 square feet
Tons: 1,824 GRT
Power: 1,000 HP diesel Caterpillar D399 engine
Hull: steel

Photo by Thad Koza

EAGLE

One of five sister ships built for sail training in Germany in the 1930s, *Eagle* was included in reparations paid to the United States following World War II and the Coast Guard took her over as a training ship. Aboard the *Eagle*, cadets have a chance to put into practice the navigation, engineering, and other skills they are taught at the Coast Guard Academy. As underclassmen, they fill positions normally taken by the enlisted crew of a ship, including watches. They handle the more than 20,000 square feet of sail and more than 20 miles of rigging. Over 200 lines must be coordinated during a major ship maneuver, and the cadets must learn the name and function of each. As upperclassmen, they perform officer-level functions. For many, their tour of duty aboard the *Eagle* is their first experience of life at sea and it is here that they learn to serve as the leaders they will one day become in the Coast Guard. *Eagle* is safely maintained and operated by six officers and 49 crew who are stationed on board for two to three years at a time. This experienced core provides leadership and coaching to over 700 trainees and 60 short term temporary crew each year.

Who sails: US Coast Guard cadets and officer candidates
Program type: Military training
Season: Summer cruises with cadets, Fall and Spring cruises with officer candidates
Built: 1936: Hamburg, Germany, Blohm & Voss
Crew: 55
Contact: Commanding Officer, USCGC EAGLE, 45 Mohegan Ave., New London, CT 06320 USA
Tel: 860-439-1562
Website: www.facebook.com/coastguardcuttereagle

SPECIFICATIONS

Flag: USA
Rig: Barque, 3-masted
Homeport: Galveston, Texas
Normal cruising waters: Coastal waters near Galveston
Sparred length: 205'
LOA: 155'
LOD: 150'
Draft: 10'
Beam: 28'
Rig height: 110'
Freeboard: 10'
Sail area: 12,000 square feet
Tons: 411 GRT
Power: 450 HP diesel
Hull: iron

ELISSA

Who sails: School groups from middle school through college; individuals of all ages
Program type: Sail training for crew and apprentices; sea education in maritime history based on informal, in-house training; dockside interpretation
Season: April to November
Built: 1877: Aberdeen, Scotland, Alexander Hall and Sons Yard
Coast Guard certification: Cargo and Miscellaneous Goods (Subchapter I)
Crew: 40 **Trainees-passengers:** 85 daysails
Contact: Texas Seaport Museum/Galveston Historical Foundation, Pier 21, No. 8, Galveston, TX 77550 USA
Tel: 409-763-1877 **Fax:** 409-763-3037
E-mail: elissa@galvestonhistory.org
Website: www.tsm-elissa.org

In 1975, a rusted iron hulk lay in the waters of Piraeus, Greece. Nearly 100 years earlier, she had sailed the world's oceans as a proud square-rigged sailing ship. Cut down, leaking and decrepit, she waited a cable's length from the scrap yard. Today, *Elissa* remains one of the hallmarks of maritime preservation. Lovingly restored and maintained, she sails again, continuing a far longer life than most ships are ever granted. She tests her readiness annually in a series of sea trials amid the oil rigs and shrimpers off Galveston Island. Working under professional officers, her volunteer crew completes an extensive dockside-training program. As funds allow, she makes longer voyages.

SPECIFICATIONS

Flag: USA
Rig: Barque, 3-masted (lateen mizzen)
Homeport: Manteo, North Carolina
Normal cruising waters: Inland sounds of North Carolina
Sparred length: 78'
LOA: 68' 6"
LOD: 55'
LWL: 59'
Draft: 8'
Beam: 16' 6"
Rig height: 65'
Sail area: 1,920 square feet
Tons: 97 GRT
Hull: wood

ELIZABETH II

Built with private funds to commemorate the 400th Anniversary of the English colonization of the America's, *Elizabeth II* is named for a vessel that sailed from Plymouth, England on the second of the three Roanoke voyages sponsored by Sir Walter Raleigh between 1584 and 1587. She probably carried marines, colonists and supplies to establish a military garrison to support England's claim to the New World. *Elizabeth II's* sail training program teaches volunteer crew about America's 16th century maritime heritage. In addition to classroom instruction and dockside training, crewmembers participate in the care and maintenance of the vessel. Voyages are scheduled during the spring and fall seasons. Sponsorship for the volunteer crew program is provided by the nonprofit Friends of Elizabeth II, Inc.

Who sails: Volunteer crew
Program type: Sail training for volunteer crew and apprentices; dockside interpretation
Season: Spring and fall
Designer: W. A. Baker and Stanley Potter
Built: 1983: Manteo, North Carolina, O. Lie-Nielsen, Creef-Davis Shipyard
Contact: Kim Sawyer, Executive Director, Roanoke Island Festival Park, One Festival Park, Manteo, NC 27954 USA
Tel: 252-475-1500 **Fax:** 252-475-1507
E-mail: Kim.Sawyer@ncdcr.gov
Website: www.roanokeisland.com

SPECIFICATIONS

Flag: Chile
Rig: Barquentine, 4-masted
Homeport: Valparaiso, Chile
Normal cruising waters:
Worldwide
Sparred length: 371'
Draft: 19' 8"
Beam: 42' 8"
Hull: steel

Photo by Thad Koza

ESMERALDA

Program type: Sail training vessel of the Chilean Navy
Design: Camper & Nicholson
Built: 1952 – 1954, Cadiz, Spain
Contact: Embassy of the Republic of Chile, 1732 Massachusetts Avenue, NW, Washington, DC 20036 USA
Tel: 202-785-1746 **Fax:** 202-887-5579

The pride of the Chilean Navy, *Esmeralda* was built in Cadiz, Spain from plans used to build Spain's *Juan Sebastian de Elcano*. Both vessels were constructed from Camper & Nicholson design at the same yard, though some 27 years apart. The only difference between these two elegant 4-masters are the additional fore-and-aft sail on the *Sebastian's* foremast, designating her as a topsail schooner, and the slightly flatter angle of *Esmeralda's* bowsprit. Esmeralda was completed in 1954. Her distinctive figurehead represents a giant Andes condor, the national bird of Chile.

SPECIFICATIONS

Flag: France
Rig: Topsail schooner
Homeport: Brest, France
Sparred length: 124'
Draft: 12'
Beam: 24'
Hull: wood

Photo by Thad Koza

ETOILE

Along with her sister ship *La Belle Poule*, the schooner *Etoile* serves the French Navy in the training of future officers. Designed with the hull shape and the rigging of fishing vessels from Breton, *La Belle Poule* and *Etoile* were built in 1932 in the fishing port of Fecamp in northern Normandy, France. During World War II, both vessels relocated to Portsmouth, England, where they served the Free France Forces. They are permitted to fly the French ensign with the imposed Cross of Lorraine in recognition of their service during the war.

Program type: Sail training vessel of the French Navy
Built: 1932: Fecamp, Normandy, France
Contact: Embassy of France, 4101 Resevoir Road, NW, Washington, DC 20007 USA
Tel: 202-944-6000 **Fax:** 202-944-6166

SPECIFICATIONS

Flag: The Netherlands
Rig: Barque
Homeport: The Hague, The Netherlands
Normal cruising waters: Worldwide
Sparred length: 185'
LOA: 159'
LOD: 143'
LWL: 132'
Draft: 12'
Beam: 24'
Rig height: 109'
Freeboard: 4'
Sail area: 11,000 square feet
Tons: 303 GRT
Hull: steel

EUROPA

Who sails: Youth trainees, individuals, families, and groups of all ages
Program type: Sail training for paying trainees; fully accredited sea education in maritime history; special expeditions to Antarctica; dockside interpretation during port visits
Season: Year-round
Built: 1911: Hamburg, Germany, Stülcken
Crew: 12 **Trainees-voyage crew:** 90 daysails, 50 overnight
Contact: Rederij Bark EUROPA, PO Box 23183, 3001 KD Rotterdam The Netherlands
Tel: +31 (0) 10 281 0990
Fax: +31 (0) 10 281 0991
E-mail: info@barkeuropa.com
Website: www.barkeuropa.com

Europa was launched in Hamburg in 1911 for use as a lightship in the entrance of the river Elbe. In her second life, which started after an 8 year refit in 1994, the *Europa* recommenced sailing as a sail-training vessel. The professional crew of 14 seafarers involve the voyage crew/trainees as much as possible in running and sailing this traditionally rigged barque. The "guest crew" sail the ship in accordance to their individual abilities and ambition and no former sailing experience is needed. They learn how to stand watches, take turns at steering or as lookout, take in or set sails, scrub the decks and practice traditional seafaring/seamanship skills. Following her annual Antarctic voyages, the *Europa* "follows the sun" in the wake of the old sailing routes into the Northern Hemisphere. In the summer of 2012 *Europa* is planning to take part in the "Sail Training International" races to Portugal, Spain & Ireland; for 2013 plans are coming together to go to Australia together with the Dutch three-masted topsail schooner *Oosterschelde* to participate in Tall Ships Races in Australia and New Zealand. From there *Europa* will be living up to her nickname "Ocean Wanderer" by sailing together with *Oosterschelde* from Auckland around Cape Horn to the Falklands.

Flag: USA
Rig: Brigantine
Homeport: Los Angeles, California
Normal cruising waters:
Southern California and offshore
islands
Sparred length: 110' 8"
LOA: 90'
LOD: 81' 7"
LWL: 72' 6"
Draft: 11'
Beam: 21' 9"
Rig height: 87' 8"
Sail area: 4,540 square feet
Tons: 99 GRT
Power: 315 HP diesel
Hull: wood

Photo by Lee Uran

EXY JOHNSON

The Los Angeles Maritime Institute (LAMI) launched the twin brigantines, *Exy Johnson* and *Irving Johnson*, in 2002 for the TopSail Youth Program. With ships named in honor of sail training pioneers and seven-time circumnavigators with youth crew aboard their ship, *Yankee*, TopSail recognizes that the shipboard environment is challenging yet nurturing, encouraging exploration and self-reliance. TopSail is notably effective with youth who are not coping well with the demands of society and are at risk of dropping out of school and giving up. The 2007 research findings from the University of Edinburgh-Sail Training International study describe TopSail as "highly successful, developing personal and social confidence, and the ability to work together with others." With the premise that 'school is where the kids are...', TopSail youth engage in building cooperation, courage, confidence and character in the real-world classroom of the sea. LAMI is a volunteer-driven, youth-focused, educational 'family' organization. We welcome the skills and enthusiasm of people of all ages and all walks of life to sail with youth, maintain the tall ships, and be involved in many other ways.

Who sails: Youth/school groups from diverse communities, mostly from middle schools in urban areas
Program type: Educational sailing adventures for youth and adult groups
Season: Year-round
Coast Guard certification: Sailing School Vessel (Subchapter R), Passenger vessel (Subchapter T)
Contact: Los Angeles Maritime Institute, Berth 73, Suite 2, San Pedro, CA 90731 USA
Tel: 310-833-6055 **Fax:** 310-548-2055
Website: www.LAMITopSail.org

SPECIFICATIONS

Flag: Canada
Rig: Brigantine
Homeport: Ottawa, Ontario, Canada
Normal cruising waters:
Great Lakes and East Coast
(summer), Caribbean (winter)
Sparred length: 110'
LOD: 82'
LOA: 62'
Draft: 6'
Beam: 24' 6"
Rig height: 80'
Freeboard: 8'
Sail area: 4,000 square feet
Tons: 124 GRT
Power: 235 HP diesel
Hull: fiberglass on steel

FAIR JEANNE

Who sails: Middle school, high school, college, adults
Program type: Sail training for paying trainees; overnight voyages; sea education in maritime history with formal organizations and as informal; in-house programming; dockside interpretation; bursary programs available
Season: Spring, summer and fall
Designer: Captain Thomas G. Fuller
Built: 1982: Ottawa, Ontario, Canada, T. G. Fuller
Certification: Sailing School Vessel, inland/near coastal
Crew: 6 high school and university officers
Trainees-passengers: 36 daysails; 24 overnight
Contact: Bytown Brigantine, Inc., 2700 Queensview Drive, Ottawa, Ontario K2B 8H6 Canada
Tel: 613-596-6258 **Fax:** 613-596-4335
E-mail: info@tallshipsadventure.org
Website: www.tallshipsadventure.org

Designed and built in 1982 by the late Captain Thomas G. Fuller, *Fair Jeanne* was first sailed as a private yacht. Captain Fuller was one of Canada's most decorated WWII naval war heroes, earning the name "Pirate of the Adriatic". His wartime experience taught him the value of instilling confidence and resourcefulness in our youth while at sea. More than 100,000 nautical miles and almost 30 years later, *Fair Jeanne* is now in service as a sail training vessel for Bytown Brigantine, a non-profit charitable organization dedicated to providing adventure through the time honored traditions inherent in square rigged sailing. During the summer months she provides programs for youth 14-19 years old, and during the spring and fall she also provides programs for school groups and adults.

SPECIFICATIONS

SPECIFICATIONS

Flag: Sweden
Rig: Schooner
Homeport: Karlskrona, Sweden
Sparred length: 129'
Draft: 13' 9"
Beam: 23'
Hull: steel

Photo by Thad Koza

FALKEN

Falken and her sister ship *Gladan* are twin schooners built in 1947, in the same yard and according to the same plans. Differentiated only by their sail numbers, these two vessels train future officers of the Swedish Royal Navy, as they have since their commissioning.

Program type: Sail training vessel of the Swedish Royal Navy
Built: 1947
Contact: Embassy of Sweden, 1501 M Street, NW, Suite 900, Washington, DC 20005-1702 USA
Tel: 202-467-2600 **Fax:** 202-467-2699

SPECIFICATIONS

Flag: USA
Rig: Topsail schooner
Homeport: Dundalk, Maryland
Normal cruising waters:
Chesapeake Bay, East Coast of US
Sparred length: 47'
LOD: 40'
LWL: 30'
Draft: 4' 9"
Beam: 10' 6"
Sail area: 1,000 square feet
Tons: 9 GRT
Power: 25 HP diesel
Hull: fiberglass

FAREWELL

Who sails: Groups and individuals of all ages
Program type: Sail training for paying trainees; sea education in maritime history; passenger day sails and overnight passages; dockside interpretation
Season: April through November
Designer: P. Van Dine
Built: 1972: Andy Merrill
Crew: 6
Contact: Captain Linda Gunn, 8500 Cove Road, Dundalk, MD 21222 USA
Tel: 410-961-4054
E-mail: schoonergirl@comcast.net
Website: www.schoonerfarewell.com

Peter Van Dine designed *Farewell* and traded the design with Andy Merrill for guitar lessons for he and his wife. Over a two year period, Andy built *Farewell* in his backyard in Annapolis, MD and launched her in 1972. *Farewell* was home to Andy and his family until 1982. The second owner purchased *Farewell* in 1994 to use as a coastal sail training vessel for three pre-teen sons. In 1996, the owner and the three boys cruised from Annapolis, MD to Camden, ME. The ship competed in the Great Chesapeake Bay Schooner Race each year from 1994 to 1998. In early 1999, her present owner, Captain Linda Gunn, purchased *Farewell*. During the past several years, *Farewell* has participated in Tall Ships America events and several maritime festivals and celebrations, including the homecoming of the USS *Constellation*, the Baltimore Preakness Schooner Race, and the Leukemia & Lymphoma Society Bridge to Bridge race. *Farewell* has also continued the tradition of competing in the Great Chesapeake Bay Schooner Race.

SPECIFICATIONS

Flag: USA
Rig: Square topsail sloop
Homeport: South Haven, Michigan
Normal cruising waters: Upper Great Lakes
Sparred Length: 101'
LOD: 56' 3"
Draft: 8' 9"
Beam: 16' 10"
Rig Height: 82'
Sail area: 3,180 square feet
Tons: 49.2 GRT
Power: diesel
Hull: wood

FRIENDS GOOD WILL

"We have met the enemy and they are ours…", Commander Oliver Hazard Perry, U.S.N., Battle of Lake Erie, September 10, 1813. This famous dispatch, dashed off within an hour after the great guns fell silent, went on to reference a merchant sloop turned man-o-war. That sloop was *Friends Good Will*. The Michigan Maritime Museum launched a replica of this fateful vessel in 2004. Scarano Boatbuilding, Inc. of Albany, New York, designed and built *Friends Good Will*, to be rigged and sailed by Museum volunteers. The vessel serves as an historic flagship for the preservation of traditional maritime skills. The Michigan Maritime Museum is developing programs and curriculum, utilizing its Padnos Boat Shed as a rig shop and its ample exhibit space to assist in educating members, visitors, school groups of all ages and special tours about Michigan's maritime history and culture. Combining these resources with dockside interpretation and a day sail program throughout the summer, *Friends Good Will* employs traditional materials and skills to keep Michigan's rich maritime heritage alive.

Who sails: Museum members, school groups, individuals and families
Program Type: Sail Training for museum members and crew; passenger day sails; dockside interpretation, historical reenactment at home port and during port visits; education in history, geography, navigation, marine science for school groups of all ages. Affiliated with Sea Scout Ship #5191, South Haven, Michigan.
Designer: Scarano Boatbuilding, Inc.
Built: 2004: Albany, NY, Scarano Boatbuilding, Inc.
Coast Guard certification: Passenger Vessel (Subchapter T)
Crew: 13 **Trainees-passengers:** 28 daysails
Contact: Michigan Maritime Museum, 260 Dyckman Avenue, South Haven, Michigan 49090 USA
Tel: 269-637-8078 **Fax:** 269-637-1594
E-mail: info@michiganmaritimemuseum.org
Website: www.MichiganMaritimeMuseum.org

SPECIFICATIONS

Flag: USA
Rig: Full-rigged ship
Homeport: Salem, Massachusetts
Normal cruising waters:
Massachusetts Bay, Buzzards Bay
Sparred length: 171'
LOA: 116'
LOD: 104'
LWL: 99'
Draft: 11' 3"
Beam: 30'
Rig height: 125'
Freeboard: 10'
Sail area: 9,409 square feet
Tons: 99 GRT
Power: twin 300 HP diesels
Hull: wood

Photo by S.Waterworth/NPS

FRIENDSHIP OF SALEM

Who sails: All age groups through school programs as well as general public on day sails and weekly programmed trips.
Program type: Dockside programs and hands on interpretation as an historic site exhibit; informal sea education in maritime history. Special events at other ports and dockside leasing for special events at Salem.
Season: Open for tours all year
Designer: Bay Marine, Inc., Barrington, RI
Built: 1998: Scarano Boats, Albany, NY; 1999-2002: Salem, MA., Dion Yacht Yard, NPS & USS Constitution Naval Detachment
Coast Guard certification: Passenger Vessel (Subchapter T)
Crew: 5 **Trainees-passengers:** 30 daysails
Contact: Colleen Bruce, Chief, Marine and Special Programs, Salem Maritime National Historic Site, 160 Derby Street, Salem, MA 01915 USA
Tel: 978-740-1694 **Fax:** 978-740-1685
E-mail: colleen_bruce@nps.gov
Website: www.nps.gov/sama and www.salem-web.com/frndship

Friendship, a full size replica of a Salem East Indiaman, built for the National Park Service and berthed at Salem Maritime National Historic Site in Salem, Massachusetts, was launched in August 1998. Although she represents a specific vessel built in Salem in 1797, she is typical of a class of commercial carriers commonly employed in both the East India and transatlantic trades during the early years of the new American republic. Her historic predecessor is credited with 15 voyages to the Far East, South America, Mediterranean, and northern Europe. She had the misfortune of being taken as a prize of war by the British Royal Navy on a return voyage from Archangel, Russia, in 1812. Sold by the British government in 1813, her ultimate fate remains a mystery. Today's *Friendship* is built from wood laminates and solid timbers and was designed as a passenger carrying and sail training vessel while exhibiting the look and function of an historic vessel. *Friendship* is accessible to the public for dockside tours.

SPECIFICATIONS

Flag: USA
Rig: Brigantine
Homeport: Fairhaven, Massachusetts
Normal cruising waters: Southern New England
Sparred length: 74'
LOD: 54'
LWL: 47'
Draft: 7'
Beam: 15'
Rig height: 65'
Freeboard: 5'
Sail area: 9,409 square feet
Tons: 39 GRT
Power: Detroit 4-71 175 BHP
Hull: wood

FRITHA

The S/V *Fritha*, is a 74-foot tall ship used for training purposes at Northeast Maritime Institute and is widely available for charters to the public. Launched in 1986 in New Zealand and named for the heroine in Paul Gallico's book, The Snow Goose, the brigantine *Fritha* was built by traditional methods to unparalleled standards of excellence in materials and craftsmanship. The *Fritha's* home waters of Southern New England offer some of the most beautiful scenery and the best sailing in the world. Interesting ports and anchorages include Buzzard's Bay, Elizabeth Islands, Martha's Vineyard and Nantucket, and are only a few hours' sail from *Fritha's* home port of Fairhaven, Massachusetts. The *Fritha* can also meet you in places outside of her home waters as well. With a licensed captain and professional crew, your sailing adventure aboard the brigantine *Fritha* will create memories that last a lifetime. Fritha can accommodate up to six passengers and is ready to take family and friends on an exciting and educational adventure. Learn navigation, knot tying and the art of square rigged sailing. The crew encourages guests to help haul the sails during your time aboard. *Fritha* is owned and operated by Northeast Maritime Institute.

Who sails: Students of the Northeast Maritime Institute
Program type: Sail training
Designer: Murray Peterson
Built: 1985: New Zealand, McMullan and Wing
Coast Guard certification: Uninspected Passenger Vessel (Subchapter C)
Crew: 2 **Trainees-passengers:** 6 daysails, 6 overnight
Contact: Northeast Maritime Institue, 32 Washington Street, Fairhaven, MA 02719 USA
Tel: 508-992-4025 **Fax:** 508-992-1236
E-mail: fritha@northeastmaritime.com
Website: www.northeastmaritime.com

SPECIFICATIONS

Flag: USA
Rig: Barquentine, 3-masted
Homeport: Philadelphia, Pennsylvania
Normal cruising waters: Delaware River and the Atlantic Coast
Sparred length: 177'
LOA: 150'
LOD: 140'
LWL: 133'
Draft: 17'
Beam: 26"
Rig height: 100'
Sail area: 8,910 square feet
Tons: 299 GRT
Power: diesel
Hull: wood, copper clad

GAZELA

Who sails: Volunteers who support the Philadelphia Ship Preservation Guild
Program type: Sail training for crew and apprentices; sea education based on informal in-house programming; dockside interpretation both in homeport and on out-port visits
Built: 1883: Cacihas, Portugal, major rebuild 1901: Setubal, Portugal
Crew: 35 (volunteer)
Contact: Philadelphia Ship Preservation Guild, 301 S.Columbus Blvd., Philadelphia, PA 19106 USA
Tel: 215-238-0280 **Fax:** 215-238-0281
E-mail: office@gazela.org
Website: www.gazela.org

The wooden barquentine, *Gazela Primeiro*, was originally built to fish for cod in the Grand Banks. Now owned and operated by the Philadelphia Ship Preservation Guild, a nonprofit volunteer organization, the *Gazela* sails as a goodwill ambassador for the Commonwealth of Pennsylvania and the Ports of Philadelphia, Pennsylvania and Camden, New Jersey. Our mission extends beyond historic preservation to community outreach through such activities as maritime education of disadvantaged youth. *Gazela* has been featured in several major motion pictures including "Interview with the Vampire" and "The Widow of St. Pierre", as well as several documentaries including "The Irish in America".

SPECIFICATIONS

Flag: USA
Rig: Sloop
Homeport: Newport, Rhode Island
Normal cruising waters:
North Atlantic and Caribbean
Sparred length: 69' 8"
LOA: 69' 8"
LOD: 68'
LWL: 53' 11"
Draft: 6' 8" – 13' 5"
Beam: 18' 7"
Rig height: 85' 6"
Freeboard: 5'
Sail area: 2,091 square feet
Tons: 53 GRT
Power: diesel
Hull: fiberglass

GERONIMO

The sailing vessel *Geronimo* sails year round between the Canadian maritime and the greater Carribean. Trainees are taught Nautical Science and Oceanography/Marine Biology while on board. During the academic year, *Geronimo* carries students from St. George's School on 6-week long voyages. During these trips, the students stand watch, learn the intricacies of handling a modern sailing vessel and conduct research on sea turtles working in conjunction with the Archie Carr Center for Sea Turtle Research University of Florida, Gainsville. In the summer months, the vessel makes three shorter trips along the east coast. Summer trainees range in age from high school to adult.

Who sails: High school students through adults
Program type: Marine/nautical science
Season: Year-round
Designer: Ted Hood Design Group
Built: 1998: Portsmouth, RI, New England Boatworks
Coast Guard certification: Sailing School Vessel (Subchapter R)
Crew: 3 **Trainees-passengers:** 8
Contact: Captain Deborah Hayes, Program Director, St. George's School, 372 Purgatory Road, PO Box 1910, Newport, RI 02840 USA
Tel: 401-842-6747 **Fax:** 401-842-6696
E-mail: Deborah_Hayes@stgeorges.edu
Website: www.sailgeronimo.org

SPECIFICATIONS

Flag: Sweden
Rig: Schooner
Homeport: Karlskrona, Sweden
Sparred length: 129'
Draft: 13' 9"
Beam: 23'
Hull: steel

Photo by Thad Koza

GLADAN

Program type: Sail training vessel of the Swedish Royal Navy
Built: 1947
Contact: Embassy of Sweden, 1501 M Street, NW, Suite 900, Washington, DC 20005-1702
Tel: 202-467-2600 **Fax:** 202-467-2699

Gladan and her sister ship *Falken* are twin schooners built in 1947, in the same yard and according to the same plans. Differentiated only by their sail numbers, these two vessels train future officers of the Swedish Royal Navy as they have since their commissioning.

SPECIFICATIONS

Flag: Colombia
Rig: Barque, 3-masted
Homeport: Cartegena, Colombia
Normal cruising waters:
Worldwide
Sparred length: 249' 4"
LOA: 212'
LOD: 189'
LWL: 184'
Draft: 14' 9"
Beam: 34' 9"
Rig height: 126' 4"
Freeboard: 21' 7"
Sail area: 15,075 square feet
Tons: 934 GRT
Power: twin 256 HP KV
Hull: steel

GLORIA

Built in Bilbao, Spain for the Colombian Navy in 1966, the 3-masted barque *Gloria* is used as a school ship for the cadets of the Colombian Naval Academy. She carries a compliment of 150 men and women, ranging from enlisted to midshipmen and officers. The cruises are aimed at training officers in their third year at the Naval Academy, to implement their academic knowledge in the areas of star navigation, seamanship, leadership and teambuilding. *Gloria* is a proud goodwill ambassador of the Colombian Navy. During her service she has made 46 cruises, navigating over 500,000 nautical miles and visiting 143 different ports around the world.

Who sails: Midshipmen, enlisted and officers of the Colombian Navy
Program type: Sail training vessel of the Colombian Navy
Season: Year-round
Designer: Sener
Built: 1969: Bilbao, Spain, A. T. Celaya
Certification: Colombian Naval Vessel
Crew: 69 **Trainees-passengers:** 80 students
Contact: Embassy of Colombia, 2118 Leroy Place, NW, Washington, DC 20008
Tel: 202-387-8338 **Fax:** 202-232-8643
E-mail: embassyofcolombia@colombiaemb.org
Website: www.colombiaemb.org

SPECIFICATIONS

Flag: USA
Rig: Barque, 3-masted (lateen mizzen)
Homeport: Jamestown Settlement, Virginia
Normal cruising waters:
Chesapeake Bay, US East Coast
Sparred length: 88'
LOA: 74'
LOD: 65'
LWL: 56'
Draft: 7'
Beam: 17'
Rig height: 72'
Freeboard: 7' 6"
Sail area: 2,420 square feet
Power: twin 115 HP diesel
Hull: wood

GODSPEED

Who sails: Crew consisting of Jamestown Settlement staff and volunteers. Age 18 years and older
Program type: Sail training and dockside interpretation
Season: Year-round
Designer: Tri-Coastal Marine
Built: 2006: Rockport Marine, Inc., Rockport, Maine
Coast Guard certification: Passenger Vessel (Subchapter T), Attraction Vessel
Crew: 12 **Trainees-passengers:** 20
Contact: Capt. Eric Speth, Maritime Program Manager, Jamestown Settlement, PO Box 1607, Williamsburg, VA 23187 USA
Tel: 757-253-4838 **Fax:** 757-253-7350
Website: www.historyisfun.org

Godspeed is a full-scale re-creation of one of the three ships that brought America's first permanent English colonists to Virginia in 1607. Together with the *Susan Constant* and *Discovery*, *Godspeed* is on exhibit at Jamestown Settlement, a living-history museum of 17th-century Virginia, and hosts about a half-million visitors every year. Jamestown Settlement is administered by the Jamestown-Yorktown Foundation, a Virginia state agency. Built at Rockport Marine in Maine and commissioned at Jamestown Settlement in 2006, *Godspeed* is a third-generation re-creation. The first was built for the 1957 350th-anniversary commemoration of the founding of Jamestown. *Godspeed, Susan Constant* and *Discovery* are based on the historically documented tonnages of the original ships and 17th-century principles of tonnage measurement. With a crew of staff and volunteers, *Godspeed* and *Susan Constant* periodically sail to other ports in the Chesapeake Bay region to participate in commemorative and community events and host educational programs. A volunteer sail-training program is offered to individuals 18 and older.

SPECIFICATIONS

Flag: Germany
Rig: Barque
Homeport: Kiel, Germany
Normal cruising waters:
Worldwide
Sparred length: 293'
Draft: 15' 6"
Beam: 39'
Sail Area: 21,140 square feet
Hull: steel

GORCH FOCK II

Built from the same plans and in the same shipyard (Blohm & Voss in Hamburg, Germany) as the original, *Gorch Fock II* boasts contemporary safety features and the latest navigational equipment. She is an eminent replacement for her namesake (now the training vessel *Tovarishch* from Ukraine). Since her launch in 1958, *Gorch Fock II* has logged thousands of nautical miles in her twice-yearly voyages and has hosted more than ten thousand cadets for training cruises. The barque is named for a popular German writer of sea stories, Hans Kinau (1880 – 1916), who used the pseudonym Gorch Fock (fock means "foresail" in German). Kinau became part of the romantic mythology of the sea when he perished aboard the cruiser *Weisbaden*, which was sunk during the Battle of Jutland on 31 May 1916. The training vessel of the German Navy, *Gorch Fock II* is a proud symbol of Germany's distinguished sailing and shipbuilding traditions.

Program type: Sail training vessel of the German Navy.
Built: 1958: Hamburg, Germany, Blohm & Voss
Crew: 73 **Trainees-passengers:** 200
Contact: Embassy of the Federal Republic of Germany, 4645 Reservoir Road, NW, Washington, DC 20007 USA
Tel: 202-298-8140 **Fax:** 202-298-4249

SPECIFICATIONS

Flag: Sweden
Rig: Full-rigged ship
Homeport: Göteborg, Sweden
Normal cruising waters: Worldwide
Sparred length: 192'
LOA: 156'
LWL: 134'
Draft: 17' 2"
Beam: 36'
Rig height: 154'
Sail area: 21,140 square feet
Power: 2 x Volvo Penta TAMD 163A
(16 liter) 550 HP
Hull: wood

GÖTHEBORG

Who sails: Adults of all ages
Program type: Sail training for paying trainees; overnight passages; dockside interpretation
Season: Year-round
Designer: Joakim Severinson
Built: 2005: Svenska Ostindiska Companiet, Goteborg, Sweden
Certification: Special Purpose Ship
Crew: 20 **Passengers-trainees:** 50 overnight
Contact: Emanuel Persson, Svenska Ostindiska Companiet, Eriksberg Pir 4, Göteborg, 41763 Sweden
Tel: +46317793450
E-mail: info@soic.se
Website: www.soic.se

One of the Swedish East India Company's ships, the East Indiaman *Götheborg*, ran aground at the entrance to Gothenburg (Göteborg) in Sweden in 1745. The ship was fully laden with goods such as tea, porcelain, silk and spices, and had almost reached dock after her third voyage to China. After almost 250 years a group of divers rediscovered the shipwreck and a marine archaeological excavation opened the door to a bygone century of adventurous voyages and trade with China. It also awakened the dream of rebuilding the ship and once again sailing across the oceans. During the years 1995-2005 *Götheborg* was built using old methods and the same materials as for the original ship. In 2005 the ship set sail on her first expedition to China. Today, *Götheborg* voyages across the oceans promoting cultural exchange, peaceful trade and international relations. EXPEDITION AMERICA: In the autumn of 2012, *Götheborg* will embark on an expedition to the USA and Canada, with several stopovers during the year of 2013. Join the adventure at www.expeditionamerica.com
www.facebook.com/swedishshipgotheborg
www.twitter.com/gotheborg

SPECIFICATIONS

Flag: Ecuador
Rig: Barque
Homeport: Guayquil, Ecuador
Normal cruising waters:
Worldwide
Sparred length: 257'
LOA: 221'
LOD: 218'
LWL: 184'
Draft: 15' 4"
Beam: 34' 9"
Sail area: 15,784 square feet
Power: diesel
Hull: steel

GUAYAS

Guayas was built in the Celaya Shipyard in Bilbao, Spain. She is named after the Chief of Huancavilcas, a native culture in the Ecuadorian coastal region. Commissioned in 1977, the *Guayas* is proud to serve as a goodwill ambassador for the Ecuadorian Navy. The ship carries a complement of 16 officers, 43 midshipmen, and 94 enlisted men, including the ship's band. During a cruise, considered one semester at the Ecuadorian Naval Academy, midshipmen apply, in a very challenging environment, theoretical principals of navigation, seamanship and other subjects learned in the classroom.

Who sails: Ecuadorian Naval Academy cadets
Program type: Sail training for Ecuadorian Naval Academy cadets
Season: Year-round
Designer: Celaya
Built: 1976: Bilbao, Spain, Celaya Shipyard
Certification: Ecuadorian Naval Vessel
Crew: 76
Contact: Naval Attaché, Embassy of Ecuador, 2535 15th Street NW, Washington, DC 20009 USA
Tel: 202-265-7674 **Fax:** 202-667-3482

SPECIFICATIONS

Flag: USA
Rig: Gaff topsail schooner, 2-masted
Homeport: Islesboro, Maine
Normal cruising waters: North Atlantic Ocean and Caribbean Sea, Canada to South America
Sparred length: 131'
LOA: 95'
LOD: 90'
LWL: 85'
Draft: 9' 7"
Beam: 24'
Rig height: 91'
Freeboard: 5'
Sail area: 4,200 square feet
Tons: 94 GRT
Power: 220 HP diesel
Hull: wood

HARVEY GAMAGE

Who sails: Individuals and school groups from middle school through college; affiliated institutions include Proctor Academy, University of Maine, Center for Coastal Studies, Outward Bound, and other schools
Program type: Traditional seamanship training combined with accredited academic studies
Season: Year-round
Designer: McCurdy & Rhodes
Built: 1973: South Bristol, Maine, Harvey F. Gamage Shipyard
Coast Guard certification: Sailing School Vessel (Subchapter R), Passenger Vessel (Subchapter T)
Crew: 8 - 11 including instructors
Student-trainees: 24 overnight
Contact: Ocean Classroom Foundation, PO Box 205, 1 Oak Street, Boothbay Harbor, ME 04538 USA
Tel: 800-724-7245
E-mail: mail@oceanclassroom.org
Website: www.oceanclassroom.org

Owned by the Ocean Classroom Foundation, the schooner *Harvey Gamage* offers programs of education under sail to the youth of America. Programs range from four month semesters-at-sea to week-long programs with schools and youth groups. Trainees sail the ship and learn traditional seamanship skills under the captain and crew, and they explore maritime subjects with the onboard academic staff. Ocean Classroom's Discovery™ program is a semester-at-sea for qualified high school students, fully accredited by Proctor Academy. The voyage covers more than 6,000 nautical miles, connecting South American shores to the Canadian Maritimes. Students live and work as sailors on a true voyage of discovery, while they study maritime history, maritime literature, marine science, applied mathematics, and navigation. Discovery™ is offered Fall and Spring Terms. Other programs include SEAmester™, OceanBound and Summer Seafaring Camps. The Ocean Classroom Foundation also owns and operates the schooners *Spirit of Massachusetts* and *Westward*.

SPECIFICATIONS

Flag: USA
Rig: Square topsail ketch
Homeport: Grays Harbor, Aberdeen,Washington
Normal cruising waters: West Coast of North America
Sparred length: 103'
LOD: 65'
LWL: 62'
Draft: 6'
Beam: 22'
Rig height: 75'
Freeboard: 3'
Sail area: 4,200 square feet
Tons: 64 GRT
Power: twin diesels
Hull: wood

HAWAIIAN CHIEFTAIN

Hawaiian Chieftain is a 103-foot square-rigged topsail ketch owned and operated by Grays Harbor Historical Seaport Authority. Built in Lahaina, Hawaii in 1988, she is a contemporary interpretation of a traditional design based on the European trading vessels that called in Hawaii during the 18th-century. Each year, *Hawaiian Chieftain* sails the Pacific Coast from British Columbia to San Diego in company with the *Lady Washington* providing "Voyages of Discovery" sailing and dockside educational programs. This hands-on history program teaches 4th & 5th grade students about the exploration of the Pacific Coast during the 1790s. The ships offer dockside tours and sea battle reenactment, sails for the public, as well as a crew training program, "Two Weeks Before the Mast." Summer programs include "Family Camp" and "Youth Camp" for ages 12 to 16. *Hawaiian Chieftain* programs are designed to educate, excite, inspire and empower students and the general public. *Hawaiian Chieftain* also offers sail training and team building for adults, private charters, and natural history cruises.

Who sails: Individuals and groups
Program type: Sail training for apprentices and paying trainees; maritime heritage programs for schools, homeschools and youth organizations; public programs include summer camps, three-hour sails, dockside tours and passages
Season: Year-round
Designer: Raymond R. Richards
Built: 1988: Lahaina, Maui, Hawaii, Lahaina Welding Co.
Coast Guard certification: Passenger Vessel (Subchapter T)
Crew: 8 **Trainees-passengers:** 45 overnight
Contact: Capt. Les Bolton, Executive Director, Grays Harbor Historical Seaport Authority, PO Box 2019, Aberdeen, WA 98520 USA
Tel: 800-200-5239 **Fax:** 360-533-9384
E-mail: les@historicalseaport.org
Website: www.historicalseaport.org

SPECIFICATIONS

Flag: USA
Rig: Dipping lug
Homeport: Grays Harbor, Aberdeen, Washington
Normal cruising waters: Grays Harbor, Puget Sound, Western Washington
Sparred length: 26'
LOA: 25'
LOD: 25'
LWL: 25'
Draft: 20"
Beam: 7'
Rig height: 16'
Sail area: 316 square feet
Tons: 3,800 LBS
Hull: wood

HEWITT R. JACKSON

Who sails: Students in grades elementary through college and groups and individuals of all ages
Program type: Sail training for volunteer and paying crew and trainees in cooperation with accredited institutions and other organized groups; sea education in maritime history, marine science, and ecology; passenger day sails; dockside interpretation
Designer: Stewart Hoagland, Hewitt Jackson
Built: 1993: Aberdeen, WA, Grays Harbor Historical Seaport Authority
Coast Guard certification: Sailing School Vessel (Subchapter R)
Crew: 2 **Trainees-passengers:** 8 – 13 day sails
Contact: Capt. Les Bolton, Executive Director, Grays Harbor Historical Seaport Authority, PO Box 2019, Aberdeen, WA 98520 USA
Tel: 800-200-5239 **Fax:** 360-533-9384
E-mail: les@historicalseaport.org
Website: www.historicalseaport.org

On May 12, 1792 Captain Robert Gray sailed his ship, *Columbia Rediviva*, over the bar of the "Great River of the West" and named it Columbia's River in honor of his ship. Captain Gray never would have entered that river had it not been for the information he received from the first American vessel to enter the river, *Columbia's* longboat. Unnamed and unheralded, ship's longboats were the workhorses of the 16th- to 19th-century. Powered by either oars or sails, these versatile seaworthy craft carried all manner of cargo from ship to shore and back again. Grays Harbor Historical Seaport Authority built two 18th-century ship's longboat reproductions in 1993. Noted maritime historian and artist Hewitt R. Jackson, who worked closely with naval architect Stewart Hoagland and Seaport Director Les Bolton to ensure both historical accuracy and the meeting of specific program needs, painstakingly researched the design for the Seaport longboats. Powered by ten oars, or up to a 3-masted dipping lugsail rig, these versatile vessels are ideal for exploring the protected inland waterways of Washington. Programs are customized to the needs and interests of specific groups.

SPECIFICATIONS

Flag: USA
Rig: Gaff schooner, 2-masted
Homeport: Suttons Bay, Michigan
Normal cruising waters: Grand Traverse Bay, Lake Michigan
Sparred length: 77'
LOA: 61' 6"
LOD: 61' 6"
LWL: 53'
Draft: 7'
Beam: 17'
Rig height: 66'
Freeboard: 4'
Sail area: 1,800 square feet
Tons: 41 GRT
Power: 130 HP diesel
Hull: steel

INLAND SEAS

The *Inland Seas* Education Association (ISEA) was created in 1989 to teach culturally diverse students from throughout the state of Michigan, the Midwest and beyond about the science and heritage of the Great Lakes. ISEA's award-winning experiential educational programs are designed for students in grades 5 – 12 and are modified for learners of all ages. More than 90,000 participants have experienced the Great Lakes Schoolship Program, including students from over 140 Michigan communities. Summer shipboard experiences for all ages include astronomy, history, and science programs on Grand Traverse Bay and Lake Michigan. The goal of every ISEA program is to encourage young people to pursue academic interests related to the Great Lakes, particularly the sciences, and to provide enhanced public understanding and stewardship of the Great Lakes for future generations. The heart of the Schoolship Program is the work of 200 dedicated and professionally trained volunteers who donate nearly 8,000 hours annually aboard the Schoolship.

Who sails: School groups and individuals of all ages
Program type: Sail training for volunteer and paying trainees; sea education in marine science, maritime history, and ecology for students from elementary through college, adults, and at-risk youth; dockside interpretation during port visits
Season: May through early October
Designer: Charles W. Wittholz, Woodin & Marean
Built: 1994: Palm Coast, FL, Treworgy Yachts
Coast Guard certification: Passenger Vessel (Subchapter T)
Crew: 5 **Trainees-passengers:** 32 daysails, 10 overnight
Contact: Thomas M. Kelly, Executive Director, Inland Seas Education Association, PO Box 218, Suttons Bay, MI 49682 USA
Tel: 231-271-3077 **Fax:** 231-271-3088
E-mail: isea@schoolship.org
Website: www.schoolship.org

SPECIFICATIONS

Flag: USA
Rig: Brigantine
Homeport: Los Angeles, California
Normal cruising waters: Southern California and offshore islands
Sparred length: 110' 8"
LOA: 90'
LOD: 81' 7"
LWL: 72' 6"
Draft: 11'
Beam: 21' 9"
Rig height: 87' 8"
Sail area: 4,540 square feet
Tons: 99 GRT
Power: 315 HP diesel
Hull: wood

Photo by Volker Correll

IRVING JOHNSON

Who sails: Youth/school groups from diverse communities, mostly middle schoolers from 'at-risk' urban areas
Program type: Educational sailing adventures for youth and adult groups
Season: Year-round
Coast Guard certification: Sailing School Vessel (Subchapter R), Passenger Vessel (Subchapter T)
Contact: Los Angeles Maritime Institute, Berth 73, Suite 2, San Pedro, CA 90731 USA
Tel: 310-833-6055 **Fax:** 310-548-2055
Website: www.LAMITopSail.org

In April of 2002, the Los Angeles Maritime Institute launched the twin brigantines *Exy Johnson* and *Irving Johnson.* Named in honor of the Johnsons and their lifelong commitment to character-building sailing adventures, the brigantines were constructed on the waterfront in San Pedro, California. Designed for LAMI's TopSail Youth Program, the brigantines were built especially to meet the needs of middle school youth. The TopSail Youth Program uses sail training to provide youth with real-life challenges that develop the knowledge, skills and attitudes needed to live healthy, productive lives. TopSail enriches, validates and challenges conventional school curricula by bringing biology, history, mathematics, physics, geography, literature and the environment to life in the real world classroom of the sea. Irving McClure Johnson began training for a sailor's life as a teenager. In 1929 he sailed around Cape Horn on the barque *Peking.* Captain Johnson met his wife Electa, "Exy", sailing trans-Atlantic aboard *Wanderbird.* The Johnsons sailed around the world seven times with youth crew on two different *Yankees,* then cruised European and African waters in their third *Yankee,* a ketch.

SPECIFICATIONS

Flag: Poland
Rig: Barquentine
Homeport: Gdynia, Poland
Normal cruising waters: Baltic Sea
Sparred length: 161'
LOA: 140'
LOD: 137'
LWL: 121'
Draft: 13' 9'
Beam: 26'
Rig height: 115'
Freeboard: 5'
Sail area: 377 square feet
Hull: steel

Photo by Thad Koza

ISKRA

The ship took her name after a 3-masted gaff schooner, *Iskra*, which sailed under the Polish navy ensign for 50 years between 1927 and 1977. ORP *Iskra* was built in 1982 in Gdanska Shipyard. She is a 3-masted barquentine with different rigging on all three masts. The foremast has five square sails; main sail is gaff-rigged; and mizzen is Bermudian. The main purpose of the ship is to train Polish Naval Academy cadets on their summer practices. Every year since 1987, she has participated in the Cutty Sark Tall Ships' Races. During her years of sailing, the ship has won numerous prizes including the United Nations Peace Medal in 1990, the Cutty Sark Trophy in 1989, the Fair Play Prize in the 1999 Cutty Sark Tall Ships Race, and the Polish Navy's Best Ship Prize (five times). The letters ORP in front of her name are the abbreviation for "Ship of the Republic of Poland" and indicate that the ship belongs to the Polish Navy. The name *Iskra* means "spark".

Who sails: Cadets of the Polish Naval Academy
Program type: Training vessel
Designer: Zygmunt Choren
Built: 1982: Gdanska Shipyard
Contact: Commanding Officer, ORP Iskra, JW 1449 ORP ISKRA, Gdynia, Wojewodztwo Pomorskie, 81-103 Gdynia 3 Poland
Tel: 48-58-626-25-54
Fax: 48-58-626-25-54
E-mail: iskra2@poczta.fm

SPECIFICATIONS

Flag: USA
Rig: Ship, 3-masted
Homeport: Mystic, Connecticut
Sparred length: 118' 6"
LOA: 100' 8"
Draft: 12'
Beam: 25' 3"
Rig height: 98' 6"
Tons: 213 GRT
Hull: iron

JOSEPH CONRAD

Who sails: Individuals and organized groups ages 10 – 15
Program type: Sail training; dockside visitation for school groups and individuals
Season: June – August
Designer: Burmeister and Wain
Built: 1882: Copenhagen, Denmark, Burmeister & Wain
Contact: Mystic Seaport Watercraft Department, PO Box 6000, Mystic, CT 06355-0990 USA
Tel: 860-572-5322 **Fax:** 860-572-5355
Website: www.mysticseaport.org

For over 60 years, young people have come to Mystic Seaport, our nation's leading maritime museum, to learn to sail and live on board the tall ship *Joseph Conrad*. Each morning, campers tackle the wind and current of the Mystic River and then set off for an active afternoon investigating the Museum's unique exhibitions. After a late-day sail session, some "R and R" and dinner, campers spend their evenings with new friends, stargazing in a planetarium, climbing the rigging of the *Conrad* or enjoying a lively sea music sing-a-long. The *Joseph Conrad* program is open to individual boys and girls and organized groups ages 10 – 15. No prior experience is required for beginner sessions, only a desire to participate and learn. Intermediate sessions are for those who have attended a previous beginner session or have had sailing experience. All must hold current Red Cross swimmers certification or its equivalent.

SPECIFICATIONS

Flag: Spain
Rig: Topsail schooner, 4-masted
Homeport: Cadiz, Spain
LOA: 305' 6"
Draft: 23' 7"
Beam: 42' 7"
Rig height: 164'
Power: GM358 diesel
Hull: iron

JUAN SEBASTIAN DE ELCANO

The official training vessel for the midshipmen and ensigns of the Spanish Navy, *Juan Sebastian de Elcano* was launched in 1927 and delivered to the Spanish navy in 1928. Her hull is made of iron and she has four masts, each named after other training ships which preceded her (*Blanca*, *Almansa*, *Asturias*, and *Nautilus*). She is named in honor of *Juan Sebastion de Elcano*, captain of Ferdinand Magellan's last exploratory fleet. The ship also carries the *de Elcano* coat of arms–a terraqueous globe and the motto "Primus Circumdedisti Me" (first to circumnavigate me) which emperor Charles I conferred on *de Elcano* after he returned to Spain having completed Magellan's global expedition. She has sailed in more than 50 training voyages, including six circumnavigations of the globe.

Who sails: Midshipmen of the Spanish Navy
Program type: Training vessel of the Spanish Naval Academy
Designer: Nicholson, England
Built: 1927: Cadiz, Spain, Shipyard Echevarrieta y Larrinaga
Certification: Spanish Naval Vessel
Crew: 250 – 270 including midshipmen
Contact: Office of the Naval Attache, Embassy of Spain, 4801 Wisconsin Avenue, NW, 3rd floor, Washington, DC 20016 USA
Tel: 202-244-2166 **Fax:** 202-362-3993

SPECIFICATIONS

Flag: Antigua
Rig: Brigantine
Homeport: St John's, Antigua
LOA: 151'
Draft: 11' 2"
Beam: 25'
Hull: steel

KAISEI

Program type: Sail training voyages with an emphasis on studying the North Pacific Gyre and other gyres, specifically concentrating on the marine debris/ocean trash issue. Massive amounts of debris have collected in the global ocean. We study how to conduct effective cleanup missions. Our marine debris equipment collection think tank has four types of equipment to be utilized for dealing with different types and sizes of ocean trash. We also study processing techniques that could be employed to recycle these materials into building materials, diesel fuel, etc. Major research expeditions have been conducted in the summers of 2009 & 2010. These expeditions are critical to understanding the logistics needed for major cleanup expeditions which are in planning.
Built: 1990
Contact: Ocean Voyages Institute, 1709 Bridgeway, Sausalito CA 94965 USA
Tel: 415-332-4681 **Fax:** 415-332-7460
E-mail: Mary@oceanvoyagesinstitute.org & ryan@oceanvoyagesinstitute.org
Website: www.oceanvoyagesinstitute.com

Launched in 1990, *Kaisei* has already traversed the globe and sailed thousands of people to far reaching ports. *Kaisei* has visited over 15 countries, crewed by volunteers from over 26 nations. Her voyages have created a powerfully diverse network of supporters; dissolving racial, ethnic, religious, political, and age barriers around the world. *Kaisei* has sailed International Peace Missions with citizens of political "hot spots" such as joint crews made up of Japanese and Korean citizens. *Kaisei* is now operated by Ocean Voyages Institute, a non-profit organization (501-c-3) founded in 1979 by a group of international sailors, educators, and conservationists with a mission of teaching the maritime arts and sciences, and researching and preserving the world's oceans. *Kaisei* has become a flagship for the global ocean, heralding the importance of stopping the flow of plastic trash into the global ocean and beginning large scale cleanup of the world's oceans.

SPECIFICATIONS

Flag: Bulgaria
Rig: Barquentine
Homeport: Varna, Bulgaria
Sparred length: 159'
Draft: 11'
Beam: 27'
Hull: steel

Photo by Thad Koza

KALIAKRA

Completed in 1984, *Kaliakra* trains future officers for the Bulgarian Navy and is a sister ship to *Iskra*. Her home port is Varna on the Black Sea, although she has been a frequent participant in European and American tall ship gatherings. As initially rigged, only four yardarms crossed her foremast because of variations in deck thickness that affected the height of the foremast. Since her refitting in 1992, however, she carries five yardarms in her barquentine configuration. Her figurehead is a stylized version of a Bulgarian mythological figure.

Program type: Training vessel of the Bulgarian Navy
Built: 1984
Contact: Embassy of the Republic of Bulgaria, 1621 22nd Street NW, Washington, DC 20008 USA
Tel: 202-387-7969 **Fax:** 202-234-7973

SPECIFICATIONS

Flag: USA
Rig: Full-rigged ship
Homeport: Wilmington, Delaware
Normal cruising waters:
Mid-Atlantic and Northeast
Sparred length: 141'
LOA: 93'
LOD: 91'
LWL: 89' 2"
Draft: 12' 5"
Beam: 24' 11"
Rig height: 105'
Freeboard: 8'
Sail area: 7,600 square feet
Tons: 168 GRT
Power: 2 Caterpillar 3208 180 HP
Hull: wood

KALMAR NYCKEL

Who sails: School groups from elementary through college, as well as individuals and families
Program type: Crew training for volunteers; education programs for school children, dockside interpretation during port visits
Season: April through October
Designer: Tom Gillmer
Built: 1997: Wilmington, Delaware, Allen C. Rawl
Coast Guard certification: Passenger Vessel (Subchapter T)
Crew: 8 **Passengers:** 49 daysails
Contact: Kalmar Nyckel Foundation, 1124 East Seventh Street, Wilmington, DE 19801 USA
Tel: 302-429-7447 **Fax:** 302-429-0350
E-mail: officemanager@kalmarnyckel.org or info@kalmarnyckel.org
Website: www.kalmarnyckel.org

The *Kalmar Nyckel*, the tall ship of Delaware, is a re-creation of the first Swedish colonial settlement ship to arrive in America in 1638, which established the colony of New Sweden in what is now Wilmington, Delaware. Launched in the fall of 1997, commissioned in May of 1998, and USCG certified in June of 2000, this ornately carved 17th Century Dutch pinnace sails the Northeast and Mid-Atlantic regions seasonally, carrying out her mission of education and goodwill. She transforms Delaware's history into hands-on educational opportunities for children through adults, from teaching fourth and sixth graders history and physics to conducting her bi-annual volunteer crew sail training. She provides economic development opportunities, private charters both underway and dockside, public sails and public tours, and statewide marketing initiatives on a national scale, serving as Delaware's tall ship ambassador. A professional captain, mates and a volunteer crew man the *Kalmar Nyckel*.

SPECIFICATIONS

Flag: Russia
Rig: Barque, 4-masted
Homeport: Kalingrad, Russia
Normal cruising waters:
Western European waters (summer)
Southern European waters (winter)
Sparred length: 376'
LOA: 346'
LOD: 329'
LWL: 311' 6"
Draft: 19'
Beam: 46'
Rig height: 176'
Freeboard: 27' 9"
Sail area: 36,380 square feet
Power: twin 600 HP diesels
Hull: steel

KRUZENSHTERN

Kruzenshtern was built as *Padua* in 1927 in Bremerhaven, Germany. The sister ship to *Peking*, she is the last of the "Flying P" liners still under sail. These vessels were engaged in the grain trade from Australia to Europe. In 1933, *Kruzenshtern* sailed from her homeport of Hamburg to Port Lincoln in Australia in only 67 days. At the end of World War II she was handed over to the USSR and converted into a sail training ship. Since 1990, up to 40 trainees of all ages have been welcomed onboard to sail along with the Russian students of the Baltic Academy in Kalingrad, Russia, learning the ropes, manning the helm, or climbing the rigging to set more than 30,000 square feet of sail. No previous experience is necessary. *Kruzenshtern* is supported by Tall Ship Friends, a nonprofit organization in Hamburg, Germany. The goals of Tall Ship Friends are to promote sail training on square-riggers, to contribute to the further existence of these beautiful ships, and to provide an unforgettable experience for the participants. Members of Tall Ship Friends receive the quarterly Tall Ships News (English/German) and a personal sailing log.

Who sails: Groups and individuals of all ages
Program type: Sail training for paying trainees; fully accredited sea education in traditional seamanship
Built: 1927: Bremerhaven, Germany, J.C. Tecklenborg
Certification: Special Purpose (School Vessel), Russia
Crew: 45-70 **Trainees-passengers:** 250 day-sails, 60 overnight
Contact: Wulf Marquard, Managing Director, Tall Ship Friends Germany, Schweriner Sir. 17, Hamburg, D22143 Germany
Tel: 49-40-675 635 97 **Fax:** 49-40-675 635 99
E-mail: tallshipl@aol.com
Website: www.tallship-friends.de

SPECIFICATIONS

Flag: France
Rig: Topsail schooner
Homeport: Brest, France
Sparred length: 124'
Draft: 12'
Beam: 24'
Hull: wood

Photo by Thad Koza

LA BELLE POULE

Program type: Sail training vessel of the French Navy
Built: 1932: Fecamp, Normandy, France
Contact: Embassy of France, 4101 Reservoir Road, NW, Washington, DC 20007 USA
Tel: 202-944-6000
Fax: 202-944-6166

Along with her sister ship *Etoile*, the schooner *La Belle Poule* serves the French Navy in the training of future officers. Designed with the hull shape and the rigging of fishing vessels from Breton, *La Belle Poule* and *Etoile* were built in 1932 in the fishing port of Fecamp in northern Normandy, France. During World War II, both vessels relocated to Portsmouth, England, where they served the Free France Forces. They are permitted to fly the French ensign with the imposed Cross of Lorraine in recognition of their service during the war.

SPECIFICATIONS

Flag: USA
Rig: Pungy schooner
(gaff rigged), 2-masted
Homeport: Baltimore, Maryland
Normal cruising waters:
Chesapeake Bay and the East Coast
between Maryland and Maine
Sparred length: 104'
LOD: 72'
LWL: 64' 3"
Draft: 7'
Beam: 22'
Rig height: 85'
Freeboard: 3'
Sail area: 2,994 square feet
Tons: 60 GRT
Power: twin 80 HP diesels

LADY MARYLAND

Lady Maryland is an authentic pungy schooner, an elegant boat designed to haul cargo, fish, dredge for oysters, and to carry luxury items quickly from port to port on Chesapeake Bay and along the Atlantic Coast. Instead of carrying watermelons and oysters, her mission today is to provide students with the opportunity to experience sailing a historic vessel while studying history, seamanship, marine science, and ecology on her traditional waters from Maryland to Maine. The Living Classrooms Foundation has developed a flexible educational program that can fit the needs of a variety of school and community groups. More than 50,000 students participate in LCF programs each year. The *Lady Maryland* operates educational day experiences for 32 trainees and extended live-aboard sail training and marine science programs for up to 14 people.

Who sails: Student and other organized groups, individuals, and families
Program type: Sail training with paying trainees; sea education in marine science, maritime history, and ecology for school groups from elementary school through college as well as adults
Season: March through November
Designer: Thomas Gilmer
Built: 1986: Baltimore, Maryland, G. Peter Boudreau
Coast Guard certification: Passenger Vessel (Subchapter T)
Crew: 6 day sails, 8 overnight **Trainees-passengers:** 32 daysails, 12-14 overnight
Contact: Living Classrooms Foundation, 802 South Caroline Street, Baltimore, MD 21231-3311 USA
Tel: 410-685-0295 **Fax:** 410-752-8433
Website: www.livingclassrooms.org

SPECIFICATIONS

Flag: USA
Rig: Brig
Homeport: Grays Harbor, Aberdeen, Washington
Normal cruising waters: Washington, West Coast of North America
Sparred length: 112'
LOA: 87'
LOD: 66' 9"
LWL: 58'
Draft: 11'
Beam: 24'
Rig height: 89'
Freeboard: 6'
Sail area: 4,400 square feet
Tons: 99 GRT
Power: diesel
Hull: wood

LADY WASHINGTON

Who sails: School groups from elementary school through college, individuals, and families
Program type: Sail training for crew, apprentices, and paying trainees; sea education in maritime history in cooperation with accredited institutions based on informal, in-house programming; passenger day sails, overnight passages, and family camps; dockside interpretation
Season: Year-round
Designer: Ray Wallace
Built: 1989: Aberdeen, Washington, Grays Harbor Historical Seaport Authority
Coast Guard certification: Passenger Vessel (Subchapter T)
Crew: 12 **Trainees-passengers:** 48 daysails, 8 overnight
Contact: Capt. Les Bolton, Executive Director, Grays Harbor Historical Seaport Authority, PO Box 2019, Aberdeen, WA 98520 USA
Tel: 800-200-5239 **Fax:** 360-533-9384
E-mail: les@historicalseaport.org
Website: www.historicalseaport.org

As a privateer during the American Revolution, the original *Lady Washington* fought to help the colonies gain their independence from England. In 1788, she became the first American vessel to visit the West Coast of North America, opening trade between the colonies and the native peoples of the Northwest Coast. Built at Grays Harbor Historical Seaport in Aberdeen, Washington, and launched in 1989 as a Washington State Centennial project, the reproduction *Lady Washington* sails the waters of Washington State and the West Coast of North America as the tall ship ambassador for the state of Washington. With a busy year-round sailing schedule, *Lady Washington* regularly tours the West Coast, providing shipboard education programs for schools in 89 port communities in Washington, Oregon, California, British Columbia, and Alaska. More than 15,000 school children visit *Lady Washington* each year to learn about the rich and colorful maritime heritage of our nation. Crew are paid professionals and volunteer trainees.

SPECIFICATIONS

Flag: USA
Rig: Gaff topsail schooner, 2-masted
Homeport: New York, New York
Normal cruising waters: Northeast United States
Sparred length: 125'
LOD: 83'
LWL: 71'
Draft: 11'
Beam: 21'
Rig height: 91'
Freeboard: 4'
Sail area: 5,017 square feet
Tons: 54 GRT
Power: twin 85 HP diesels
Hull: wood

LETTIE G. HOWARD

The *Lettie G. Howard* is the sole surviving example of a Georges Bank fishing schooner.   A Fredonia model-fishing schooner built in Essex, Massachusetts, she exemplifies the type of craft used widely up and down the Eastern seaboard of the United States from Maine to the Gulf Coast. Operating out of Gloucester for her first eight years, the *Lettie* was similar to the schooners that carried their Long Island and New Jersey catches to New York City's Fulton Fish Market. In 1901, the *Lettie* was purchased by the E.E. Saunders company of Pensacola, Florida, for use off Mexico's Yucatan Peninsula. Completely rebuilt in 1923, she was fitted with her first auxiliary engine a year later. She remained in the Gulf of Mexico until 1968, when she was sold to the Seaport Museum in New York City. The *Lettie G. Howard* was designated a National Historic Landmark in 1989. Between 1991 and 1993, the Museum completely restored her to her original 1893 appearance, while outfitting her to accommodate trainees on educational cruises.

Who sails: School groups, colleges and universities, corporate teambuilding programs, Elderhostel, individual adults, and families
Program type: Sea education and sail training programs focusing on nautical science, fishery and maritime history, natural and social sciences
Built: 1893: Essex, MA, A. D. Story (restored at South Street Seaport Museum in 1993)
Coast Guard certification: Sailing School Vessel (Subchapter R)
Crew: 7-9 **Trainees-passengers:** 33 daysails, 13 overnight
Contact: Marine Operations, Seaport Museum New York, 12 Fulton Street, New York, New York 10038 USA
Tel: 212-748-8600 **Fax:** 212-748-8610
E-mail: marineoperations@seany.org
Website: www.seany.org

SPECIFICATIONS

Flag: Argentina
Rig: Full-rigged ship
Homeport: Buenos Aires, Argentina
Sparred length: 356'
LOD: 317'
LWL: 263'
Draft: 21' 9"
Beam: 45' 3"
Rig height: 147' 6"
Freeboard: 15'
Sail area: 28,545 square feet
Power: two 1,200 HP diesel engines
Hull: steel

LIBERTAD

Who sails: Cadets from the Military Naval School (20 – 23)
Program type: Naval training vessel
Season: May through December
Designer: Astilleros y Fabricas Navales del Estado (AFNE)
Built: 1960 (launched 1956): Rio Santiago (BA), Argentina, Astilleros y Fabricas Navales del Estado (AFNE)
Crew: 150 **Trainees-passengers:** 150
Contact: Argentine Naval Attache Office, Embassy of Argentina, 630 Indiana Avenue, NW, Washington, DC 20004 USA
Tel: 202-626-2164 **Fax:** 202-626-2180
Website: www.argnavattache-usa.org or www.ara.mil.ar

The frigate, A.R.A. *Libertad,* was initiated as a training ship in 1963 for the Argentine Navy. As a training ship, her mission is to enhance the maritime knowledge and cultural background of her midshipmen while integrating them to life at sea and instructing them on the fundamentals of the art of sailing. *Libertad* also serves as a floating ambassador representing the Argentine Republic establishing professional and friendly ties with navies around the world while preparing her cadets academically, physically and spiritually. In 1966, *Libertad* established the world record for speed crossing the North Atlantic sailing from Cape Race (Canada) to Dursey Island (Ireland) in six days and 21 hours. The International Sail Training Association (ISTA) officially recognized her record, and *Libertad* flies a pennant commemorating this achievement. Her figurehead was made by a Spanish sculptor and depicts Liberty, for which the ship is named. *Libertad* has sailed the seven seas and participates in regattas and port visits around the world.

SPECIFICATIONS

Flag: USA
Rig: Gaff topsail schooner
Homeport: Boston, Massachusetts
Normal cruising waters: East Coast US
Sparred length: 125'
LOD: 86'
LWL: 76'
Draft: 8'(min.), 13'(max.)
Beam: 25'
Rig height: 78'
Freeboard: 5'
Sail area: 4,300 square feet
Tons: 99 GRT
Power: diesel
Hull: steel

LIBERTY CLIPPER

The *Liberty Clipper* is a replica of the mid-19th century Baltimore Clippers famous for their fast passages round Cape Horn on their way to California and other Pacific ports. The *Liberty Clipper* operates in Boston Harbor during the summer, Baltimore, Maryland, in the fall and Nassau, the Bahamas, during the winter. In Boston, *Liberty Clipper* is available for charter on day and evening cruises for up to 115 passengers. Her spacious decks and on-board hospitality create an ambiance under sail that will meet the expectations of the most discriminating clients. In addition to a variety of high quality charter opportunities, during the summer months, she offers the Liberty Classroom program for Boston area youth groups, a sail training and harbor education program designed to give trainees an introduction to essential topics in seamanship, safety, and Boston's maritime history. For those interested in extended trips, *Liberty Clipper* offers three to six-day overnight cruises in the Chesapeake Bay and six-day island hopping cruises in the Bahamas where pricing includes a berth and excellent food prepared by the ship's chef.

Who sails: School groups from elementary through high school, individuals, and families
Program type: Passenger day sails and overnight passages; corporate and private charters
Designer: Charles Wiftholz
Built: 1983: Warren, RI, Blount Marine Corporation
Coast Guard certification: Passenger Vessel (Subchapter T)
Crew: 5 daysails, 10 overnight **Trainees-passengers:** 115 daysails, 28 overnight
Contact: The Liberty Fleet of Tall Ships, 67 Long Wharf, Boston, MA 02210 USA
Tel: 617-742-0333 **Fax:** 617-742-1322
E-mail: info@libertyfleet.com
Website: www.libertyfleet.com

SPECIFICATIONS

Flag: USA
Rig: Square topsail schooner
Homeport: Newport Beach, California
Sparred Length: 122'
LOA: 78'
LOD: 76'
LWL: 72'
Draft: 9'
Beam: 23'
Rig height: 94'
Freeboard: 5'
Sail Area: 4,669 square feet
Tons: 94 GRT
Power: Cat 3306B - 290 HP hundested variable pitch propeller
Hull: wood

LYNX

Who sails: Schools groups from elementary age thru college. Troops, individuals, families, and company charters
Program type: Sail training; maritime history; Life, Earth, and Physical Science; charters; team building; public sails, dockside programs
Season: Year-round
Designer: Melbourne Smith - International Historical Watercraft Society
Built: Rockport, ME, Rockport Marine; launched July 28, 2001 in Rockport, ME
Coast Guard certification: Passenger Vessel (Subchapter T)
Crew: 8 **Trainees-passengers:** 40 daysails, 6 overnight
Contact: Jeffrey Woods, Director of Operations, Lynx Educational Foundation, 509 29th Street, Newport Beach, CA. 92663 USA
Tel: 866-446-5969 **Fax:** 949-723-1958
E-mail: privateerlynx1812@verizon.net
Website: www.privateerlynx.org

The square topsail schooner *Lynx* has been designed and built to interpret the general configuration and operation of a privateer schooner or naval schooner from the War of 1812, the original *Lynx* being a "letter of marque" Baltimore Clipper commissioned during the opening days of the war. Serving effectively as a blockade-runner and offensive weapon of war, she was among the first ships to defend American freedom. Dedicated to all those who cherish the blessings of America, *Lynx* sails as a living history museum, providing inspiration and resolve at this time in our nation's history. She is fitted with period ordnance and flies flags and pennants from the 1812 era. To complement her historic character, the *Lynx* crew members wear period uniforms and operate the ship in keeping with the maritime traditions of early 19th century America. *Lynx* also operates as a sail training vessel to serve as a classroom for the study of historical, environmental, and ecological issues. In addition, she undertakes "cruises of opportunity" to the Hawaiian Islands that lead to personal growth and awareness through the experience of life at sea aboard a traditional sailing vessel.

SPECIFICATIONS

Flag: USA
Rig: Gaff topsail schooner, 2-masted
Homeport: Traverse City, Michigan
Normal cruising waters: Great Lakes
Sparred length: 92'
LOA: 55' 6"
LWL: 52'
Draft: 7' 7"
Beam: 16' 2"
Rig height: 71'
Freeboard: 2' 2"
Sail area: 2,270 square feet
Tons: 42 GRT

MADELINE

Madeline is a reconstruction of a mid-19th-century schooner, typical of the trading schooners that once sailed the Great Lakes. The original *Madeline* was the first Euro-American School in the Grand Traverse region and for a short time served as a lightship in the Straits of Mackinac. Launched in 1990, the modern *Madeline* was built over a period of five years by volunteers of the Maritime Heritage Alliance (MHA), using traditional methods and materials. From her homeport in Traverse City, Michigan, she has sailed with her volunteer crew on all five Great Lakes, visiting over 60 ports with dockside tours and historical interpretation. *Madeline* is designated as the City of Traverse City's goodwill ambassador. Crewmembers, trained as historical interpreters, share their knowledge of history, marlinespike skills, and wooden boat building. School programs with special hands-on activities are also available. The Maritime Heritage Alliance, a nonprofit organization, is dedicated to preserving, interpreting, and sharing the maritime heritage of the Great Lakes.

Who sails: Trained crew members and guests of the Maritime Heritage Alliance
Program type: Adult sail training and maritime history
Designer: Kenneth (Bob) Core
Built: 1990: Traverse City, MI, Maritime Heritage Alliance
Coast Guard certification: Dockside Attraction Vessel
Crew: 9
Contact: Maritime Heritage Alliance, 13268 S. West Bayshore, Traverse City, Michigan 49684 USA
Tel: 231-946-2647
E-mail: info@maritimeheritagealliance.org
Website: www.maritimeheritagealliance.org

SPECIFICATIONS

Flag: USA
Rig: Staysail schooner, 3-masted
Homeport: Kaneohe Bay, Hawaii
Normal cruising waters:
Hawaiian Islands
Sparred length: 96'
LOA: 85'
LOD: 75'
LWL: 63'
Draft: 8'
Beam: 20'
Rig height: 65'
Freeboard: 5'
Sail area: 2,000 square feet
Tons: 68 GRT
Power: 210 HP
Hull: steel

MAKANI OLU (GRACIOUS WIND)

Who sails: Groups and individuals of all ages
Program type: Sail training for paying trainees; fully accredited sea education in marine science, maritime history, and ecology, as well as service learning, in cooperation with accredited institutions and other organized groups, and as informal in-house programming
Season: Year-round
Designer: Thomas Kolvin
Built: 1998: St. Augustine, FL, Schrieber
Coast Guard certification: Sailing School Vessel (Subchapter R)
Crew: 5 **Trainees-passengers:** 30 daysails, 20 overnight
Contact: Matthew Claybaugh, Ph.D., President and CEO, Marimed Foundation, 45-021 Likeke Place, Kaneohe, HI 96744 USA
Tel: 808 235-1377 **Fax:** 808-235-1074
E-mail: info@marimed.org
Website: www.marimed.org

The *Makani Olu* (Gracious Wind) is owned and operated by Marimed Foundation, a non-profit organization involved with sail training since 1988. The 96-foot, 3-masted staysail schooner, retrofitted for sail training in Hawaiian waters, is the central component of a model experiential education and treatment program for at-risk adolescents built around ocean voyaging. Voyaging challenges and experiences are designed to be powerful and transformational. From *Makani Olu's* home port in Kaneohe Bay on Oahu, cadets make a series of six-day voyages throughout the Hawaiian Island chain. While learning to operate the sailing ship, the cadets learn marine, navigation and team-building skills. Elderhostel International provides sail training experiences aboard *Makani Olu* as well. These programs feature a six-day voyage that includes hands-on opportunities to sail and operate the ship and additional learning opportunities at ports-of-call. The *Makani Olu* is also available to youth, families and community organizations for sail training and team building trips.

SPECIFICATIONS

Flag: USA
Rig: Staysail schooner
Homeport: Seattle, Washington
Normal Cruising Waters: Pacific Northwest, Canada and Alaska
Sparred Length: 65'
LOA: 60'
LOD: 60'
LWL: 50'
Draft: 5' (min) 8' (max)
Beam: 16'
Rig height: 65'
Freeboard: 5'
Sail Area: 1,545 square feet
Tons: 38 GRT
Power: diesel
Hull: composite

MALLORY TODD

Named for Captain Mallory Todd, who served as master on American vessels during the Revolutionary War, the *Mallory Todd* is a modern 65-foot schooner built in the classic style with fireplaces and exceptionally intricate wood-work. Designed for long distance voyages, she has sailed the West Coast from Mexico to Alaska for 18 years. Sail training trips to the San Juan Islands, Canada, and Alaska via the Inside Passage, are blessed with the full bounty of nature. These trips are open to anyone between 18 and 80 with or without sailing experience. When at homeport in Seattle, she relieves the tedium of long-term cancer treatment with recreational outings for hospital patients and their caregivers under the auspices of the nonprofit Sailing Heritage Society. Together, part time volunteers, trainees, and professionals get the job done. Hands on tending the sails, steering, scrubbing, navigating, fishing, or clamming, each contributes where a need fits their abilities. Schooner *Mallory Todd* also offers corporate and private charters that provide a unique and delightful venue for business or recreational activities.

Who sails: All ages for volunteers, paying trainees, and apprentices
Program type: Sail training for crew, volunteers, trainees, and apprentices; sea education based on programmed and day to day events; passenger day sails for corporate team building or recreational events
Season: All year, but primarily May through September. MT is sometimes gone April and May on charters to Alaska
Designer: Perry & Todd
Built: 1981: Seattle, WA
Coast Guard certification: Passenger Vessel (Subchapter T)
Crew: 2 **Trainees-passengers:** 25 daysails, 6 overnight
Contact: Captain George Todd, Sailing Heritage Society, 10042 NE 13th Street Bellevue, WA 98004 USA
Tel: 206-381-6919 **Fax:** 206-381-9556
E-mail: info@sailingheritage.org
Website: www.sailingheritage.org

SPECIFICATIONS

Flag: USA
Rig: Gaff topsail schooner
Homeport: Traverse City, Michigan
Normal cruising waters: Great Lakes
Sparred length: 114'
LOD: 77'
LWL: 65'
Draft: 7' (min.) 11' (max.)
Beam: 21'
Rig height: 77'
Freeboard: 6'
Sail area: 3,000 square feet
Tons: 82 GRT
Power: 150 HP diesel
Hull: steel

Photo by Capt. Dav McGinnis

MANITOU

Who sails: School groups; individual, family, and corporate groups for day sails and bed & breakfast
Program type: Sail training for crew; sea education in marine science, maritime history and ecology; individual and group day sails; "Floating Bed & Breakfast"
Season: May to October
Designer: Woodin & Marean
Built: 1982: Portsmouth, NH, Roger Gagnon Steel Ship Company
Coast Guard certification: Passenger Vessel (Subchapter T)
Crew: 5 **Trainees-passengers:** 59 daysails, 24 overnight
Contact: Captain Dave McGinnis, Traverse Tall Ship Co., LLC, 13390 SW Bay Shore Drive, Traverse City, MI 49684 USA
Tel: 231-941-2000 **Fax:** 231-941-0520
E-mail: manitou@tallshipsailing.com
Website: www.talishipsailing.com

Owned and operated by Traverse Tall Ship Co., LLC, the schooner *Manitou* is one of the largest sailing vessels on the Great Lakes. This replica of a 19th century "coaster" can accommodate 24 overnight guests and 62 passengers for day excursions. *Manitou* is fully certified by the US Coast Guard and offers day sails on Grand Traverse Bay, Lake Michigan. In addition, join us for an adventurous overnight as part of our "Floating Bed & Breakfast." Wake up in the morning to hot coffee and fresh baked muffins from the galley before sitting down to a full breakfast prepared from scratch on the wood stove. For a more in-depth experience, *Manitou* offers three and four day sailing adventures to the islands, bays and coastal villages of northern Lake Michigan. In conjunction with Inland Seas Education Association, *Manitou* operates the Schoolship Program, which provides an environmental, historical, and sail training education for students during the spring. The schooner offers partial as well as private charter service to family, company, and motor coach groups.

MARY DAY

Built in 1962 by Harvey Gamage, *Mary Day* combines the best aspects of the New England centerboard coaster with modern design thinking. *Mary Day* operates out of Camden, Maine, in the windjammer trade from late May to early October. She carries 30 passengers on weeklong vacation cruises in mid-coast Maine. *Mary Day* is a pure sailing vessel. She has no engine and depends on a small yawl boat when winds fail. She has a large and powerful rig and exhibits outstanding sailing abilities. *Mary Day* carries a professional crew of six, including captain, mate, cook, two deckhands, and one galley hand. The galley and one deck position are considered entry-level positions, and a great many sailing professionals have started out or gained valuable experience on board the schooner *Mary Day*.

Who sails: Individuals and families
Program type: Sail training for crew and apprentices; passenger overnight passages; dockside interpretation in homeport
Season: May to October
Designer: H. Hawkins
Built: 1962: South Bristol, ME, Harvey Gamage Shipyard
Coast Guard certification: Passenger Vessel (Subchapter T)
Crew: 7 **Trainees-passengers:** 49 day sails, 29 overnight
Contact: Captains Barry King and Jen Martin, Penobscot Windjammer Company, PO Box 798, Camden, ME 04843 USA
Tel: 800-992-2218
E-mail: captains@schoonermaryday.com
Website: www.schoonermaryday.com

SPECIFICATIONS

Flag: USA
Rig: Gaff-rigged schooner
Homeport: Essex, Connecticut
Normal cruising waters:
Connecticut River to New York City
Sparred Length: 75'
LOD: 50'
Draft: 6'
Beam: 14'
Rig height: 50'
Freeboard: 2'
Sail area: 1,500 square feet
Tons: 14 GRT
Power: GM 471 diesel
Hull: Oak

MARY E

Who sails: Students and adult passengers of all ages
Program type: Educational sails, private sailing excursions and day sails
Season: May until October
Designer: William Donnell
Built: 1906:Thomas Hagan, Bath, Maine
Coast Guard certification: Passenger Vessel (Subchapter T)
Crew: 3 **Trainees-passengers:** 25 daysails, 6 overnight
Contact: Matt Culen or John Bosco of Halyard Enterprises, Eric Van Dormolen, of NY Maritime Restoration, 210 Bellerose Ave., East Northport, NY 11731 USA
Tel: 631-332-0699
E-mail: captericvandy@aol.com
Website: www.schoonermarye.org and www.nymaritimerestoration.com

The *Mary E* is the last Clipper Bow Schooner of 4,000 built in Bath, ME still afloat. She was a sword fishing, cargo, passenger, mail carrier, and rum running schooner that sailed out of Providence, Rhode Island. Captain Dunn sailed her to Block Island delivering goods. In 1938, her sail rig was cut down and she was converted to a motorized fishing dragger. In November of 1963 a hurricane washed her ashore. Captain Donnell, the original designer's great great-grandson, salvaged and restored her from 1965-1970 and made her a magnificent schooner once again. Since 1969, she has sailed in Camden, Rockport, Boothbay, New York City, City Island, Greenport. The *Mary E* has found her new home at the Connecticut River Museum in Essex, Connecticut. The *Mary E's* primary goal is to educate the public about the Connecticut River as well as offer a sight seeing sails for adults with the occasional pirate or shanty sing along. The *Mary E* will sail to any port in the New York and Connecticut area for special events.

SPECIFICATIONS

Flag: USA
Rig: Sloop
Homeport: Baltimore, Maryland
Normal cruising waters:
Potomac River
Sparred length: 69'
LOD: 45' 3"
Draft: 3'
Beam: 15' 7"
Rig height: 58'
Freeboard: 2'
Sail area: 1,450 square feet
Tons: 10 GRT
Hull: wood

MINNIE V

The skipjack *Minnie V*, built in Wenona, Maryland, was used to dredge oysters on the Chesapeake Bay for many years. The vessel was rebuilt by the City of Baltimore in 1981 and is now owned and operated by the Living Classrooms Foundation in partnership with Potomac Riverboat Company. *Minnie V* sails the upper Potomac River from National Harbor, Maryland and Alexandria, Virginia. While on board the *Minnie V*, passengers learn about the oyster trade, its importance to the economy of Maryland, and the hard life of a waterman as they relive history by raising the sails on one the Chesapeake's few remaining skipjacks.

Who sails: Individuals and families; school groups from middle school through college
Program type: Passenger daysails; sea education in marine science, maritime history, and ecology in cooperation with accredited schools, colleges, and other organized groups
Season: April through October
Built: 1906: Wenona, MD, Vetra
Coast Guard certification: Passenger Vessel (Subchapter T)
Crew: 2 **Trainees-passengers:** 24
Contact: Andrew Samworth, Fleet Captain LC NCR, Living Classrooms, National Capital Region, 515 M Street, Suite 222, Washington, DC 20003 USA
Tel: 301-488-0627 **Fax:** 202-488-1307
E-mail: asamworth@livingclassroomsdc.org
Website: www.livingclassroomsdc.org
www.potomacriverboatco.com

SPECIFICATIONS

Flag: Russia
Rig: Full-rigged ship
Homeport: St. Petersburg, Russia
Normal cruising waters:
West and southwest European
Sparred length: 345' 9"
LOA: 328'
LOD: 300' 9"
LWL: 254'
Draft: 18'
Beam: 44' 9"
Rig height: 149'
Freeboard: 34' 6"
Sail area: 29,997 square feet
Tons: 2,856 GRT
Power: Twin 570 HP diesels
Hull: steel

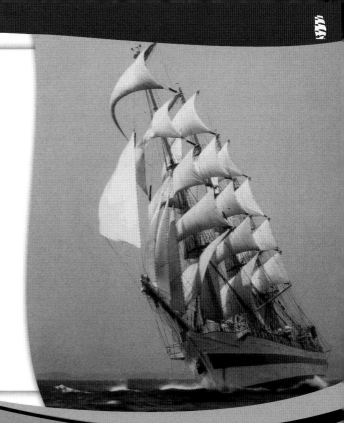

MIR

Who sails: Students and individuals of all ages. Affiliated with Tall Ship Friends clubs in France, UK, Switzerland, Austria, Ireland, and Italy
Program type: Sail training for paying trainees; fully accredited sea education in traditional seamanship; dockside interpretation during port visits
Designer: Z. Choren
Built: 1987: Gdansk, Poland, Stocznia Gdanska
Certification: Russian registered Sailing School Vessel
Crew: 45-70 **Trainees-passengers:** up to 250 daysails, 60 overnight
Contact: Wulf Marquard, Managing Director, Tall Ship Friends Germany, Schweriner Str. 17, Hamburg, D22 143 Germany
Tel: 49-40-675 635 97 **Fax:** 49-40-675 635 99
E-mail: tallshipl@aol.com
Website: www.tallship-friends.de

Mir is regarded by many as the fastest Class A sail training ship in the world. She was the overall winner of the 1992 Columbus Race and the winner of the Cutty Sark Tall Ship Races in 1996, 1997, and 1998 under the command of Captain Victor Antonov. *Mir* was launched in 1989 at the Lenin Shipyard in Gdansk, Poland, the builders of five more of the M 108 type ships: *Dar Mlodziezy, Pallada, Khersones, Druzhba,* and *Nadezhda*. *Mir* is the school ship of the Makaroz Maritime Academy in St. Petersburg, Russia, training future navigators and engineers for the Russian merchant fleet. Since 1990, up to 60 trainees of all ages are welcomed on board to sail along with the Russian students, learning the ropes, manning the helm, or climbing the rigging to set the sails. No previous experience is necessary. *Mir* is supported by Tall Ship Friends, a nonprofit organization in Hamburg, Germany. The goals of Tall Ship Friends are to promote sail training on square-riggers, to contribute to the further existence of these beautiful ships, and to provide an unforgettable experience for the participants.

SPECIFICATIONS

Flag: Romania
Rig: Barque
Homeport: Constanta, Romania
Sparred length: 328'
LOA: 266'
LOD: 241' 6
LWL: 203'
Draft: 18'
Beam: 39' 6"
Rig height: 144'
Freeboard: 8'
Sail area: 18,837 square feet
Tons: 1320 GRT
Power: 1,100 hp diesel
Hull: steel

MIRCEA

Mircea is the flagship and the training vessel of the Romanian Naval Forces. The last of a quartet of sailing school ships built in Blohm & Voss Shipyard, Hamburg, Germany, in the 1930s, Mircea and her sister ships became the models for sailing vessels built during the last three decades. During overhaul concluded in 2002, Mircea has been equipped with modern navigation and communication devices that made her up-to-date despite the 65 years of age.

Who sails: Students and cadets of the Romanian Naval Academy and Romanian Petty Officer School
Program type: Schoolship for the Romanian Naval Forces' cadets
Built: 1938: Hamburg, Germany, Blohm & Voss Shipyard
Crew: 65 **Trainees-passengers:** 120
Contact: Public Affairs Officer, Romanian Naval Academy, Fulgerului Street, Constanta, Romania 900218
Tel: +40 241 643040
Fax: +40 241 643096
E-mail: relpub@navedo.anmb.ro
Website: www.anmb.ro

SPECIFICATIONS

Flag: USA
Rig: Gaff-rigged schooner
Homeport: New London, Connecticut
Normal cruising waters:
Hudson River in Spring, Southeast New England in Summer, Chesapeake Bay in Fall
Sparred length: 110'
LOA: 83'
LOD: 83'
LWL: 78'
Draft: 7' 6" (min.) 13' (max.)
Beam: 25'
Rig height: 90'
Freeboard: 7'
Sail Area: 3,000 square feet
Tons: 100 GRT
Power: 175 HP diesel
Hull: steel

MYSTIC WHALER

Who sails: School groups from elementary school through college, as well as individuals and families ages 5 and up
Program type: Sail training for crew and apprentices; sea education in maritime history and ecology based on informal programming with organized groups such as Scouts; passenger day sails and overnight passages
Season: March through November
Designer: "Chub" Crockett
Built: 1967: Tarpon Springs, Florida, George Sutton
Coast Guard certification: Passenger Vessel (Subchapter T)
Crew: 5 **Trainees-passengers:** 65 daysails, 34 overnight
Contact: Captain John Eginton, Mystic Whaler Cruises Inc., PO Box 189, Mystic, CT 06355-0189 USA
Tel: 800-697-8420 **Fax:** 860-447-1268
E-mail: info@mysticwhaler.com
Website: www.mysticwhaler.com

Built in 1967 and rebuilt in 1993, the *Mystic Whaler* carries passengers and trainees on a variety of cruises, ranging from three hours to five days. In April, May and early June, the schooner joins *Clearwater* on the Hudson River, for environmental education programs. Sailing from New London, CT throughout the summer months, the *Mystic Whaler* offers great sailing opportunities for both novice and experienced passengers. Three-hour Lobster Dinner Cruises are popular, as are the five-hour day sails, or try an overnight of two, three or five days. In September and October, the *Mystic Whaler* travels to Baltimore, Maryland for three weeks of three-day overnight sails and to participate in the Great Chesapeake Bay Schooner Race. Some of the overnight cruises have special interest extras such as lighthouse tours, sea music, and full moon cruises. Two-week apprenticeship programs run throughout the season (June-September).

Photo by Thad Koza

SPECIFICATIONS

Flag: Russia
Rig: Ship
Homeport: Vladivostok, Russia
LOA: 359'
Draft: 21' 5"
Hull: steel

NADEZHDA

Nadezhda, the Russian word for "hope", is the last of six "DAR–class" full-rigged ships that were built in the Gdansk Shipyard in the 1980s. *Nadezhda* was completed in 1990, and delivered and commissioned to the Far Eastern State Maritime Academy in Vladivostok, Russia in 1991.

Contact: FESMA (Far Eastern State Maritime Academy), 50a Verkhneportovaya St., Vladivostok, 690059 Russia
E-mail: fesma@ints.vtc.ru

SPECIFICATIONS

Flag: USA
Rig: Brig
Homeport: Erie, Pennsylvania
Normal cruising waters: Great Lakes and connecting waters
Sparred length: 198'
LOA: 123'
LOD: 116'
LWL: 110'
Draft: 11'
Beam: 32' 6"
Rig height: 120'
Sail area: 11,600 square feet
Tons: 162 GRT
Power: twin 200 HP diesels
Hull: wood

NIAGARA

Who sails: Trainees must be at least 16 years-old, ambulatory, and of average physical fitness. No previous experience is required.
Program type: Experiential-education with focus on seamanship skills, technology of a sailing warship, and War of 1812 history.
Designer: Melbourne Smith **Built:** 1988: Erie, PA
Coast Guard certification: Sailing School Vessel (Subchapter R) and Attraction Vessel
Crew: 18 professionals **Trainees/passengers:** 22 trainees (3-week, live-aboard) and up to 50 daysail students
Contact: Caleb M. Pifer, Flagship Niagara League, c/o Erie Maritime Museum, 150 East Front Street, Suite 100, Erie, PA 16507 USA
Tel: 814-452-2744 x223
E-mail: cpifer@flagshipniagara.org
Website: www.flagshipniagara.org

The Flagship *Niagara* is one of the most historically authentic tall ships in the United States. As an accurate reproduction of Commodore Oliver Hazard Perry's victorious flagship from the War of 1812's Battle of Lake Erie, the ship represents both Pennsylvania and her homeport of Erie in ports throughout the Great Lakes. The ship currently offers three distinctive educational programs to the public. These include educational day sails, an individual trainee program, and for-credit high school and college programs. The day sail program allows the public to sail for an afternoon or evening and experience the life of a sailor. The individual training program integrates trainees into the regular crew for two to three weeks. Finally, the Flagship *Niagara's* institutional partnerships with schools have linked the vessel to some of the most prestigious educational institutions in the country. Students receive full credit for being onboard and are taught by accredited faculty from their respective institution. All students and trainees can expect a highly authentic onboard living experience, including sleeping in hammocks, and meals cooked off of a woodstove.

SPECIFICATIONS

Flag: USA
Rig: 15th century caravel redondo
Homeport: Wilmington, Delaware
Sparred length: 92'
LOA: 68'
LOD: 65'
LWL: 58'
Draft: 7'
Beam: 18'
Rig height: 54'
Freeboard: 5'
Sail area: 1,919 square feet
Tons: 37 GRT
Power: 128 HP diesel
Hull: wood

NINA

The *Nina* is a historically accurate replica of a 15th century caravel. John Sarsfield, the leading authority on caravels, was designer and builder until his death halfway through the project. Jonathan Nance, a noted British designer and archaeologist, finished the vessel and designed the sail plan and rig. She was built in Valenca, Bahia, Brazil, using only traditional tools and techniques of the 15th century. Her mission today is to educate the public on the "space shuttle" of the 15th century, and over one million students and teachers have visited the *Nina* since her completion in 1992. The ship is available for filming and charters.

Program type: Attraction vessel
Designer: John Sarsfield/Jonathon Nance
Built: 1988-1991: Valenca, Brazil, John Sarsfield/Jonathan Nance/Ralph Eric Nicholson
Coast Guard certification: Attraction Vessel
Crew: 6
Contact: Morgan P. Sanger, Captain/Director, Columbus Foundation, Box 305179, St. Thomas, VI 00803
Tel: 284-495-4618 **Fax:** 284-495-4616
E-mail: columfnd@surfbvi.com
Website: www.thenina.com

SPECIFICATIONS

Flag: USA
Rig: Viking longship (single square sail)
Homeport: Wilmington, Delaware
Normal cruising waters:
Chesapeake Bay, Delaware River,
Jersey Shore, New York Bay, Hudson
River, and Long Island Sound
Sparred length: 40'
LOD: 32'
LWL: 30'
Draft: 3'
Beam: 9'
Rig height: 30'
Freeboard: 3'
Sail area: 297 square feet
Tons: 2 GRT
Power: 19 HP Volvo Penta diesel,
or 10 oarsmen
Hull: Fiberglass

NORSEMAN

Who sails: Students and individuals of all ages
Program type: Sail training for volunteer crew
and apprentices; sea education in maritime
history relevant to Viking period; dockside
interpretation during port visits
Designer: Applecraft, Inc.
Built: 1992: Isle of Man, UK, Applecraft, Inc.
Crew: 7-12 **Trainees:** 7-12
Contact: President & Captain Dave
Segermark, Leif Ericson Viking Ship, Inc., P.O.
Box 393 Swarthmore, PA 19081-0393 USA
Tel/Fax: 410-275-8516
E-mail: info@vikingship.org
Website: www.vikingship.org

Built in 1992, the *Norseman* offers people a glimpse of
Viking culture and reminds everyone of the first discovery
of North America by Europeans Leif Ericson and his fellow
Vikings, who sailed from Greenland around the year 1000
to explore the new lands to the west. Crewmembers
appear in full Viking costume, share their interests in Viking
culture and their Scandinavian heritage, and practice their
sailing and rowing skills. Over the years, the *Norseman*
has appeared in sailing events concentrating on the Mid-
Atlantic region of the US, but traveling where invited. The
organization has also traveled to Stockholm, Sweden, St.
Petersburg, Russia, and Newfoundland, Canada. The
Norseman's sailing season runs from April to November
with the majority of events held in the summer. The
crewmembers, however, bring Viking history to local
schools and associations throughout the year. The off-
season is devoted to cleanup and training. Leif Ericson
Day is the organization's "main event" and is held in
Philadelphia, Pennsylvania area on or near October 9.

SPECIFICATIONS

Flag: United Kingdom
Rig: Schooner, 2-masted
Homeport: Road Town,
Tortola, British Virgin Islands
Normal cruising waters:
Eastern Caribbean
Sparred length: 88'
LOA: 77'
LOD: 71'
LWL: 66'
Draft: 9'
Beam: 18'
Rig height: 92'
Freeboard: 5'
Sail area: 3,100 square feet
Tons: 74 GRT
Power: 210 HP diesel
Hull: steel

OCEAN STAR

Originally launched in 1991, *Ocean Star* has sailed under the Sea|mester flag since 1998 hosting college level semester voyages aboard. Sea|mester offers 20, 40, and 80-day semesters that are based on the principles of experiential and adventure education. Learning through interaction and practical activities, the primary academic foci of oceanography, marine science, communication and leadership skills development are brought from the textbook into real-life application. Under the guidance of professional staff, our students earn college credits for both academic and vocational activities, while piloting *Ocean Star* throughout the islands of the Lesser Antilles. Along the way the crew visit up to 20 individual Caribbean islands, undertaking research and service projects with local government and private organizations. They also earn certifications in sailing and scuba diving. No experience is necessary. Programs are available to high school seniors, high school graduates and college students.

Who sails: High school graduates and college students (fall, spring, and summer)
Program type: Experiential education semesters for high school graduates and college students; accredited academics with sail training, scuba training, service projects and adventure travel
Season: Year-round
Designer: Bill Peterson
Built: 1991: Norfolk, VA, Marine Metals
Crew: 4 **Trainees-passengers:** 16
Certification: MCA (UK) inspected Small Commercial Vessel up to 24 meters LWL, Catergory 1 service
Contact: Sea|mester, P.O. Box 5477, Sarasota, FL 34277 USA
Tel: 941-924-6789 or 800-317-6789
Fax: 941-924-6075
E-mail: info@seamester.com
Website: www.seamester.com

SPECIFICATIONS

Flag: USA
Rig: Full-rigged ship
Homeport: Newport, Rhode Island
Normal cruising waters:
East Coast US and Caribbean
Sparred length: 207'
LOA: 132'
LWL: 110'
Draft: 13'
Beam: 30' 6"
Rig height: 128'
Sail area: 14,000 square feet
Tons: 74 GRT
Power: twin diesels
Hull: steel

OLIVER HAZARD PERRY

Who sails: Individuals and students groups
Program type: Sail training and education
Season: Year-round
Crew: 11 **Trainees-passengers:** 85 daysails, 35 overnight
Contact: Mr. Perry Lewis, Oliver Hazard Perry Rhode Island, 29 Touro Street, Newport, RI 02840 USA
Tel: 401-841-0080 **Fax:** 401-841-0149
E-mail: lewis@OHPRI.org
Website: www.OHPRI.org

In October 2008, Newport welcomed a 132-foot steel hull which is being completed as a 197-foot' full-rigged school ship. When construction is completed in 2013, she will be commissioned as the flagship of the State of Rhode Island with the name of *Oliver Hazard Perry* in honor of the state's naval hero of the War of 1812. Equipped with full laboratory facilities, classrooms and even complete interchangeable lab van modules, she will be equipped to serve students from middle school through college on voyages of exploration in Narragansett Bay, New England waters, Canada and the Caribbean. Accommodations will be for 46 on overnight trips and 96 for day trips. *Oliver Hazard Perry* will serve as a platform for Rhode Island public, independent and charter schools as well as for local and regional colleges and universities on waters between the Maritimes and the Caribbean. Winters will offer adult navigation and educational programs in the Caribbean and summers will take young people on scientific and experiential programs around New England. Wherever she goes, *Oliver Hazard Perry* serves as an ambassador for Rhode Island and for the state's marine trades.

SPECIFICATIONS

Flag: Canada
Rig: Marconi rigged ketch
Homeport: Esquimalt, British Columbia, Canada
LOA: 102'
LOD: 91'
LWL: 19'
Draft: 10'
Beam: 19'
Rig height: 67' 8"
Freeboard: 6' 8" (forward) 4' 9" (aft)
Sail area: 15,700 square feet
Power: 261 HP Detroit Diesel

HCMS ORIOLE

The oldest commissioned ship in the Canadian Navy has a pedigree that goes back to 1880 when George Gooderham sailed the first *Oriole* as the flagship of the Royal Canadian Yacht Club of Toronto, Ontario. Gooderham, who was for several years Commodore of the Toronto club, built *Oriole II* in 1886 and *Oriole III* in 1909. In 1921, the last of the *Orioles* - then called *Oriole IV*, was thought to be the most majestic of all R.C.Y.C. flagships. She was started by the Toronto Dominon Shipbuilding company but due to labor problems, was completed by George Lawley & Sons, a Boston shipyard. She was launched at Neponset, Massachusetts, June 4, 1921, commissioned *HMCS Oriole* June 19, 1952, and two years later the navy moved her to the West Coast to become a training vessel to VENTURE, the Naval Officer Training Center. She was purchased by the Royal Canadian Navy in 1957. HMCS *Oriole* is both the oldest vessel and the longest serving commissioned ship in the Canadian Navy. Her distinctive red, white, and blue spinnaker displays an orange Oriole.

Program type: Training vessel of the Canadian Navy
Built: 1921
Crew: 5 **Trainees-passengers:** 16
Contact: Embassy of Canada, 501 Pennsylvania Avenue, NW, Washington, DC 20001 USA
Tel: 202-682-1740 **Fax:** 202-682-7726

SPECIFICATIONS

Flag: Canada
Rig: Gaff topsail schooner
Homeport: Victoria, British Columbia, Canada
Normal cruising waters: Coastal waters of British Columbia
Sparred length: 138' 7"
LOA: 115'
LOD: 108' 7"
LWL: 89' 6"
Draft: 11' 6"
Beam: 22' 2"
Rig height: 115'
Freeboard: 3' 7"
Sail area: 7,564 square feet
Tons: 175 GRT
Power: twin diesels
Hull: wood

PACIFIC GRACE

Who sails: Students and young adults ages 13 – 25
Program type: Sail training for paying trainees
Season: March through October
Built: 1999: Victoria, British Columbia, Canada, SALTS
Certification: Passenger Vessel, Sailing School Vessel
Crew: 5 **Trainees-passengers:** 40 daysails, 30 overnight
Contact: Sail and Life Training Society (SALTS), PO Box 5014, Station B, Victoria, British Columbia V8R 6N3 Canada
Tel: 250-383-6811 **Fax:** 250-383-7781
E-mail: info@salts.ca
Website: www.salts.ca

Pacific Grace was launched at her homeport of Victoria, British Columbia in 1999. She replaces the *Robertson II*, one of Canada's last original Grand Banks fishing schooners, and is built along the lines of the old ship using traditional methods. *Pacific Grace* embarked on a nine-month offshore voyage in 2003 to the South Pacific. In 2007-08 she visited 15 countries in the South Pacific and Asia, traveling 18,000 nautical miles over 12 months. Most years, she sails coastally in southern British Columbia, Canada. During the summer months of July and August 10-day trips are available to anyone aged 13 - 25. In the spring and fall, five-day school programs are offered. Each year, over one thousand young people board *Pacific Grace* for an experience which combines all aspects of shipboard life from galley chores to helmsmanship, with formal instruction in navigation, pilotage, seamanship and small boat handling. S.A.L.T.S. is a registered charity that seeks to develop the spiritual, relational and physical potential of young people through shipboard life in a Christian environment.

SPECIFICATIONS

Flag: Canada
Rig: Square topsail schooner, 2-masted
Homeport: Victoria, British Columbia, Canada
Normal cruising waters: Coastal waters of British Columbia
Sparred length: 111'
LOA: 81'
LOD: 77' 3"
LWL: 73'
Draft: 10' 8"
Beam: 20' 6"
Rig height: 88'
Freeboard: 3' 6"
Sail area: 5,205 square feet
Tons: 98 GRT
Power: 220 HP diesel
Hull: wood

PACIFIC SWIFT

Built as a working exhibit at Expo '86 in Vancouver, British Columbia, the *Pacific Swift* has sailed over 100,000 deep-sea miles on training voyages for young crewmembers. Her offshore travels have taken her to Australia and Europe, to remote communities on Easter and Pitcairn Islands, and to many other unusual and far-flung ports of call. When not offshore, the *Swift* provides coastal sail training programs among the cruising grounds of the Pacific Northwest, which include shorter school programs in the spring and fall, and 10-day summer trips open to anyone aged 13 to 25. Each year, over one thousand young people participate in an experience, which combines all aspects of shipboard life, from galley chores to helmsmanship, with formal instruction in navigation, pilotage, seamanship, and small boat handling. Rooted in Christian values, SALTS believes that training under sail provides the human spirit a real chance to develop and mature. SALTS received the 1998 Sail Training Program of the Year Award from Tall Ships America.

Who sails: Individuals and groups
Program type: Offshore and coastal sail training
Season: March through October
Built: 1986: Vancouver, British Columbia, Canada, SALTS
Certification: Passenger vessel, Sailing School Vessel
Crew: 5   **Trainees-passengers:** 35 **Age:** 13–25
Contact: Sail and Life Training Society (SALTS), PO Box 5014, Station B, Victoria, British Columbia V8R 6N3 Canada
Tel: 250-383-6811 **Fax:** 250-383-7781
E-mail: info@salts.ca
Website: www.salts.ca

SPECIFICATIONS

Flag: Italy
Rig: Barquentine
Homeport: La Maddalena, Sardinia, Italy
Normal cruising waters:
Mediterranean
Sparred length: 226'
Draft: 16'
Beam: 33'
Hull: steel

Photo by Thad Koza

PALINURO

Who sails: Cadets of the Italian Navy
Program type: Sail training
Season: Year-round
Built: 1934
Contact: Embassy of Italy, 3000 Whitehaven Street, NW, Washington DC 20008 USA
Tel: 202-612-4400 **Fax:** 202-518-2151
Website: www.ambwashingtondc.esteri.it/ambasciata_washington

In her first incarnation, *Palinuro* enjoyed a long career fishing for cod on the Grand Banks. Built in Nantes, France in 1933, she was known originally as *Commandant Louis Richard*, and later as *Jean Marc Aline*. Purchased in 1950 by the Italian Navy, she was renamed after the helmsman in the Greek legend of Aeneas, a prince of Troy and son of Venus. Aeneas fled Troy after its destruction and sailed on a course toward Italy in search of a new homeland. Venus interceded with Neptune to allow Aeneas to reach his goal safely. Neptune agreed but exacted a life as ransom. Palinurus, the victim in this bargain, was drugged at Neptune's behest by Somnus, who then pushed the unlucky Palinurus overboard. True to his promise however, Neptune insured the safe arrival in Italy of Aeneas and his ship. After an extensive refitting in 1955, *Palinuro* began her new role as a sail training ship for future naval petty officers. Recently overhauled, *Palinuro's* white-striped color scheme echoes the style of *Amerigo Vespucci*, the other Italian naval sail training vessel. *Palinuro* sails mainly in the Mediterranean.

SPECIFICATIONS

Flag: Russia
Rig: Full-rigged ship
Homeport:
Vladivostok, Russia
Normal cruising waters:
Worldwide
Sparred length: 356' 4"
Draft: 22' 4"
Beam: 45' 9"
Hull: steel

Photo by Thad Koza

PALLADA

The sailing training ship *Pallada* was built in Gdan'sk, Poland in 1989 and was named after the Russian navy frigate *Pallada*. She is owned by the Far Eastern State Technical Fisheries University, and offers sail training to marine-college cadets. Though her homeport is in Vladivostok, which is on the far eastern coast of Russia, *Pallada* voyages widely. She has made two round-the-globe voyages, in 1992 and 2007/08. *Pallada* sails with a compliment of 143 cadets and a permanent crew of 56 officers, teachers, and professionals. With 26 sails and masts soaring 162 feet above the deck, *Pallada* combines traditional sail training with a modern maritime college curriculum.

Who sails: Marine-college cadets
Program type: Sail training and sea education for marine-college cadets
Season: Year-round
Designer: Zygmunt Choren
Built: 1989: Gdansk, Poland
Crew: 56   **Trainees-passengers:** 143
Contact: Georgy N. Kim, President, Far Eastern State Technical Fisheries University, 52-B, Ulitsa Lugovaya, Vladivostok 690087 Russia
Tel: +7 4232 44 03 06
Fax: +7 4232 44 24 32
E-mail: fish75@yandex.ru

SPECIFICATIONS

Flag: Canada
Rig: Brigantine
Homeport: Toronto, Ontario, Canada
Normal cruising waters:
Great Lakes
Sparred length: 72'
LOA: 60'
LOD: 58'
LWL: 45'
Draft: 8'
Beam: 15' 3"
Rig height: 54'
Freeboard: 4'
Sail area: 2,600 square feet
Tons: 31.63 GRT
Power: 150 HP diesel
Hull: steel

PATHFINDER

Who sails: In July and August, youth programs for ages 13-18; in May, June, and September, school groups from middle school through college, and interested adult groups
Program type: Sail training for paying trainees, including seamanship and leadership training based on informal, in-house programming; shoreside winter program; dockside interpretation. Affiliated institutions include the Canadian Sail Training Association and the Ontario Camping Association. A bursary fund is available for qualified applicants
Designer: Francis A. Maclachlan
Built: 1963: Kingston, Ontario, Canada, Kingston Shipyards
Crew: 10 **Trainees:** 25 daysails, 18 overnight
Contact: Toronto Brigantine, Inc., 215 Spadina Avenue, Suite 413, Toronto, Ontario M5T 2C7 Canada
Tel: 416-596-7117 **Fax:** 416-596-7117
E-mail: office@torontobrigantine.org
Website: www.torontobrigantine.org

Tall Ship Adventures conducts sail training on board *Pathfinder*, a square-rigged ship designed specifically for youth sail training on the Great Lakes. Since 1964 over 15,000 young people have lived and worked aboard *Pathfinder* and her sister ship, *Playfair*. Youth between the ages of 13 and 18 become the working crew on one or two week adventures, making 24-hour passages from ports all over the Great Lakes. The program is delivered by youth officers between the ages of 15 and 18, trained and qualified during Tall Ship Adventures' Winter Training Programs. The captain is the only adult on board. Every year, each ship sails over 4,000 miles, spends over 40 nights at sea, and introduces 300 trainees to the tall ship experience. *Pathfinder* is inspected by Transport Canada under guidelines established for Sail Training Vessels and the Captain and Executive Officer hold appropriate Transport Canada qualifications. *Pathfinder* is owned and operated by Toronto Brigantine, Inc., a registered charity.

SPECIFICATIONS

Flag: Cook Islands
Rig: Barque, 3-masted
Homeport: Avatiu, Rarotonga, Cook Islands
Normal cruising waters:
Worldwide service with refits in Lunenburg, Nova Scotia, Canada
Sparred length: 179'
LOA: 148'
LOD: 135'
LWL: 130'
Draft: 14' 6"
Beam: 24'
Rig height: 100'
Freeboard: 6'
Sail area: 12,450 square feet
Tons: 284 GRT
Power: 690 HP diesel
Hull: steel

PICTON CASTLE

The 284-ton Barque *Picton Castle* is a traditionally rigged and operated sail training ship based in Lunenburg, Nova Scotia, Canada but best known for her voyages around the world. Over the past decade, the ship has made five complete circumnavigations of the globe, as well as a year-long voyage around the Atlantic Basin, two trips to the Great Lakes and numerous runs up and down the east coast of the United States and Canada. Along the way, we've introduced more than 1,000 people to the challenges and rewards of square-rigged sailing. In 2006, Tall Ships America named us its Sailing Training Program of the Year. In May 2012, the *Picton Castle* will cast off on another epic voyage, this time to Europe, Africa, the Caribbean and rarely explored Spanish Main. Applications are now being accepted. Join Capt. Daniel Moreland and his crew on this voyage of one year, 15,000 nautical miles, all under sail. As a training ship, all on board work, stand watch, and learn the ways of a square-rigged sailing ship. Onboard workshops are conducted in wire and rope rigging, sail making, boat handling, navigation and practical seamanship. The ship is outfitted to the highest standard with safety gear and equipment. She is a strong, seaworthy home afloat for adventurers devoted to learning the art of deep-water sailing.

Who sails: Men and women ages 18 and older (16 years and up on shorter training cruises)
Program type: Deep water sail training; maritime education in cooperation with various institutes and organized groups; comprehensive instruction in the arts of seafaring under sail; dockside school visits and receptions; charitable educational/medical supply to isolated islands
Season: Year-round
Designer: Masting and rigging, decks and layout: Daniel Moreland, MM - Stability, calculations and ballasting: Daniel Blachley, NA/ME Webb Institute
Certification: Registered and certified as a Sail Training Vessel for worldwide service by the Cook Islands Ministry of Transportation
Crew: 12 **Trainees:** 38 coed
Contact: Barque Picton Castle, PO Box 1076, Lunenburg, Nova Scotia B0J 2C0 Canada
Tel: 902-634-9984 **Fax:** 902-634-9985
E-mail: info@picton-castle.com
Website: www.picton-castle.com

SPECIFICATIONS

Flag: USA
Rig: Snow brig
Homeport: Dana Point, California
Normal cruising waters: Point Conception to Ensenada, Mexico
Sparred length: 130'
LOD: 98'
Draft: 9'
Beam: 24' 6"
Rig height: 104'
Freeboard: 8'
Sail area: 7,600 square feet
Tons: 99 GRT
Power: diesel
Hull: wood

PILGRIM

Who sails: Student groups and individual volunteers
Program type: Maritime living history and volunteer sail training
Season: Year-round
Designer: Ray Wallace
Built: 1945: Holbaek, Denmark, A. Nielsen
Coast Guard certification: Uninspected Vessel
Crew: 35 **Dockside visitors:** 50
Contact: Karin Wyman, Maritime Director, Ocean Institute, 24200 Dana Point Harbor Drive, CA 92629 USA
Tel: 949-496-2274 **Fax:** 949-496-4715
E-mail: kwyman@ocean-institute.org
Website: www.ocean-institute.org

The Pilgrim is a full-scale replica of the ship immortalized by Richard Henry Dana in his classic book *Two Years Before the Mast*. Owned and operated by the Ocean Institute, *Pilgrim* is dedicated to multidisciplinary education. During the school year, the Ocean Institute has an 18-hour, award-winning living history program that offers a hands-on exploration of literature, California history, and group problem solving in which crewmembers recreate the challenge of shipboard life. Students live like sailors of the 1830s as they hoist barrels, row in the harbor, stand night watches, swab the decks, and learn to cope with a stern captain. On summer evenings, audiences are treated to the sights and sounds of the sea as the *Pilgrim's* decks come alive with theatrical and musical performances. In late summer, the *Pilgrim* sails on her annual cruise with an all volunteer crew to ports along the California coast as a goodwill ambassador for the City of Dana Point. She returns in September to lead the annual tall ship parade and festival.

PINTA

The *Pinta* was built in Valenca, Bahia, Brazil at the same shipyard as our foundation's *Nina*. Construction started in January 2002 and was completed in April 2005. For three years she toured 20 Islands in the Caribbean and in April of 2009 started touring with the *Nina* in her Tall Ship Tour. Together the vessels are a spectacular venue for dockside charters as well as their regular daytime tours.

Program type: Attraction vessel
Designer: Jonathan Nance, Morgan Sanger
Built: Nicholson Shipyard, Valenca, Brazil
Crew: 6
Contact: Morgan P. Sanger, Captain/Director, Columbus Foundation, Box 305179, St. Thomas, VI 00803
Tel: 284-495-4618 **Fax:** 284-495-4616
E-mail: columfnd@surfbvi.com
Website: www.thenina.com

SPECIFICATIONS

Flag: USA
Rig: Gaff topsail schooner, 2-masted
Homeport: New York, New York
Normal cruising waters: New York Harbor, Hudson River, and Atlantic Coast
Sparred length: 102'
LOD: 65'
LWL: 58' 11"
Draft: 4' 8" (min.) 12' (max.)
Beam: 21' 6"
Rig height: 79'
Sail area: 2,700 square feet
Tons: 43 GRT
Power: diesel
Hull: steel

PIONEER

Who sails: School groups from elementary school through college, charter groups, museum members, and the general public
Program type: Sail training for crew and volunteers; hands-on education sails designed to augment school curriculums in history, ecology, marine science, physics, and math; corporate and private charters, Elderhostel programs, and public sails
Season: April through October
Built: 1885: Marcus Hook, PA, Pioneer Iron Works (rebuilt 1968; Somerset, MA)
Coast Guard certification: Passenger Vessel (Subchapter T)
Crew: 4
Contact: Marine Operations, Seaport Museum New York, 12 Fulton Street New York, NY 10038 USA
Tel: 212-748-8600 **Fax:** 212-748-8610
Email: marineoperations@seany.org
Website: www.seaportny.org

The first iron sloop built in the United States, *Pioneer* is the only surviving American iron-hulled sailing vessel. Built in 1885 by the *Pioneer* Iron Foundary in Chester, Pennsylvania, she sailed the Delaware River, hauling sand for use in the iron molding process. Ten years later *Pioneer* was converted to a schooner rig for ease of sail handling. In 1966, the then abandoned vessel was acquired and rebuilt by Russell Grinnell, Jr. of Gloucester, Massachusetts. In 1970, the fully restored schooner was donated to the Seaport Museum New York. Today historic *Pioneer* serves as a vital education platform. Students of all ages can come on history and other curricular subjects during the hands-on program. *Pioneer* also offers corporate and private charters, Elderhostel day programs, and public sails.

SPECIFICATIONS

Flag: USA
Rig: Schooner
Homeport: Marathon, Florida
Normal cruising waters: Florida Keys
Sparred length: 71'
LOD: 56'
LWL: 54'
Draft: 6'
Beam: 16'
Rig height: 48'
Freeboard: 4'
Sail area: 1,600 square feet
Tons: 40 GRT
Power: 150 HP Yanmar
Hull: steel

PIRATES LADY

Originally built as a cargo schooner, *Pirates Lady* now sails the waters of the Florida Key during the summer as part of the High Adventure Program with Boy Scouts of America. The program consists of sail training, navigation, and coral reef education. Sailing, snorkeling, diving and fishing make the program exciting for the participants. During the winter months *Pirates Lady* carries guests on afternoon and sunset sails from her dock in Marathon. She is also available for private charters and informal in-house sea education programs. *Pirates Lady* has participated in the Great Chesapeake Bay Schooner Race. The schooner is available to travel to participate in special events.

Who sails: Adults and groups of all ages
Program type: Passenger daysails; private charters; informal sea education; sail training for paying trainees
Designer: Merrit Walter
Built: 1984: Patchogue, NY, Greg Brazier
Coast Guard certification: Passenger Vessel (Subchapter T)
Crew: 2 **Trainees:** 28 daysails
Contact: Schooner Pirates Lady, 1280 Oceanview Avenue, PO Box 500010, Marathon, FL 33050 USA
Tel: 305-481-1289
E-mail: schoonerpirateslady@yahoo.com
Website: www.schoonerpirateslady.com

SPECIFICATIONS

Flag: Canada
Rig: Brigantine
Homeport: Toronto, Ontario, Canada
Normal cruising waters: Great Lakes
Sparred length: 72'
LOA: 60'
LOD: 58'
LWL: 45'
Draft: 7' 6"
Beam: 16'
Rig height: 54'
Freeboard: 4'
Sail area: 2,600 square feet
Tons: 33 GRT
Power: 110 HP diesel
Hull: steel

PLAYFAIR

Who sails: In July and August, youth programs for ages 13-18; in May, June, and September, school groups from middle school through college, and interested adult groups
Program type: Sail training for paying trainees, including seamanship and leadership training based on in-house programming; shoreside winter program; dockside interpretation. Affiliated institutions include the Canadian Sail Training Association and the Ontario Camping Association. A bursary fund is available for qualified applicants.
Designer: Francis A. Maclachian
Built: 1973: Kingston, Ontario, Canada, Canada Dredge and Dock Co.
Crew: 10 **Trainees:** 25 daysails, 18 overnight
Contact: Toronto Brigantine, Inc., 215 Spadina Avenue, Suite 413, Toronto, Ontario M5T 2C7 Canada
Tel: 416-596-7117 **Fax:** 416-596-7117
E-mail: office@torontobrigantine.org
Website: www.torontobrigantine.org

Tall Ship Adventures conducts sail training on board *Playfair*, a square-rigged ship designed specifically for youth sail training on the Great Lakes. Since 1964, over 15,000 young people have lived and worked aboard *Playfair* and her sister ship, *Pathfinder*. Youth between the ages of 13 and 18 become the working crew on one or two week adventures, making 24-hour passages from ports all over the Great Lakes. The program is delivered by youth officers between the ages of 15 and 18. Our youth officers are trained and qualified during Tall Ship Adventures' Winter Training Programs. The captain is the only adult on board. Every year, each ship sails over 4,000 miles, spends over 40 nights at sea, and introduces 300 trainees to the tall ship experience. *Playfair* is inspected by Transport Canada under guidelines established for Sail Training Vessels and the Captain and Executive Officer hold appropriate Transport Canada qualifications. *Playfair* is owned and operated by Toronto Brigantine, Inc., a registered charity.

SPECIFICATIONS

Flag: Poland
Rig: Barkentine
Homeport: Gdynia, Poland
Sparred Length: 154'
Draft: 11' 6"
Beam: 26'
Hull: steel

Photo by Thad Koza

POGORIA

Pogoria holds the distinction of being the first completed square-rigger by Polish naval architect Zygmunt Choren. Built for the Steel Workers Union in 1980, *Pogoria* has served as the background for a movie and as a floating classroom for West Island College of Quebec, Canada. She is now the flagship of the Polish Sail Training Association in Gdansk. Pogoria's hull design served as the model for three other vessels: *Iskra* for the Polish navy, *Kaliakra* for the Bulgarian navy, and *Oceania,* a specially rigged oceanographic vessel from Gdynia, Poland. Trainees live in the four, eight, ten and twelve person cabins, and each of them has his/her own bunk. They are divided into four watches of eight to ten each. Three of those do four hours on watch and eight off while the fourth one is the galley watch, helping the cook and keeping the ship tidy. Most of the watch time is spent on look-out, taking the helm, keeping the log and trimming sails. One doesn't have to go aloft, but most trainees do for the experience and thrill of handling square sails. The usual trainee age is between 15 and 25.

Who sails: Youth ages 15 - 25
Program type: Sail training
Crew: 8 **Trainees-passengers:** 40
Built: 1984: Escanoba, MI, T. D. Vinette
Contact: Sail Training Association Poland, PO Box 113, 81-964 Gdynia 1, Poland
Tel: +48 58 614770 **Fax:** +48 58 206225
Website: www.pogoria.pl

SPECIFICATIONS

Flag: USA
Rig: Topsail schooner
Homeport: Baltimore, Maryland
Normal cruising waters: East and Gulf Coasts, Canada, Great Lakes and Europe
Sparred length: 157'
LOA: 105'
LOD: 100'
LWL: 91'
Draft: 12' 6"
Beam: 26' 4"
Rig height: 107'
Freeboard: 4' 4"
Sail area: 9,018 square feet
Tons: 97 GRT
Power: 2-165 HP Caterpillar diesel
Hull: wood

PRIDE OF BALTIMORE II

Who sails: Minimum professional crew member age is 18; overnight guest crew/trainee minimum age is 16. Day sail minors must be accompanied by an adult and supervised one-on-one. There is no maximum age limit.

Program type: U.S. historical education; charters; daysails; team building; and overnight guest crew/trainees.

Season: Spring, summer, fall

Designer: Thomas C. Gillmer **Built:** 1987-88: Baltimore, MD, G. Peter Boudreau

Coast Guard certification: Passenger Vessel (Subchapter T)

Crew: 12 **Professionals:** 6 paying guest crew/trainees for overnight sails; 35 paying day sail guests

Contact: Linda E. Christenson, Esq., Executive Director, Pride of Baltimore, Inc., 1801 South Clinton St., Suite 250, Baltimore, MD 21224 USA
Tel: 410-539-1151; toll-free 888-557-7433
E-mail: pride2@pride2.org
Website: www.pride2.org

Pride of Baltimore II is a reproduction of an 1812-era Baltimore-built topsail schooner. Owned and operated by Pride of Baltimore, Inc., a 501(c)(3) non profit, *Pride of Baltimore II's* mission is to promote Maryland's importance to U.S. and maritime history, in particular the War of 1812 and the penning of "The Star-Spangled Banner" during the 1814 Battle of Baltimore at Fort McHenry, and to serve as a visual representative of entrepreneurship in every port she visits. *Pride of Baltimore II* is available for chartered onboard dockside (107 persons) and sailing (35 persons) receptions in each of her destinations as well as public daysails.

She accommodates up to six paying guest crew/trainees between ports of call. *Pride of Baltimore II* maintains an international sailing schedule. She sails with two rotating professional captains and a crew of eleven. Crew positions are open to qualified male and female sailors.

SPECIFICATIONS

Flag: USA
Rig: Square topsail sloop
Homeport: Newport, Rhode Island
Normal cruising waters:
Narragansett Bay, Rhode Island
Sparred length: 110'
LOA: 65'
LOD: 61'
LWL: 59'
Draft: 10'
Beam: 20'
Rig height: 94'
Sail area: 3,470 square feet
Tons: 59 GRT
Power: 170 HP diesel

Photo by Thad Koza

PROVIDENCE

The original sloop *Providence* was built in Providence, Rhode Island in 1768 by John Brown. It was later purchased as the first war ship by the Continental Navy. It participated in over 60 battles and captured 40 British ships. Her last captain was John Paul Jones who later became the father of the American Navy. He is buried at the U.S. Naval Academy in Annapolis, Maryland.
The replica was built in 1975 in Portsmouth, Rhode Island. Today it participates in tall ship events, sail training, educational programs, movies and special events.

Designer: Charles W. Wittholz
Built: 1976: Melville, RI
Coast Guard certification: Passenger vessel (Subchapter T) pending
Crew: 5 **Trainees-passengers:** 40 daysails, 4-6 overnight
Contact: Thorpe Leeson, Owner
Tel: 401-241-6965
E-mail: thorpe1@aol.com
Website: www.tallshipprovidence.com

SPECIFICATIONS

Flag: USA
Rig: Gaff schooner, 2-masted
Homeport: New Haven, Connecticut
Normal cruising waters: Long Island Sound
Sparred length: 91'
LOA: 65'
LOD: 62'
LWL: 58'
Draft: 4' 5" - 11'
Beam: 20'
Rig height: 77'
Freeboard: 5' 2"
Sail area: 2,400 square feet
Tons: 41 GRT
Power: 135 HP diesel
Hull: wood

QUINNIPIACK

Who sails: School groups from middle school through college, individuals and families
Program type: Sail training; marine science, maritime history, and ecology in cooperation with primary and secondary schools, colleges, community groups and as informal, in-house programming; dockside interpretation during port visits; passenger day sails
Season: April – November
Designer: Philip Shelton
Built: 1984: Milbridge, ME, Philip Shelton
Coast Guard certification: Passenger Vessel (subchapter T)
Crew: 5 **Trainees-passengers:** 40 daysails, 4-6 overnight
Contact: Schooner Inc., 60 South Water Street, New Haven, CT 06519 USA
Tel: 203-865-1737 **Fax:** 203-624-8816
E-mail: director@schoonerinc.org or captain@schoonerinc.org
Website: www.schoonerinc.org

Built in 1984 for the passenger service, *Quinnipiack* serves as the primary vessel for Schooner Inc., an organization dedicated to teaching environmental education programs focused on Long Island Sound. Since 1975, Schooner Inc. has taught programs in classrooms, on the shore, and aboard the *Quinnipiack* and a fleet of smaller sailing vessels. Participants of all ages learn about the importance of protecting Long Island Sound. Sail training programs teach students life skills including teamwork, communication, self-reliance, responsibility and interdependence. Hands on learning activities include collection and identification of marine life, water chemistry, plankton and benthic studies, sail training and seamanship. Expedition is an overnight program for high school and college students that combines marine science, sail training and teambuilding in an intensive three-day or five-day program. During the summer Schooner Inc. offers weeklong programs for grades K-12 and public sails and charters. The *Quinnipiack* also participates in tall ship festivals and other events outside of New Haven.

SPECIFICATIONS

Flag: USA
Rig: Full rigged ship
Homeport: Culver, Indiana
Normal cruising waters: Lake Maxinkuckee in Culver, Indiana
Sparred length: 65'
LOA: 54'
LOD: 50'
Draft: 5'
Beam: 13'
Rig height: 49'
Freeboard: 5'
Tons: 25 GRT
Power: diesel

R. H. LEDBETTER

The *R.H. Ledbetter* is the flagship of the Culver Summer Naval School, located on Lake Maxinkuckee in Culver, Indiana. The 3-masted square-rigger, named in honor of Georgia philanthropist and Culver alumnus Robert H. Ledbetter, was built in 1983-84 by the T. D. Vinette Co. of Escanaba, Michigan. Culver Summer Camps offer two simultaneous coed six-week camps from mid-June to early August (Woodcraft for ages 9-13, and Upper Camp for 13-17) and 10 two-week specialty camps from early June to mid-August. Administered by The Culver Educational Foundation, which also operates the Culver Academy, the camps use the facilities of the 1,800-acre wooded campus along the north shore of Indiana's second-largest lake.

Who sails: Students and Alumni of Culver Academy
Program type: Sail training for students of Culver Academy; sea education in cooperation with organized groups such as the American Camping Association; dockside interpretation while in home port
Designer: Marine Power
Built: 1984: Escanoba, MI, T. D. Vinette
Contact: Anthony Mayfield, Director, Culver Summer Camps, 1300 Academy Road, RD# 138, Culver, IN 46511 USA
Tel: 800-221-2020 **Fax:** 574-842-8462
E-mail: mayfiea@culver.org
Website: www.culver.org

SPECIFICATIONS

Flag: USA
Rig: Gaff schooner
Homeport: Chicago, Illinois
Normal cruising waters:
Great Lakes
Sparred length: 77'
LOA: 57'
LOD: 54'
LWL: 49'
Draft: 6' 6"
Beam: 17' 6"
Rig height: 73'
Freeboard: 4' 6"
Sail area: 2,100 square feet
Tons: 41 GRT
Power: 125 HP diesel
Hull: wood

RED WITCH

Who sails: School groups from elementary school through college; individuals and families, professional groups
Program type: Sail training for volunteer or paying trainees; sea education in marine science and maritime history in cooperation with accredited institutions and organized groups; passenger day sails, evening sails, and private parties
Season: May through October
Designer: John Alden **Built:** 1986: Bayou La Batre, Alabama, Nathaniel Zirlott
Coast Guard certification: Passenger Vessel (Subchapter T)
Crew: 4 **Trainees-passengers:** 49
Contact: Captain Bruce L. Randall, Lakeshore Maritime Collective, Tall Ship Adventures of Chicago, 401 E. Illinois Street, Suite 332 Chicago IL 60611 USA
Tel: 312-404-5800 **Fax:** 312-222-9048
E-mail: info@redwitch.com
Website: www.redwitch.com

Red Witch is typical of the schooners that once plied Lake Erie and the Great Lakes. She was built in the tradition of the schooners which were the workhorses of America's 19th century transportation system. Designed by John G. Alden, the *Red Witch* has a hull of cyprus on oak, wooden blocks, and a gaff rig. Although traditional in appearance, the schooner was purpose-built for charter and day cruise service. She has full amenities for up to 49 passengers. Since 2004, *Red Witch's* home port has been Chicago. She has sailed as far as Hawaii and worked in San Diego before coming to the Great Lakes. As Ohio's Bicentennial flagship, she represented the state on goodwill cruises to Michigan, Indiana, Wisconsin, and Illinois as well as Ontario, Canada during 2003. In 2006, she represented the city of Chicago in their Tall Ships® Festival. In addition to private charters and daysails, *Red Witch* offers sea chanty concert cruises, Chicago Special Event cruises, and freshwater whale watching (none seen yet, but still trying!) Sail training programs for school groups, as well as disadvantaged and at-risk youth, are conducted.

ROBERT C. SEAMANS

Along with the SSV *Corwith Cramer*, the SSV *Robert C. Seamans* is owned and operated by the Sea Education Association (SEA) of Woods Hole, Massachusetts. Built in 2001 and named for a former SEA trustee and chairman of the board, the 134-ft steel brigantine is a highly sophisticated oceanographic research/sailing vessel built in the US. She is outfitted with an oceanographic wet/dry laboratory, classroom, library, and computer laboratory. SEA Semester students investigate and study the ocean from multiple perspectives. Our 12-week SEA Semester programs are tailored to meet a wide variety of undergraduate majors and interests. Every SEA Semester begins with a shore component in Woods Hole, Massachusetts followed by an open ocean research cruise aboard the SSV *Corwith Cramer* or the SSV *Robert C. Seamans*. Each program combines elements of oceanography, maritime history and culture, environmental studies, public policy, and nautical science. SEA Semester programs offer 17-18 credits from Boston University; the Summer Session and Trimester Program offer 12.

Who sails: College students admitted by competitive selection from over 150 colleges and universities worldwide. Also high school students participating in summer seminar programs.
Program type: SEA programs combine 6 weeks of academic study on campus in Woods Hole, MA with 6 weeks of oceanographic research at sea. Courses on shore include oceanography, nautical science, and maritime studies. Program offerings include SEA Semester (college level, 12 weeks, 17-18 credits), SEA Summer Session (college level, 8 weeks, 12 credits), and SEA seminars for high school students.
Designer: Woodin & Marean, Inc., Wiscasset, ME
Built: 1987
Coast Guard certification: Sailing School Vessel (Subchapter R) for Ocean service
Crew: 6 professional mariners and 4 scientists
Trainees-passengers: 24-25
Contact: Sea Education Association (SEA), PO Box 6, Woods Hole, MA 02543 USA
Tel: 508-540-3954 OR 800-552-3633
Fax: 508-540-0558
E-mail: admissions@sea.edu
Website: www.sea.edu

SPECIFICATIONS

Flag: USA
Rig: Schooner
Homeport: St. Croix, US Virgin Islands
Normal cruising waters:
New England (summer); Caribbean
(winter)
Sparred length: 137'
LOD: 112'
LWL: 89'
Draft: 12' 5"
Beam: 25'
Rig height: 103'
Freeboard: 4'
Sail area: 5,600 square feet
Tons: 260 GRT
Power: 400 HP diesel
Hull: wood

Photo by Kate Wood

ROSEWAY

Who sails: Middle school through college
students; individuals of all ages
Program type: Sea education in community
and leadership, cross-cultural partnerships, and
environmental stewardship through sail training;
dockside interpretations, port appearances, day
sails, and private charters.
Season: Year-round
Designer: John F. James & Sons
Built: 1925: Essex, MA, John F. James & Sons
Coast Guard certification: Passenger Vessel
(subchapter T)
Crew: 10
Contact: Abby Kidder, Executive Director,
World Ocean School, PO Box 701, Camden,
ME 04843 USA
Tel: 207-236-7482 **Fax:** 207-236-7482
E-mail: wos@worldoceanschool.org
Website: www.worldoceanschool.org

The World Ocean School on *Roseway*, creates and
provides a method of experiential education at sea that
affords teenage students a practical application for their
studies as well as cultivating teamwork, community service,
environmental responsibility, and cross-cultural friendships
so that they gain insight into becoming empowered,
motivated and engaged citizens. The 137-foot *Roseway*
was built in 1925 in Essex, Massachusetts as a private
fishing yacht. She was purchased by the Boston Pilots
Association in 1941. The *Roseway* was the last pilot
schooner in the United States when she was retired in
1973. In September 2002, she was donated to the World
Ocean School. Today, after 78 years of service, she is one
of the last Grand Banks schooners built in Essex, and a
registered U.S. National Historic Landmark.

SPECIFICATIONS

Flag: Portugal
Rig: Barque
Homeport: Lisbon, Portugal
Normal cruising waters:
Worldwide
Sparred length: 293' 6"
Draft: 17'
Beam: 39' 6"
Hull: steel

SAGRES

Sagres II sails under the Portuguese flag as a naval training ship. She was built in 1937 at the Blohm & Voss shipyard in Hamburg, Germany, and is virtually a sister ship to *Eagle, Mircea, Tovarishch,* and *Gorch Fock II*. Originally named *Albert Leo Schlageter*, she served under American and Brazilian flags before being acquired by Portugal in 1962. At that time she replaced the first *Sagres*, which was built in 1896 as the *Rickmer Rickmers*. The original *Sagres* has now been restored and serves as a museum ship in Hamburg, Germany. The name *Sagres* is derived from the historic port that sent forth many famed Portuguese explorers and navigators. It served as the home and base for Prince Henry the Navigator (1394-1460). His court in *Sagres* was responsible for the geographic studies and practical explorations that made Portugal master of the seas in the early 15th century. A bust of Prince Henry serves as the figurehead on the bow of *Sagres II*, and the ship is easily identified by the traditional Portuguese crosses of Christ (Maltese crosses) that mark the square sails on her fore- and mainmasts.

Who sails: Cadets of the Portuguese Navy
Program type: Training vessel for the Portuguese Navy
Season: Year-round
Built: 1937: Hamburg, Germany, Blohm & Voss Shipyard
Contact: Portuguese Defense and Naval Aftaché, Embassy of Portugal, 2012 Massachusetts Ave., NW, Washington, DC 20008 USA
Tel: 202-232-7632
Fax: 202-328-6827
E-mail: ponavnir@mindspring.com

SPECIFICATIONS

Flag: USA
Rig: Mast head sloop
Homeport: Port Jefferson, NY
Normal cruising waters: Long Island Sound, New York City
Sparred length: 32'
LOD: 31'
LWL: 23' 6"
Draft: 5'
Beam: 8' 5"
Rig height: 40'
Freeboard: 2' 6"
Sail area: 496 square feet
Tons: 5 GRT
Power: Nanni, Kubota 14 HP
Hull: wood

SAIL'S UP

Who sails: Individuals and groups of all ages
Program type: Open boat for personal education and public sailing
Season: May-October
Designer: Robert G. Henry Jr.
Built: 1958: Bremen, Germany, DeDood and Son Yacht Works, International 500
Coast Guard certification: Uninspected Small Passenger Vessel (subchapter C)
Crew: 2 **Passengers-trainees:** 6 daysails
Contact: Captain Eric Van Dormolen, Halyard Enterprises/ NY Maritime Restoration, 210 Bellerose Avenue, East Northport, NY 11731 USA
Tel: 631-332-0699
E-mail: captericvandy@aol.com
Website: www.nymaritimerestoration.com

The sloop *Sail's Up* in her past life was named *Isis* and *Gwahir*. She is one of 15 wooden built International 500's. She sailed as a private vessel until she had burned and sunk in New Rochelle, NY in the 1980's. After her first salvage she moved to the Connecticut River where she continued to sail as a private vessel and was home for a local carpenter. She was hauled at a marina in Deep River, CT for about a decade. The ship was then donated to NY Maritime Restoration where, after three years of work, she was restored to classic sailing condition by a team of skilled shipwrights and dedicated novices. The restoration included replacement of keel, deadwood, sternpost and 1/3 of the planking. She can be seen at the pier, in Port Jefferson at the Village Center, where many visiting tall ships gather during the season. Tall ships transiting the area can come and run their own programs or work with us to sail with passengers (If interested in sailing in Port Jefferson for a short or long term program contact Eric). *Sail's Up* sails with educational and private charter groups.

SPECIFICATIONS

Flag: USA
Rig: Ketch
Homeport: Portland, Maine
Sparred length: 63'
LOD: 53'
LWL: 45'
Draft: 7'
Beam: 16'
Rig height: 85'
Freeboard: 4'
Sail area: 1,500 square feet
Tons: 34 GRT
Power: Ford Lehman
Hull: steel

SAMANA

The instructional mission for the School of Ocean Sailing is to teach offshore ocean sailing and ocean navigation in a live-aboard setting. In our sailing school we offer seven and eight-day courses. Your classroom and sailing school home is a modern, well-founded, romantic, beautiful, fast, and very sea-kindly sailing vessel. *Samana*, a 52-foot steel offshore sailing ketch, was built in 1975 in Holland. The School of Ocean Sailing operates winters out of Saint Thomas, USVI, sailing the Atlantic Ocean and the Caribbean Sea surrounding the USVIs and BVIs. During the summers, the sailing school operates in the North Atlantic Ocean off the coast of Maine. The curriculum is a rich blend of technical skill, confidence building, and common sense coupled with a spirit of adventure and romance. Instruction centers on the principal objectives underlying the knowledge of ocean sailing, coastal navigation, or celestial navigation. The School of Ocean Sailing is able to accommodate beginners just learning to sail a large ocean vessel, and to students interested in advanced ocean navigation or celestial navigation.

Who sails: Individuals of all ages
Program type: Sail training for paying trainees; ocean sailing, celestial navigation, offshore passage making
Designer: Van de Wiele
Built: 1975: The Netherlands
Crew: 2   **Trainees-passengers:** 6
Contact: Captain Larry Wheeler, School of Ocean Sailing, TLC #1, 5600 Royal Dane Mall, Suite 12, St. Thomas, VI 00802
Tel: 207-321-9249
E-mail: svsamana@sailingschool.com
Website: www.sailingschool.com

SPECIFICATIONS

Flag: USA
Rig: Staysail schooner
Homeport: Sausalito,
California / San Francisco Bay
Normal cruising waters:
Northern California to Mexico
Sparred Length: 82'
LOA: 82'
LOD: 65'
Draft: 8' 6"
Beam: 17'
Rig Height: 75'
Freeboard: 4'
Tons: 59 GRT
Power: 210 HP Cummins 6BT
Hull: steel

SEAWARD

Who sails: elementary schools, teenagers, &
adults
Program type: maritime and environmental
education through hands-on programs ranging
from 3 hours to week-long voyages
Season: April through November in San
Francisco Bay and Northern California coastal
waters; December to March in coastal waters of
California and Mexico
Designer: Russ Woodin
Built: 1988: Paul Bramsen, St. Augustine,
Florida
Coast Guard certification: Passenger Vessel
(Subchapter T) for Ocean waters
Crew: 4-5 **Trainees-passengers:** 40 daysails,
14 overnight
Contact: Call of the Sea, 3020 Bridgeway,
#278, Sausalito, CA 94965 USA
Tel: 415 331-3214 **Fax:** 415 331-1412
E-mail: info@CalloftheSea.org
Website: www.CalloftheSea.org

Call of the Sea and the schooner *Seaward's* mission is to
inspire people of all ages and backgrounds, and especially
youth, to connect with the sea, San Francisco Bay, and
seafaring. Our hands-on programs focus on the ocean
and bay environment, our nautical heritage, seamanship,
teamwork, and leadership. *Seaward* is well-suited to both
the 'inside' waters of the bay and the 'outside' waters
beyond the Golden Gate and our programs range from
three hour Bay sails for all ages to challenging week-long
coastal voyages with teenagers. We offer wintertime
voyages along the Mexican coast for adults and youth
groups. *Seaward* is also available for collaborative
programs with educational partners as well private charters
and public sails.

SPECIFICATIONS

Flag: Russia
Rig: Barque, 4-masted
Homeport: Murmansk, Russia
Normal cruising waters:
Worldwide
Sparred length: 386'
Draft: 27'
Beam: 48'
Hull: steel

SEDOV

Sedov is the world's largest tall ship still in service and was one of the last barques built for deepwater cargo carrier service from South America and Australia to the German ports of Bremen and Hamburg. Constructed in 1921 as *Magdalene Vinnen* in Kiel, Germany, she sailed for the Bremen firm of F. A. Vinnen. Following the German commercial tradition, she was christened in honor of one of the owner's female family members. After being sold to the shipping conglomerate Norddeutscher Lloyd in 1936, she was renamed *Kommodore Johnson* and served as a sail training vessel. After World War II, she was appropriated by the Russian Ministry of Fisheries and was renamed for the Soviet polar explorer and oceanographer Georgij Sedov (1877 – 1914). *Sedov* is the largest square-rigger still in service from the days of deepwater cargo sailing. She is ten feet longer than the other giant Russian barque, *Kruzenshtern*. Besides her physical statistics, such as masts that rise 184 feet above the deck and a length of 386 feet, *Sedov* boasts its own bakery, workshop, and first-aid station.

Who sails: Students of the Murmansk State Technical University
Program type: Sail training vessel
Designer: 1921: Friedr. Krupp, A.G. Germaniawerft, Kiel, Germany
Crew: 70 crew, 120 cadets **Trainees-passengers:** 50 guest passengers
Contact: Murmansk State Technical University
Website: http://eng.mstu.edu.ru/

SPECIFICATIONS

Flag: Sultanate of Oman
Rig: Barquentine
Homeport: Muscat, Oman
Sparred length: 171'
Draft: 15'
Beam: 28'
Hull: wood

Photo by Thad Koza

SHABAB OF OMAN

Program type: Sail training vessel of the Royal Navy of Oman
Contact: Embassy of the Sultanate of Oman, 2535 Belmont Road, NW Washington, DC 20008 USA
Tel: 202-387-1980
Fax: 202-745-4933

Built in Scotland in 1971 as a sail training vessel, *Shabab of Oman* was acquired by the Sultanate of Oman in 1979. *Shabab of Oman*, which means "youth of Oman," serves as a training ship for the royal navy of Oman and also trains young men from other Omani government bureaus. The sculptured figurehead on her bow is a replica of the fifteenth-century Omani mariner Ahmed bin Majed, who helped the Portuguese sailor Vasco da Gama explore Africa and India. The turban-clad Majed cuts a rakish figure, wearing a green sash and red "khunjar," a traditional dagger. The red coat-of-arms of the sultanate is recognizable on the sails of *Shabab of Oman* and consists of a khunjar superimposed on a pair of crossed scimitars.

SPECIFICATIONS

Flag: USA
Rig: Square topsail schooner, 2-masted
Homeport: Vineyard Haven, Massachusetts
Normal cruising waters: Southern New England
Sparred length: 152'
LOA: 108'
LWL: 101'
Draft: 11'
Beam: 23'
Rig height: 94'
Freeboard: 3' (amidships)
Sail area: 7,000 square feet
Tons: 85 GRT

SHENANDOAH

While the *Shenandoah* is not a replica, the vessel's design bears a strong resemblance to that of the US Revenue Cutter *Joe Lane* of 1851. For her first 25 years, the rakish square topsail schooner was painted white, but she now wears the black and white checkerboard paint scheme of the 19th century Revenue Service. She is the only non-auxiliary power square-rigged vessel operating under the American flag. Her hull form and rig, anchors, and all materials of construction adhere closely to mid-19th century practice. Every summer, *Shenandoah* plies the waters of southern New England visiting the haunts of pirates and the homeports of whaling ships. *Shenandoah* runs six-day sailing trips for kids ages 9-16 from mid-June through mid-September. She is also available for day sailing and private charter.

Who sails: School groups from elementary through college and individuals of all ages
Program type: Sail training for paying trainees ages 9-16; private charters and day sails are also available
Season: June to September
Coast Guard certification: Passenger Vessel (Subchapter T)
Crew: 9 **Trainees-passengers:** 35 daysails, 30 overnight
Contact: Captain Robert S. Douglas, The Black Dog Tall Ships, PO Box 429, Vineyard Haven, MA 02568 USA
Tel: 508-693-1699 **Fax:** 508-693-1881
Website: www.theblackdogtallships.com

SPECIFICATIONS

Flag: USA
Rig: Sloop
Homeport: Newport, Rhode Island
Normal cruising waters:
Narragansett Bay, Rhode Island
Sparred length: 46'
LOA: 46'
LOD: 42'
LWL: 40'
Draft: 6' 6"
Beam: 11' 1"
Rig height: 63'
Freeboard: 3' 6"
Sail area: 961 square feet
Power: 47 HP diesel
Hull: aluminum

SIGHTSAILER

Who sails: Ages 6 and over
Program type: Public daysails and private charters
Season: May - October
Coast Guard certification:
Crew: 2
Trainees-passengers: 14 daysails, 16 private charters
Contact: Contact: John Hirschler, Sightsailing, Inc., 32 Bowen's Wharf, Newport, RI 02840 USA
Tel: 800-709-7245 or 401-849-3333
E-mail: info@sightsailing.com
Website: www.sightsailing.com

Fast and fun! *Sightsailer* has a towering sail plan allowing her to sail in the lightest of winds and give a lively sailing experience once the wind pipes up! *Sightsailer* sails with a maximum of 14 guests for daysails and 16 for private charters. There is a large, comfortable cushioned cockpit complete with back and footrests and two stern seats. When the wind is light to moderate, guests may also sit up on deck. Guests may take the wheel and experience the thrill of sailing a very light, highly responsive boat or simply sit back and relax. Guests board *Sightsailer* at historic Bowen's Wharf in downtown Newport, RI. Shortly after departure the sails are raised and *Sightsailer* sails through Newport Harbor, past Goat Island and Fort Adams and into Narragansett Bay. The scenery is stunning-yachts, seaside estates, the Pell-Newport Bridge, and the sailing is generally first rate. The crew is more than happy to answer guests' questions or get them involved in sailing the boat. *Sightsailer* is also available for private charters.

SPECIFICATIONS

Flag: USA
Rig: Sloop
Homeport: Baltimore, Maryland
Normal cruising waters:
Chesapeake Bay and the Delaware
River
Sparred length: 76'
LOD: 50'
Draft: 3' 5"
Beam: 16'
Rig height: 68'
Freeboard: 2' 5"
Sail area: 1,767 square feet
Tons: 14 GRT
Power: 150 HP diesel

SIGSBEE

The skipjack *Sigsbee* was built in 1901 in Deal Island, Maryland and worked as an oyster dredge boat until the early 1990s. She was named after Charles D. Sigsbee, who was the Commanding Officer of the battleship *Maine*. The vessel was rebuilt by the Living Classrooms Foundation in 1994, and now sails Chesapeake Bay with students on board. While sailing on board the *Sigsbee*, students learn the history of skipjacks and the oyster industry, marine and nautical science, and gain an appreciation of Chesapeake Bay and the hard work of the watermen of a bygone era.

Who sails: Students and other organized groups, individuals, and families
Program type: Sail training with paying trainees; sea education in marine and nautical science, maritime history, and ecology for school groups from elementary through college
Season: April through November
Built: 1901: Deal Island, Maryland
Rebuilt: 1994: Baltimore, Maryland
Coast Guard certification: Passenger Vessel (Subchapter T)
Crew: 4 **Trainees-passengers:** 30 daysails, 15 overnight , age: 13+;   **Dockside visitors:** 30
Contact: Christine Truett, Director of Education, Living Classrooms Foundation, 802 South Caroline Street, Baltimore, MD 21231-3311 USA
Tel: 410-685-0295 **Fax:** 410-752-8433
Website: www.livingclassrooms.org

SPECIFICATIONS

Flag: Venezuela
Rig: Barque
Homeport: La Guaira, Venezuela
Normal cruising waters: Worldwide
Sparred length: 270'
Draft: 14' 6'''
Beam: 35'
Hull: steel

Photo by Thad Koza

SIMON BOLIVAR

Program type: Training vessel of the Venezuelan Navy
Contact: Embassy of the Bolivarian Republic of Venezuela, 1099 30th Street, NW Washington, DC 20007 USA
Tel: 202-342-2214 **Fax:** 202-342-6820

Simon Bolivar was one of four barques built in Spain for Latin American countries. Similar in design and rigging, the four ships are nearly identical sister ships: *Gloria* from Columbia, *Guayas* from Ecuador, *Cuauhtemoc* from Mexico, and *Simon Bolivar*. All four are frequent visitors to the United States and at major tall ship gatherings. The 270-foot *Simon Bolivar* was completed in 1980 and named for the "great liberator" of northern South America. Bolivar (1783-1830) was instrumental in the independence of Columbia, Ecuador, Panama, Peru, and Venezuela. *Simon Bolivar* embodies the spirit of idealism and freedom of her namesake. Her figurehead is an allegorical depiction of Liberty and was designed by the Venezuelan artist Manuel Felipe Rincon.

SPECIFICATIONS

Flag: Canada
Rig: Marconi-rigged schooner
Homeport: Lunenburg, Nova Scotia, Canada
Normal cruising waters: Atlantic Canada and East Coast of the United States
LOA: 67'
LOD: 56' 5"
LWL: 43' 5"
Draft: 7'
Beam: 15'
Freeboard: 3' 4"
Sail area: 1,500 square feet
Tons: 26.57 GRT
Power: diesel
Hull: wood

Photo by Lynda Rosborough

SORCA

Four generations of the Stevens family have handcrafted sailing schooners – from Amos Stevens at the beginning of the century to his great-grandson Murray. The Stevens have earned a reputation of being world-class boat builders and have been described as building boats that have become an extension of themselves. Originally built in 1978, *Sorca* (Gaelic word meaning "brightness") was extensively updated and upgraded at Berthon's shipyard in the UK and is well proven in both coastal cruising and numerous safe, speedy transatlantic crossings. In 1984 she sailed as a tall ship in the trans-Atlantic race from Halifax, Nova Scotia to Liverpool, England. *Sorca* returns as a tall ship vessel under the ownership of Think Sail Inc., a Nova Scotia registered not-for-profit corporation. Established in 2008, Think Sail delivers a sail training program with qualities synonymous with its Canadian and international counterparts. Think Sail Inc. offers sail training, private and corporate charters, and vacation charters.

Who sails: Students and other organized groups, individuals, and families
Program type: Sail training, private and corporate charters, sailing vacations
Season: May through October
Designer: Murray D. Stevens
Built: 1978: Lunenburg, Nova Scotia, Stevens Boatyard
Crew: 2-4 **Trainees-passengers:** 12 daysails, 12 overnight
Contact: Think Sail Inc., TD Centre, 1791 Barrington Street, Suite 300, Halifax, Nova Scotia B3J 3K9 Canada
Tel: 902-429-1271 **Fax:** 902-429-5237
Email: info@think-sail.com
Website: www.think.sail.com

SPECIFICATIONS

Flag: USA
Rig: Gaff schooner, 3-masted
Homeport: Stamford, Connecticut
Normal cruising waters:
Long Island Sound
Sparred length: 80'
LOD: 65'
Draft: 3' (centerboards up),
8' (centerboards down)
Beam: 14'
Rig height: 60'
Freeboard: 3' 6"
Sail area: 1,510 square feet
Tons: 32 GRT
Power: diesel
Hull: steel

SOUNDWATERS

Who sails: School groups from elementary through college; individuals and families
Program type: Sea education in marine science and ecology in cooperation with accredited institutions and other groups, and as informal, in-house programming
Season: April to November
Designer: William Ward
Built: 1986: Norfolk, Virginia, Marine Metals, Inc.
Coast Guard certification: Passenger Vessel (Subchapter T)
Crew: 3 - 5 instructors **Trainees-passengers:** 42 daysails, 15-20 overnight
Contact: SoundWaters Inc., Cove Island Park, 1281 Cove Road, Stamford, CT 06902 USA
Tel: 203-323-1978 **Fax:** 203-967-8306
E-mail: connect@soundwaters.org
Website: www.soundwaters.org

SoundWaters, Inc. is a non-profit education organization dedicated to protecting Long Island Sound and its watershed through education. *SoundWaters* offers shipboard and land-based programs to 35,000 children and adults from Connecticut and New York. The schooner *SoundWaters* is the platform for a variety of programs includes seamanship, navigation, helmsmanship, and field exploration of marine ecosystems. *SoundWaters* crew includes environmental educators, biologists, naturalists, and a licensed captain. In addition, SoundWaters, Inc. operates the SoundWaters Community Center for Environmental Education, featuring educational exhibits and displays, classroom and community meeting space, a wet lab, and cutting-edge "green" construction. The organization also conducts many free outreach programs, which are offered through public schools and community centers.

SPECIFICATIONS

Flag: Bermuda
Rig: Bermudian
Homeport: Hamilton, Bermuda
Normal cruising waters: Bermuda
waters and Western Atlantic
Sparred length: 112'
LOA: 112'
LOD: 88'
LWL: 75'
Draft: 9' 6"
Beam: 23'
Rig height: 93'
Freeboard: 5'
Sail area: 4,437 square feet
Tons: 92 GRT
Power: Cat 3126 Mechanical
385 HP diesel
Hull: cold-moulded epoxy

SPIRIT OF BERMUDA

The purpose-built sail training vessel is based on civilian Bermudian-type schooners built between 1810-1840. Bermudians, enslaved and free, built the schooners in the period prior to the Emancipation of Slavery in the British Empire (August 1, 1834). The original hull shape was adapted from the Bermuda-built RN "Shamrock" class, fast dispatch and patrol vessels that ran from the RN Dockyard, Bermuda, northwest to Halifax and Southwest to Jamaica to contain the rebel colonies. The Bermuda rig was innovated on the coastal Bermuda sloops that abounded in the 17th, 18th and early part of the 19th century. Faced with impassable pathways by land, locals had evolved the lateen rig to short-tack up(wind) the island and up to the fishing banks to windward of Bermuda.

Who sails: 14+ years
Program type: Extra-curricular team (high school) and curricular learning expeditions (middle school 3)
Season: Year-round
Designer: Bill Nash / Langan Design Associates, Newport, RI
Built: 2006: Rockport, ME, Rockport Marine
Coast Guard certification: Passenger vessel (Subchapter T)
Crew: 3 professional, 8 volunteer **Trainees-passengers:** 40 inside the reef, 26 coastal
Contact: Bermuda Sloop Foundation, Suite 1151, 48 Par-la-Ville Road, Hamilton HM11 Bermuda
Tel: 441-737-5667 **Fax:** 441- 297-5776
E-mail: info@bermudasloop.org
Website: www.bermudasloop.org/

SPECIFICATIONS

Flag: USA
Rig: Schooner
Homeport: Dana Point, California
Normal cruising waters:
Southern California
Sparred length: 118'
LOD: 86'
LWL: 79'
Draft: 10'
Beam: 24'
Rig height: 100'
Freeboard: 6'
Sail area: 5,000 square feet
Power: HP diesel
Tons: 64 GRT
Hull: wood

SPIRIT OF DANA POINT

Who sails: School groups from elementary school through college; adult education groups; families and individuals of all ages
Program type: Sail training for volunteer crew or trainees; sea education in marine science, maritime history, and ecology based on informal in-house programming and in cooperation with other organizations; day sails and overnight passages
Season: Year-round
Designer: Howard Chapelle **Built:** 1983: Costa Mesa, California, Dennis Holland
Coast Guard certification: Passenger Vessel (Subchapter T)
Crew: 7 **Trainees-passengers:** 75 daysails, 30 overnight
Contact: Ocean Institute, 24200 Dana Point Harbor Drive, CA 92629 USA
Tel: 949-496-2274 **Fax:** 949-496-4715
E-mail: oi@ocean-institute.org
Website: www.ocean-institute.org

A young colony, in a new land, dreamed of independence and built some of the fastest and best sailing ships in the world. These ships were the result of ingenuity, independence and a strong desire to accomplish something. It was Dennis Holland's life dream to build an accurate replica from the period when America fought for independence and world recognition. Armed with talent, determination, a little money and plans he purchased from the Smithsonian Institute, he laid the keel in his yard on May 2, 1970. Thirteen years later, this fast privateer was launched and his vision became reality. Today at the Ocean Institute this dream continues as young students step aboard and back in time. During their voyages, students relive the challenges and discoveries of early ocean exploration. Through a series of national, award-winning living history programs, the *Spirit of Dana Point* serves as an excellent platform for our youth to directly experience life at sea, as it has been for hundreds of years. She sails throughout Southern California for more than 150 days a year.

SPECIFICATIONS

Flag: USA
Rig: Gaff tops'l schooner, 2-masted
Homeport: Boston, Massachusetts
Normal cruising waters: North Atlantic Ocean and Caribbean Sea, Canada to South America
Sparred length: 125'
LOA: 98'
LOD: 95'
LWL: 88'
Draft: 10' 6"
Beam: 24'
Rig height: 103'
Freeboard: 5'
Sail area: 7,000 square feet
Tons: 90 GRT
Power: 235 HP diesel
Hull: wood

SPIRIT OF MASSACHUSETTS

Owned by the Ocean Classroom Foundation, the schooner *Spirit of Massachusetts* offers programs of education under sail to the youth of America. Programs range from four month semesters-at-sea to week-long programs with schools and youth groups. Trainees sail the ship and learn traditional seamanship skills under the Captain and crew, and they explore maritime subjects with the onboard academic staff. Ocean Classroom's Discovery™ program is a semester-at-sea for qualified high school students, fully accredited by Proctor Academy. The voyage covers more than 6,000 nautical miles, connecting South American shores to the Canadian Maritimes. Students live and work as sailors on a true voyage of discovery, while they study maritime history, maritime literature, marine science, applied mathematics,and navigation. Discovery™ is offered Fall and Spring Terms. Other programs include SEAmester™, OceanBound and Summer Seafaring Camps. The Ocean Classroom Foundation also owns and operates the schooners *Harvey Gamage* and *Westward*.

Who sails: Individuals and school groups from middle school through college; affiliated institutions include Proctor Academy, University of Maine, Center for Coastal Studies, Outward Bound, and other schools
Program type: Traditional seamanship training combined with accredited academic studies
Season: Year-round
Designer: Melbourne Smith and Andrew Davis
Built: 1984: Boston, MA, New England Historic Seaport
Coast Guard certification: Sailing School Vessel (Subchapter R), Passenger Vessel (Subchapter T)
Crew: 8 - 11 including instructors **Student-trainees:** 22 overnight
Contact: Executive Director, Ocean Classroom Foundation, PO Box 205, 1 Oak Street, Boothbay Harbor, ME 04538 USA
Tel: 800-724-7245
E-mail: mail@oceanclassroom.org
Website: www.oceanclassroom.org

SPECIFICATIONS

Flag: USA
Rig: Schooner
Homeport: Charleston, South Carolina
Normal Cruising Waters: North Atlantic, Caribbean Sea, and the Canadian Maritimes
Sparred length: 140'
LOD: 91'
LWL: 88'
Draft: 10' 5"
Beam: 24'
Rig Height: 125'
Freeboard: 3' 9"
Sail Area: 6,462 square feet
Tons: 94 GRT
Power: two 230 HP Cummins diesel
Hull: wood

SPIRIT OF SOUTH CAROLINA

Who sails: South Carolina students and educators
Program type: Under-sail educational programs in marine science, maritime history, and seamanship, including both day trips and live-aboard programming
Season: Year-round
Designer: Tri-Coastal Marine
Built: 2007: Sea Island Boat Builders
Coast Guard certification: Passenger Vessel (subchapter T) Sailing School Vessel (subchapter R) pending
Crew: 9 **Trainees-passengers:** 40 daysails, 21 overnight
Contact: South Carolina Maritime Foundation (SCMF), PO Box 22405, Charleston, SC 29413 USA
Tel: 843-722-1030
E-mail: info@scmaritime.org
Website: www.scmaritime.org

The *Spirit of South Carolina*, owned and operated by the South Carolina Maritime Foundation, was launched in March 2007. Her lines are reminiscent of an 1870s pilot schooner that was built in Charleston, SC. The *Spirit of South Carolina* operates mainly as a sailing school vessel offering a unique education platform for the students of the Palmetto State. The hands-on programs conducted aboard are designed to challenge and engage students while promoting responsibility, teamwork, and stewardship for both their community and their environment. Programs vary in duration from day sail programs to multi-day and multi-week voyages. When not sailing in South Carolinas waters, the vessel also serves as the states floating 'Goodwill Ambassador' promoting the resourcefulness and vibrancy of South Carolinians.

SPECIFICATIONS

Flag: Canada
Rig: Brigantine
Homeport: Kingston, Ontario, Canada
Normal cruising waters: Lake Ontario and adjacent waters
Sparred length: 72'
LOA: 60'
LOD: 57'
LWL: 46'
Draft: 8' 6"
Beam: 15'
Rig height: 54'
Freeboard: 4' 6"
Sail area: 2,560 square feet
Tons: 34 GRT
Power: 165 HP diesel
Hull: steel

ST. LAWRENCE II

The *St Lawrence II* is a purpose built sail training vessel in operation since 1957, primarily on the Great Lakes. She was designed to be manageable by a young crew, yet complex enough with her brigantine rig to introduce teenagers to the challenge of square-rig sailing. The ship is owned and operated by Brigantine, Inc., a nonprofit charity staffed by local volunteers who share the conviction that the lessons of responsibility, self-reliance, and teamwork provided by sail training are especially applicable to teenagers. Brigantine, Inc. is one of the pioneering sail training programs in North America. Cruises in this hands-on program range from six to ten days or more in length. *St. Lawrence II*'s crew complement of 28 is comprised of 18 new trainees, plus a crew of watch officers, petty officers, cook, and bosun, all aged 13 to 18. The captain is usually the only adult onboard. The ship's teenage officers are graduates of Brigantine, Inc.'s winter training program, involving lessons in seamanship, navigation, and ship's systems, as well as the ongoing maintenance of the ship.

Who sails: School groups and individuals of all ages
Program type: Sail training with paying trainees
Season: April to November (sailing); October to March (winter program)
Designer: Francis McLachlan/Michael Eames
Built: 1953: Kingston, Ontario, Canada, Kingston Shipyards
Crew: 10 **Trainees-passengers:** 36 daysails, 18 overnight
Contact: Brigantine, Inc., 53 Yonge Street, Kingston, Ontario K7M 6G4 Canada
Tel: 613-544-5175 **Fax:** 613-544-9828
E-mail: briginc@kos.net
Website: www.brigantine.ca

SPECIFICATIONS

Flag: USA
Rig: Barque, 3-masted
Homeport: San Diego, California
Normal cruising waters: Coastal waters between San Diego, California and northern Baja California, Mexico
Sparred length: 278'
LOD: 210'
LWL: 200'
Draft: 21' 6"
Beam: 35'
Rig height: 148'
Freeboard: 15'
Sail area: 18,000 square feet
Tons: 1,197 GRT
Hull: iron

STAR OF INDIA

Who sails: Selected volunteers, permanent crew, and invited passengers
Program type: Sail training for crew and apprentices; sea education in maritime history; dockside interpretations
Designer: Edward Arnold
Built: 1863: Ramsey, Isle of Man, UK, Gibson, McDonald & Arnold
Coast Guard certification: Museum Attraction Vessel
Contact: Scott Baldwin, San Diego Maritime Museum, 1492 N. Harbor Drive, San Diego CA 92101 USA
Tel: 619 234 9153 x 120
E-mail: sbaldwin@sdmaritime.org
Website: www.sdmaritime.org

The *Star of India* is the world's oldest active ship. She was built at Ramsey shipyard on the Isle of Man and launched as the *Euterpe* in 1863. She began her working life as a cargo ship in the India trade and was nearly lost on her first two voyages, surviving a mutiny, collision, cyclone and the death of her captain. In 1871, she embarked on a quarter century of hauling emigrants to New Zealand. She circumnavigated the globe 21 times during this service. She was sold to American owners in 1898 and renamed the *Star of India* in 1906. By 1923, steam power had replaced sails on merchant ships and the *Star of India* was laid up in Oakland. A group of San Diegans purchased the ship and had her towed to San Diego in 1927. Depression and war delayed the beginning of her restoration until the late 1950s. In 1976, with her restoration complete, she sailed on San Diego Bay for the first time in 50 years. The *Star of India* is now the pride of the Maritime Museum of San Diego's fleet of historic ships. She is maintained by a dedicated group of volunteers and skilled craftsman and sails at least once a year.

SPECIFICATIONS

Flag: Norway
Rig: Barque
Homeport: Bergen, Norway
Sparred length: 321' 6"
Draft: 17'
Beam: 41'
Hull: steel

STATSRAAD LEHMKUHL

Statsraad Lehmkuhl is Norway's largest and oldest square-rigged sailing ship. She is a 3-masted barque built in 1914 at the J. C. tecklenborgwerft yard in Bremerhaven, Germany, as a training ship for the German merchant navy and originally christened *Grossherzog Fridrich August*. In 1923, she was purchased by agents in Bergen for the Norwegian Shipowners Association on the initiative of secretarty of state Kristoffer Lehmkuhl. For his work in promoting the cause of cadet ships and for his contributions to the creation of an independent Norwegian government in 1905, the ship was renamed in his honor. In 1924 the training ship was transferred to the Bergen Schoolship Association, which operated the vessel through difficult years until 1979 under the direction of Hilmar Reksten. In 1979, the ship was donated to the Statraad Lehmkuhl Foundation. The board of directors of this foundation comprises representatives of national and local governments, the Maritime Museum of Bergen, the firm of Hilmar Reksten, and the City of Bergen. Today she carries young people across oceans to discover the romance of the sea and the adventure of sailing.

Who sails: Norwegian Navy, schools, companies, public institutions, organizations or large groups of friends
Program type: Sail training for paying trainees, 5-7 hour day cruises and 4-10 day sailing cruises
Built: 1914: Johann C. Tecklenborg AG, Bremerhaven-Geestemünde
Crew: 17 **Trainees-passengers:** 350 daysails, 150 overnight
Contact: Statsraad Lehmkuhl, Skur 7 Bradbenken 2 NO- 5003 Norway
Tel: 55 30 17 00 **Fax:** 55 30 17 01
E-mail: lehmkuhl@lehmkuhl.no
Website: www.lehmkuhl.no

SPECIFICATIONS

Flag: USA
Rig: Square topsail schooner
Homeport: Chestertown, Maryland
Normal cruising waters: Chesapeake Bay
Sparred length: 97'
LOD: 53'
LWL: 53'
Draft: 8'
Beam: 17'
Rig height: 72'
Freeboard: 5'
Tons: 43 GRT
Power: Single screw diesel
Hull: wood

SULTANA

Who sails: School & adult groups as well as individuals of all ages
Program type: Under-sail educational experiences in environmental science and history, including both day trips and live-aboard programming
Season: April to November
Designer: Benford Design Group, St. Michael's, Maryland
Built: 2001: Chestertown, Maryland, Swain Boatbuilders, LLC
Coast Guard certification: Passenger Vessel (Subchapter T)
Crew: 5 **Trainees-passengers:** 32 daysails, 11 overnight
Contact: Drew McMullen, President, Sultana Projects, Inc., PO. Box 524, Chestertown, MD 21620 USA
Tel: 410-778-5954 **Fax:** 410-778-4531
E-mail: dmcmullen@sultanaprojects.org
Website: www.sultanaprojects.org

The schooner *Sultana* is a full scale reproduction of a 1767 vessel of the same name used by the British Royal Navy to enforce the notorious "Tea Taxes" on the North American coastline in the years preceding the American Revolution. *Sultana* is notable as one of the most thoroughly documented vessels from the American Colonial period. The schooner's original logbooks, crew lists, correspondence, and design drawings have all survived intact to the present day. Owned an operated by Sultana Projects, Inc., a non-profit, 501(c)(3) organization based in historic Chestertown, Maryland, the new *Sultana* sails as a floating classroom; providing unique, hands-on educational opportunities for children and adults that focus on the history and environment of the Chesapeake Bay and its watershed. *Sultana's* educational programs are designed to compliment and support national, state and local curriculum goals - but just as importantly, they are meant to excite students about the process of learning. Again and again teachers have found that a trip on *Sultana* can help to bring subjects like history, science, math and reading to life.

Flag: USA
Rig: Schooner
Homeport: Kings Point, New York
Normal cruising waters: Coastal New England and Mid-Atalantic
Sparred length: 101'
LOA: 79'
LOD: 78'
LWL: 67'
Draft: 10'
Beam: 18' 6"
Rig height: 97'
Freeboard: 5'
Tons: 54 GRT
Power: 1 MAN 300HP diesel powering twin hydraulic pods
Hull: wood

SUMMERWIND

Summerwind was originally built in 1929 at the yard of C.A. Morse of Thomaston, ME. Following a long career on the east coast of the United States including service in the Coastal Picket Patrol during World War II, she was brought to the Med. where she operated as a passenger vessel for several decades. In 2007 she was repatriated to the United States where a complete two year rebuild was undertaken. After being relaunched in 2009, she was donated to the United States Merchant Marine Academy where she now serves as a sail training vessel for Midshipmen and flagship of the fleet.

Who sails: United States Merchant Marine Academy training vessel
Program type: Sail training and seamanship
Designer: John G. Alden
Built: 1929: Thomaston, ME/ Palm Beach, FL, C.A. Morse/Moores Marine
Certification: Merchant Marine Academy Training Vessel
Crew: 2 **Trainees-passengers:** 20 daysails, 12 overnight
Contact: CDR Chris Gasiorek, USMS/ Sailing Master/Director of Waterfront Activities, Department of Waterfront Activities, Yocum Sailing Center, 300 Steamboat, Kings Point, NY 11024 USA
Tel: 516-726-6034
E-mail: gasiorekc@usmma.edu
Website: www.usmma.edu/waterfront

SPECIFICATIONS

Flag: USA
Rig: Junk schooner
Homeport: Philadelphia, Pennsylvania
Normal cruising waters: Delaware River, Delaware Bay, Chesapeake Bay
Sparred length: 54'
LOA: 48'
LOD: 42' 6"
LWL: 38'
Draft: 4' 6"
Beam: 11' 6"
Rig height: 50'
Freeboard: 2' 6"
Sail Area: 833 square feet
Tons: 15 GRT
Power: Yanmar 54 HP diesel
Hull: steel

SUMMER WIND

Who sails: Individuals ages 10+
Program type: Passenger daysails, private charters
Season: April 1 to October 31
Designer: Thomas E. Colvin
Built: 1979: Deltaville, VA
Coast Guard certification: Uninspected Small Passenger Vessel (Subchapter C)
Crew: 2 **Trainees-passengers:** 6 daysails, 6 overnight
Contact: : Tom Kirwan, American Sailing Tours, Inc., 26 Elizabeth Court South, Marlton, New Jersey 08053 USA
Tel: 215-900-7758 **Fax:** 856-810-2607
E-mail: tom@AmericanSailingTours.com
Website: www.AmericanSailingTours.com

The *Summer Wind* is a 48-foot, Junk-rigged, steel-hulled Colvin Gazelle owned and operated by American Sailing Tours, Inc. in Philadelphia. The *Summer Wind* sails up to six times daily, doing 90-minute sailing tours on the Delaware River, as well as private charters to Cape May and the Chesapeake Bay. With lots of great music and some history lessons not taught anywhere else, the *Summer Wind* has quickly become a top attraction in Philadelphia. The Intern Program provides live-aboard opportunities to learn all aspects of sail handling, boat handling, maintenance and repair, deck safety and navigation. Interns cover all the material required to sit for the Captains license exam. The *Summer Wind* is also a member of the American Schooner Association. Captain Tom Kirwan is also a volunteer crew member with the tall ship *Kalmar Nyckel*.

SPECIFICATIONS

Flag: Mexico
Rig: Schooner
Homeport: Cabo San Lucas, Mexico
Normal cruising waters: Mexican Riviera
Sparred length: 105'
LOA: 87'
LOD: 84'
LWL: 70'
Draft: 10' 6"
Beam: 19' 6"
Rig Height: 85'
Freeboard: 5'
Sail Area: 3,079 square feet
Tons: 187 GRT
Power: 1209 HP diesel
Hull: wood (English Oak)

SUNDERLAND

The *Sunderland* is a tall ship built in Lowestoft, England by Samuel Richards in 1885. Her first name was *Civil Lord* and then changed to *Sunderland* when she worked out of the town of Sunderland, England. The *Sunderland*, designed for fishing and carrying cargo, had its first career sailing the North Sea where she fished for 50 years. This vessel is built of English oak on oak with a typical English plum stem, which creates a lengthening of the waterline and gives her an advantage in sailing speed. English oak is a wood of longevity and it is next to impossible to find lumber of length and age to build such a ship as this today. Her career went from a fishing and cargo vessel to a yacht when she had her first motor installed in 1935. She then sailed to the Americas where she was chosen to film the movie "Captains Courageous" making this her second career. *Sunderland* was also filmed in the movie "Troy" with Brad Pitt. Now on her third career, she sails out of Cabo San Lucas doing Historical Pirate Sailing Cruises.

Who sails: Individuals and groups of all ages
Program type: Passenger trade, daysails, Historical pirate sailing cruises
Season: October 1 – August 1
Designer: Samuel Richards
Built: 1885: Lowestoft, England
Certification: Mexico Safety Certification
Crew: 4-6 **Trainees-passengers:** 145 daysails, 6 overnight
Contact: Jesse Chamberlain & Clinton Schue, Florida Caribbean Cruise Association, Calle Gomex Farias, Sin Numbero 2ª, El Medano, BCS 23453 Mexico
Tel: MX 011-52-624-105-0955
E-mail: TheCaboPirateShip@gmail.com
Website: www.TheCaboPirateShip.com

SPECIFICATIONS

Flag: USA
Rig: Full-rigged ship
Homeport: San Diego, Californian
Normal cruising waters:
San Diego Bay
LOA: 179'
LOD: 135'
Draft: 13'
Beam: 30'
Rig Height: 130'
Sail Area: 13,000 square feet
Tons: 263 GRT
Hull: wood

HMS SURPRISE

Who sails: Museum vessel at this time
Program type: No programs as yet
Designer: Admiralty
Built: 1970: John Fitzhugh Millar, Lunenburg, Nova Scotia
Contact: Scott Baldwin, San Diego Maritime Museum, 1492 N. Harbor Drive, San Diego CA 92101 USA
Tel: 619-234-9153 x120
E-mail: sbaldwin@sdmaritime.org
Website: www.sdmaritime.org

"HMS" *Surprise* is a 179' full rigged ship. Her designers and builders made painstaking efforts to recreate a 24 gun frigate of Great Britains' Nelson era Royal Navy. The result is a replica vessel unmatched in its authenticity and attention to detail. Originally christened "HMS" *Rose* when she was launched in 1970, she served as a sail training vessel operating out of several east coast ports for over 30 years. The ship underwent extensive modifications for the production of the film "Master and Commander: The Far Side of the World" in 2002. The Maritime Museum of San Diego purchased "HMS" *Surprise* from 20th Century Fox in October, 2004. Plans include restoring the ship to seaworthy condition.

SPECIFICATIONS

Flag: USA
Rig: Barque, 3-masted
(lateen mizzen)
Homeport: Jamestown Settlement,
Virginia
Normal cruising waters:
Chesapeake Bay
Sparred length: 116'
LOA: 96'
LOD: 83'
LWL: 77'
Draft: 11' 6"
Beam: 24' 10'
Rig height: 95'
Freeboard: 11'
Sail area: 3,902 square feet
Tons: 180 GRT
Power: twin 135 HP diesels
Hull: wood

SUSAN CONSTANT

Susan Constant is a full-scale re-creation of the flagship of a small fleet that brought America's first permanent English colonists to Virginia in 1607. Together with the smaller *Godspeed* and *Discovery*, *Susan Constant* is on exhibit at Jamestown Settlement, a living history museum of 17th-century Virginia. Jamestown Settlement is administered by the Jamestown Yorktown Foundation, an agency of the Commonwealth of Virginia. While no plans or renderings of the original *Susan Constant*, *Godspeed*, and *Discovery* have ever been located, the replicas are based on the documented tonnages of the 17th century ships, and *Susan Constant's* design incorporates research information that emerged after the first replicas were built. With a crew of staff and volunteers, *Susan Constant* and *Godspeed* periodically sail to other ports in the Chesapeake Bay region to participate in commemorative and community events and host educational programs.

Who sails: Crew consisting of Jamestown Settlement staff and volunteers age 18 years and older
Program type: Sail training and dockside interpretation.
Season: Year-round
Designer: Stanley Potter
Built: 1991: Jamestown Settlement, VA, Allen C. Rawl
Coast Guard certfication: Attraction Vessel
Crew: 25
Contact: Captain Eric Speth, Maritime Program Manager, Jamestown Settlement, PO Box 1607, Williamsburg, VA 23187 USA
Tel: 757-253-4838
Fax: 757-253-7350
Website: www.historyisfun.org

SPECIFICATIONS

Flag: USA
Rig: Square topsail schooner
Homeport: Los Angeles, California
Normal cruising waters: Coastal California and offshore islands
Sparred length: 92'
LOA: 70'
LOD: 66'
LWL: 62'
Draft: 10'
Beam: 18'
Rig height: 74'
Freeboard: 5'
Sail area: 4,000 square feet
Tons: 46 GRT
Power: Diesel
Hull: wood

SWIFT OF IPSWICH

Who sails: Youth/school groups from diverse communities, especially pre-teens and other youth and adult groups seeking character-building/team-building sailing adventures
Program type: Educational sailing adventures
Season: Year-round
Designer: Howard I. Chappelle
Built: 1938: Ipswich, MA, William A. Robinson
Coast Guard certfication: Passenger Vessel (Subchapter T)
Crew: 6 **Trainees-passengers:** 49 daysails, 31 overnight - Age: 10+
Contact: Los Angeles Maritime Institute, Berth 73, Suite 2, San Pedro, CA 90731 USA
Tel: 310-833-6055 **Fax:** 310-548-2055
Website: www.LAMItopsail.org

The Los Angeles Maritime Institute is currently making a major investment in the restoration of the square topsail schooner *Swift of Ipswich*. Once completed, she will return to the TopSail Youth Program, alongside the twin brigantines, *Irving Johnson* and *Exy Johnson*, providing character building sail training adventures for youth. As LAMI's original vessel, *Swift of Ipswich* is a learning environment that nurtures the development of knowledge, skills and attitudes that are necessary for the education of today's youth, but difficult to teach in a traditional classroom. About two thirds the size of one of LAMI's twin brigantines, *Swift* is especially well suited for working with smaller, younger groups who might be overwhelmed by the size and complexity of the LAMI brigantines. Built to the lines of an historic Revolutionary War privateer, *Swift of Ipswich* was once the personal yacht of actor James Cagney and has been known as a floating landmark mostly serving youth in Southern California for over 60 years.

SPECIFICATIONS

Flag: USA
Rig: Gaff schooner, 2-masted
Homeport: Marion, Massachusetts
Normal cruising waters:
Coastal New England (summer),
offshore Atlantic Ocean (school year)
Sparred length: 115'
LOA: 92' 10"
LOD: 84' 6"
LWL: 78' 8"
Draft: 10' 4"
Beam: 21' 8"
Rig height: 95'
Sail area: 3,540 square feet
Tons: 100 GRT
Power: 300 HP diesel
Hull: iron

TABOR BOY

Tabor Boy has been engaged in sail training as a seagoing classroom for Tabor Academy students since 1954. Offshore voyaging and oceanographic studies go together in the curriculum, with cruises to destinations as distant as Mexico and Panama adding adventure to the experience. Many Tabor Academy graduates go on to the US Merchant Marine, Naval, or Coast Guard academies. The schooner also offers seven summer orientation voyages for newly enrolled freshmen and sophomore students. During this time, trainees are fully involved in sail handling while studying Gulf of Maine marine wildlife and ecology. Winter programs feature sailing and snorkeling in the US and British Virgin Islands to observe and study coral reef ecosystems.

Who sails: Enrolled students at Tabor Academy
Program type: Seamanship and oceanography for high school students
Built: 1914: Amsterdam, The Netherlands, Scheepswerven & Machinefabrik
Coast Guard certification: Sailing School Vessel (Subchapter R)
Crew: 6 **Trainees-passengers:** 23 - Age: 14-18
Contact: Captain James E. Geil, Master, Tabor Boy, Tabor Academy, 66 Spring Street, Marion, MA 02738 USA
Tel: 508-748-2000 **Fax:** 508-291-6666
E-mail: jgeil@taboracademy.org
Website: www.taboracademy.org

SPECIFICATIONS

Flag: India
Rig: Barque, 3-masted
Homeport: Kochi, India
Normal cruising waters:
Worldwide
Sparred length: 177'
Draft: 15'
Beam: 28'
Sail area: 10,392 square feet
Power: twin 320 HP diesels
Hull: steel

Photo by MAX

TARANGINI

Who sails: Officer cadets of the First Training Squadron and officers of the Indian Navy
Program type: Sail training and seamanship for cadets and officers of the Indian Navy
Season: Year-round
Design: Colin Mudie
Built: 1997: Goa, India, Goa Shipyard Limited
Crew: 27 **Trainees:** 30
Contact: Indian Embassy, 2107 Massachusetts Ave NW, Washington DC 20008 USA
or
The Commanding Officer, INS Tarangini, c/o Fleet Mail Office, Kochi - 682004
Tel: 202-939-7060 **Fax:** 202-986-6717
E-mail: navy@indiangov.org

INS *Tarangini* was commissioned into the Indian Navy in 1997 as a cadet training ship forming part of the First Training Squadron based in Kochi. The name *Tarangini* comes from Hindi world, "Tarang", which means waves. Besides being an ideal platform for seamanship the ship primarily provides character building and sail training to officer cadets of the First Training Squadron of the Indian Navy. In addition cadets from the Indian Naval Academy and National Defence Academy are also trained from time to time. She provides an ideal setting for firsthand experience of the natural elements to the cadets embarking on a naval career. Training includes general points and terms used in sailing , parts of sails and rigging, setting and furling of sails, watch keeping, safety and sail maneuvers such as tacking, wearing, and boxhauling. INS *Tarangini* fosters the old fashioned and time tested virtues of courage, camaraderie and endurance. She instills among the trainees the indefinable "sea sense", which encompasses the qualities of humanity and prudence which are inseparable from safe and successful seafaring. Onboard, opportunities for developing physical and moral courage, esprit-de-corps, loyalty and respect for authority, arise as a matter of routine.

SPECIFICATIONS

Flag: Cook Islands
Rig: Gaff ketch with a yard for square sail and raffee
Homeport: Avatui, Rarotonga, Cook Islands, South Pacific Ocean
Normal cruising waters: Cook Islands and central South Pacific
LOA: 130'
Draft: 14'
Beam: 26'
Rig height: 80'
Freeboard: 6'
Sail area: 7,500 square feet
Tons: 290 GRT
Cargo: General goods, foodstuffs, frozen goods, building and gardening supplies, marine supplies, fishing gear, dry goods, medical and educational supplies
Power: 900 HP Deutz Diesel
Hull: steel

TIARE TAPORO

The *Tiare Taporo* is an auxiliary-sail passenger/cargo trading vessel established to carry cargo, freight, inter-island passengers, trade in supplies and goods, and carry out medical and government missions in the South Pacific Islands and other remote tropical routes. In addition to her staff crew and passengers, this ship will reserve berths for six apprentices in vocational training to become advanced professional seafarers. In their time aboard, the apprentices will receive instruction and experience in all ship's departments (Deck, Chartroom, Engine, Small Boats, Bosun, Galley/Steward), learn about all aspects of ship's operations applicable to this and other ships, and become well-rounded and broadly-experienced mariners. This apprenticeship is established for young mariners who have sailed previously perhaps in a sea education programs or who have had a start in other vessels or other marine experiences. This opportunity can also benefit those seeking an increase in tonnage or scope. Instruction in ship handling, boat handling, ocean winds and weather, anchoring/mooring, coral piloting and navigation, celestial navigation, diesel mechanics, cargo and passenger care, welding, wire splicing, rope-work and a great deal more. Voyage routes will primarily be within the Cook Islands in the mid South Pacific, sailing from Rarotonga for Aitutaki, Mangaia, Atiu, Puka Puka, Manihiki, Mauke,Tongareva, Rakahanga, Mitiaro, Palmerston and Suwarrow with occasional voyages to Samoa, Fiji and Tahiti.

Who sails: Young mariners seeking to advance and increase their skill levels and broaden their deep-sea and tropical island sailing experience.
Program type: professional vocational maritime training under sail
Season: Year-round
Designer: Hull: George T. Davie & Sons Ltd, Quebec; Rig and layout: D. Moreland - Master Steam, Motor and Sail, any gross tons, oceans
Built: 1963: The ship rigging and conversion is a project of Dawson Moreland & Co. Ship Riggers, Boat Builders and Vessel Outfitters of Lunenburg, Nova Scotia, Canada.
www.doryshop.com - www.lunenburgschooners.com
Crew: 9 **Apprentices:** 6 **Passengers:** 29 interisland, 12 international
Contact: Pacific Schooners Ltd., Box 102, Aitutaki, Cook Islands, South Pacific Ocean
E-mail: garth@gmb-marine.com
Website: www.pacificschooners.com

SPECIFICATIONS

Flag: USA
Rig: Square topsail schooner, 3-masted
Homeport: Long Beach, California
Normal cruising waters: Channel Islands and beyond
Sparred length: 156'
LOD: 123'
LWL: 101'
Draft: 13' 6"
Beam: 31'
Rig height: 110'
Freeboard: 6'
Sail area: 8,500 square feet
Tons: 229 GRT
Power: 575 HP Deutz diesel
Hull: steel

TOLE MOUR

Who sails: School groups 4th grade through college; educational adult groups; individuals
Program type: Live-aboard educational voyages focusing on sail training and marine science
Designer: Ewbank, Brooke, and Associates
Built: 1988: Whidbey Island, WA, Nichols Brothers
Coast Guard certification: Sailing School Vessel (Subchapter R)
Crew: 13 **Trainees-passengers:** 53 daysails, 36 overnight
Contact: CIMI Tall Ship Expeditions, PO Box 1360, Claremont, CA 91711 USA
Tel: 1-800-645-1423 **Fax:** 909-625-7305
Website: www.guideddiscoveries.org or www.tolemour.org

Tole Mour is a 156-foot, 3-masted square topsail schooner owned and operated by the non-profit organization, Guided Discoveries. With her incredibly seaworthy construction, 15 sails, hands-on science equipment, professional crew dedicated to teaching, and close proximity to Southern California's biologically rich Channel Islands, she is the ultimate platform for sail training and marine science education. The *Tole Mour* has been carrying out the work of Catalina Island Marine Institute (CIMI) since 2001. CIMI Tall Ship Expeditions, founded in 1998, is a Guided Discoveries program that is dedicated to "taking young people to sea in order to build character and minds." CIMI Tall Ship Expeditions offers live-aboard voyages during the school year, summer, and winter, that focus on sail training and marine science education and range from 2 to 21 days in length. *Tole Mour* accommodates groups of up to 36 and ages ten to adult. She sails the waters of Southern California's eight off–shore islands and beyond.

SPECIFICATIONS

Flag: USA
Rig: Gaff schooner
Homeport: Newport, Rhode Island
Sparred length: 93'
LOA: 70'
LOD: 70'
LWL: 58'
Draft: 8' 5"
Beam: 18' 6"
Rig height: 85'
Freeboard: 4' 5"
Sail area: 4,800 square feet
Tons: 83 GRT
Power: diesel
Hull: wood/epoxy

TREE OF LIFE

The Schooner *Tree of Life*, launched in 1991, was built in Nova Scotia, Canada. She sleeps 12 in three cabins and the foc'sle. Her hull is a composite of strip planked clear fir and Kevlar saturated in epoxy and sheathed in fiberglass. Her deck is fir, spars are spruce, and brightwork is Honduran Mahogany. The interior is paneled in koa and teak. The *Tree of Life*, her owners, a crew of four plus two trainees, sailed out of Newport Oct. 2002 on a three year circumnavigation. In 2003, *Tree of Life* spent five months in Auckland, New Zealand via Bora Bora, the Southern Cooks and Fiji for the America's Cup. She sailed the Indian Ocean to Capetown, South Africa, the Atlantic to Antigua for Classic Race Week, St Barth's, St Martin, Turks & Caicos, the Bahamas, Palm Beach and home to Newport, RI. The owners were on board for the duration of the voyage. The *Tree of Life*, at home in Newport Harbor, now sails throughout New England waters as she awaits prospective owners to return her to the world's oceans.

Who sails: Adult individuals and families
Program type: Sail training for volunteer and trainees; sea education in marine science and maritime history
Designer: Ted Brewer
Built: 1991: Covey Island, Canada
Crew: 4 **Trainees-passengers:** 2
Contact: Sheri & John Laramee, Owners, 443 Bellevue Avenue, Newport, RI 02840 USA
Tel: 401-640-9777 or 401-732-6464
E-mail: JohnOnTree@aol.com
Website: www.schoonertreeoflife.com

SPECIFICATIONS

Flag: USA
Rig: Topsail schooner
Homeport: Bridgeport, Connecticut
Normal cruising waters: East Coast, Long Island Sound, New England and Great Lakes
Sparred length: 118'
LOD: 90'
LWL: 83'
Draft: 9' 6"
Beam: 22'
Rig height: 96'
Freeboard: 3' 6"
Sail area: 9,688 square feet
Tons: 98 GRT
Power: 350 HP diesels
Hull: steel from German U-Boats

UNICORN

Who sails: Girls age 13 – 21; male and female executives
Program type: Sail training vessel for teenage girls, women, executive teams, private groups and film work
Built: 1947: Alphen, The Netherlands
Crew: 6 - 10 **Trainees-passengers:** 12 daysails, 6 overnight
Contact: Dawn Santamaria, 2 Gravel Hill Road, Asbury, NJ 08802 USA
Tel: 908-713-1808
E-Mail: dawn@tallshipunicorn.com
Website: www.tallshipunicorn.com

From metals of old German submarines to majestic tall ship, STV *Unicorn* sails the sea with proven on-board leadership and development programs for teenage girls, executive women and executive teams. Holland-built in 1947, STV *Unicorn* partners with Sisters Under Sail Corp. to deliver a non-profit leadership development program for teenage girls, whose mission is to build confidence, enhance self-esteem, develop social conscience and teach the value of sisters working together towards a common goal. The vessel welcomes young women from around the globe to sail aboard with *Unicorn's* all-female professional crew. *Unicorn* also partners with BeamPines, Inc., a human resources consulting firm in New York City, to offer on-board executive development and team building programming. HR consultants work closely with *Unicorn's* crew to create an effective learning environment that drives results.

SPECIFICATIONS

Flag: The Netherlands
Rig: Ketch
Homeport: Den Helder, The Netherlands
LOA: 76'
Draft: 8' 6"
Beam: 18'
Hull: steel

Photo by Thad Koza

URANIA

Urania is the flagship of the Royal Netherlands Naval College. Every executive officer who has graduated from the naval college over the past 40 years trained on the *Urania*. Generally she sails with three officers, two petty officers, and 12 cadets. She is a very active ship and has been the recipient of the prestigious Friendship Trophy four times, which is awarded by Sail Training International annually to a ship that best demonstrates the spirit of sail training. Her original wishbone rig was modified to her present Bermudian ketch rig in the late 1950s.

Program type: Training vessel of the Royal Netherlands Naval College
Built: 1928
Crew: 5 **Trainees-passengers:** 12
Contact: Royal Netherlands Embassy, 4200 Linnean Avenue, NW, Washington, DC 20008 USA
Tel: 202-244-5300 **Fax:** 202-362-3430

SPECIFICATIONS

Flag: USA
Rig: Square topsail sloop
Homeport: Traverse City, Michigan
Normal cruising waters:
Great Lakes
Sparred length: 87'
LOA: 55'
LWL: 49'
Draft: 7'
Beam: 16'
Rig height: 96'
Freeboard: 6'
Power: diesel
Hull: wood, plank on frame

WELCOME

Who sails: Families and adults of all ages
Program type: Sail training for volunteer crew and trainees; sea education in maritime history; overnight passages; dockside interpretation
Season: June – October
Designer: Fred Ford
Built: 1976: Mackinaw City, MI, State of Michigan
Coast Guard certification: Moored Attraction Vessel
Crew: 5
Contact: Maritime Heritage Alliance, 13268 S. West Bayshore, Traverse City, Michigan 49684 USA
Tel: 231-946-2647 **Fax:** 231-946-6750
E-mail: info@MaritimeHeritageAlliance.org
Website: www.MaritimeHeritageAlliance.org

The *Welcome* is a 55-foot armed sloop, a replica of the original *Welcome* built in 1775 at Fort Michimackinac during the Revolutionary War, which later became a British military vessel. The Mackinac Island State Park Commission built *Welcome* for the 200th anniversary of Independence Day. The vessel sailed the Great Lakes for a number of years before serving as a dockside museum in Mackinac City. In December of 1992 the Maritime Heritage Alliance (MHA), a nonprofit organization located in Traverse City, MI, was awarded the vessel for reconstruction. Volunteers of the MHA, having built the schooner *Madeline*, used traditional boat building skills to restore this magnificent vessel. In 2009, *Welcome* returned to the Straits of Mackinac for the first time in 20 years, providing dockside tours and historical interpretation.

SPECIFICATIONS

Flag: USA
Rig: Staysail schooner, 2-masted
Homeport: Rockland, Maine
Normal cruising waters: North Atlantic Ocean and Caribbean Sea, Canada to South America
Sparred length: 125'
LOD: 94'
LWL: 82'
Draft: 12'
Beam: 22'
Rig height: 105'
Freeboard: 7'
Sail area: 7,000 square feet
Tons: 138 GRT
Power: 500 HP diesel
Hull: steel

WESTWARD

Owned by the Ocean Classroom Foundation, the schooner *Westward* offers programs of education undersail to the youth of America. Programs range from four month semesters-at-sea to week-long programs with schools and youth groups. Trainees sail the ship and learn traditional seamanship skills under the Captain and crew, and they explore maritime subjects with the onboard academic staff. Ocean Classroom's Discovery™ program is a semester-at-sea for qualified high school students, fully accredited by Proctor Academy. The voyage covers more than 6,000 nautical miles, connecting South American shores to the Canadian Maritimes. Students live and work as sailors on a true voyage of discovery, while they study maritime history, maritime literature, marine science, applied mathematics, and navigation. Discovery™ is offered Fall and Spring Terms. Other programs include SEAmester™, OceanBound and Summer Seafaring Camps. The Ocean Classroom Foundation also owns and operates the schooners *Harvey Gamage* and *Spirit of Massachusetts*.

Who sails: Individuals and school groups from middle school through college; affiliated institutions include Proctor Academy, University of Maine, Center for Coastal Studies, Outward Bound, and other schools
Program type: Traditional seamanship training combined with accredited academic studies
Season: Year-round
Designer: Eldridge McInnis
Built: 1961: Lemwerder, Germany, Abeking & Rasmussen
Coast Guard certification: Sailing School Vessel (Subchapter R)
Crew: 8-11 including instructors
Trainees-passengers: 24 overnight
Contact: Executive Director, Ocean Classroom Foundation, PO Box 205, 1 Oak Street, Boothbay Harbor, ME 04538 USA
Tel: 800-724-7245
E-mail: mail@oceanclassroom.org
Website: www.oceanclassroom.org

SPECIFICATIONS

Flag: USA
Rig: Gaff topsail schooner, 4-masted
Homeport: Chicago, Illinois
Normal cruising waters: Great Lakes
Sparred Length: 148'
LOA: 109'
LOD: 109'
LWL: 95'
Draft: 8' 6"
Beam: 25'
Rig height: 85'
Freeboard: 8'
Sail area: 4,839 square feet
Power: Cummins 6CTA-M 300 HP
Hull: steel

WINDY

Who sails: 5th grade and up, adults and seniors of all ages
Season: Spring and Fall
Designer: R. Marthai
Built: 1996: Detyens Shipyard/Southern Windjammer, Ltd.
Coast Guard certification: Passenger Vessels (Subchapter T)
Crew: 4 **Trainees-passengers:** 150 daysails, 26 overnight
Contact: Captain Bruce Randall, Lakeshore Maritime Collective / Tall Ship Adventures Of Chicago, 401 E. Illinois St. Ste 332, Chicago IL 60611 USA
Tel: 312-731-9689 **Fax:** 312-222-9048
E-mail: tallshipwindy@aol.com
Website: www.tallshipwindy.com

Built as a modern interpretation of the last days of commercial sail, the *Windy* is true to function while using modern materials and safety features. In 1996, *Windy* was the first 4-masted commercial sailing vessel built since 1921. She has many features not found on older tall ships like hot showers, private bunks, a great cabin, furling topsails, as well as bowthruster, shoal draft, and wing keel. With her divided and easily managed multi-sail design, there are ample opportunities for persons of all walks of life to participate in the sailing experience. During the summer at Navy Pier, Chicago, *Windy* offer hands on sailing experiences to the public as well as private charters for corporations, weddings, team building, and private parties. *Windy* was the dockside ship used as the Schooner *Rouse Simmons*, in "The Christmas Tree Ship" documentary which was first aired on the Weather Channel in December 2004.

SPECIFICATIONS

Flag: USA
Rig: Topsail schooner
Homeport: Miami, Florida
Sparred length: 78'
LOD: 62' 6"
LWL: 50'
Draft: 6'
Beam: 17' 6"
Rig height: 64'
Sail area: 2,500 square feet
Tons: 44 GRT
Power: Ford Lehman 120
Hull: steel

YANKEE

 Yankee is a replica of a 1880s privateer. She is a 78-foot topsail schooner, with wide decks and comfortable seating. Her motion on the bays around Miami is gentle, but she really sails. Food and drinks are easily prepared in her large galley. *Yankee* is also available for overnight charters. She has many private staterooms and bathrooms. She is Coast Guard certified to take out 48 passengers for the day and 20 overnight. Customize your party or experience around us.

Who sails: Groups and individuals of all ages
Program type: Sailing Charters in Miami, FL, corporate charters, teambuilding, pirate cruising, sight sailing, weddings, family gatherings, parties, hands-on sail training, overnight cruises.
Coast Guard certification: Passenger Vessel (Subchapter T)
Crew: 3 **Trainees-passengers:** 48 daysails, 20 overnight
Contact: John Watson, 830 Euclid Ave #1 Miami Beach, FL 33139 USA
Tel: 401-862-9101
E-mail: coolschooner@yahoo.com
Website: www.coolschooneryankee.com

SPECIFICATIONS

Flag: Australia
Rig: Brigantine
Homeport: Sydney, Australia
Sparred length: 144' 6"
Draft: 13'
Beam: 25' 6"
Hull: steel

YOUNG ENDEAVOUR

Program type: Sail training vessel
Built: 1987
Crew: 9 **Trainees-passengers:** 24
Contact: Embassy of Australia, 1601 Massachusetts Avenue, NW, Washington, DC 20036 USA
Tel: 202-797-3000 **Fax:** 202-797-3168

Given by the United Kingdom to the government and people of Australia in celebration of that country's bicentenary, *Young Endeavour* serves as Australia's national sail training vessel. She was dedicated with the words of Prime Minister Robert Hawke, "This ship – *Young Endeavour* – bears a name imperishably linked with Captain Cook's great voyage of discovery. And the name itself expresses a great deal of our aspirations for our country." For a land surrounded by the sea, this brigantine is a reminder of the country's maritime heritage. *Young Endeavour's* arrival in Sydney also heralded the start of a new era of sail training in Australia. *Young Endeavour* sails with a permanent crew of nine from the Royal Australian Navy and hosts a coeducational crew of 24 young people. Each year *Young Endeavor* provides hundreds of youngsters with the opportunity to participate in one of twenty ten-day voyages off the Australian coast.

SPECIFICATIONS

Flag: Belgium
Rig: Bermuda ketch
Homeport: Zeebruge, Belgium
Sparred length: 93'
Draft: 8' 6"
Beam: 22' 6"
Rig height: 105'
Hull: wood

ZENOBE GRAMME

Serving first as a coastal survey ship, *Zenobe Gramme* is now a training ship for the Belgian Navy. She is a frequent participant in sail training races and gatherings and is easily recognizable when she set her spinnaker which displays the Belgian royal coat-of-arms. *Zenobe Gramme* is named for the Belgian inventor who perfected the technology for alternating-current motors and generators in the 1860s and 1870s.

Program type: Training vessel of the Belgian Navy
Built: 1961
Contact: Embassy of Belgium, 3330 Garfield Street, NW, Washington, DC 20008 USA
Tel: 202-333-6900 **Fax:** 202-333-3079

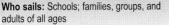

SPECIFICATIONS

Flag: USA
Rig: Gaff schooner, 2-masted
Homeport: Seattle, Washington
Normal cruising waters: Puget Sound, San Juan Islands, Canadian Gulf Islands
Sparred length: 160'
LOA: 127'
LWL: 101'
Draft: 16'
Beam: 26'
Rig height: 127'
Freeboard: 5'
Sail area: 7,000 square feet
Tons: 147 GRT
Power: diesel
Hull: wood

ZODIAC

Who sails: Schools; families, groups, and adults of all ages
Program type: Sail training for schools, groups and individuals; deckhand internships; private charters; some day-sails.
Season: March to November
Designer: William Hand, Jr.
Built: 1924: East Boothbay, ME, Hodgdon Brothers
Coast Guard certification: Passenger Vessel (Subchapter T)
Crew: 8 **Trainees-passengers:** 49 daysails, 26 overnight
Contact: Captain Tim Mehrer, Vessel Zodiac Corporation, 3 Strawberry Point, Bellingham WA 98229 USA
Tel: 206.696.4556
E-mail: richard@schoonerzodiac.com
Website: www.schoonerzodiac.com

Listed on the National Register of Historic Places since 1982, the *Zodiac* is the largest working schooner on the West Coast. Lovingly restored, she now sails with up to 49 passengers through the waters of Puget Sound, the San Juan Islands, and on international trips to Canada (SOLAS certified). A variety of one to ten day cruises include education and recreation and provide passengers with hands-on sail training, maritime programs, and shore explorations. There is an emphasis on natural resources, the environment and recycling. Built 1924 in Maine, the *Zodiac* was a luxury yacht for the Johnson and Johnson pharmaceutical heirs. She explored the Arctic and sailed in the 1928 transatlantic race. The San Francisco Bar Pilots bought her in 1931, renamed her *California,* and sailed her off the Golden Gate for more than 40 years. Retired in 1972, the schooner has been restored to her original sail plan and given back her maiden name. Her mission is now to help young sailors advance with their Coast Guard licenses, maintain herself as a national maritime treasure, and introduce traditional sailing skills to the public.

Photo by Thad Koza

Affiliate Members

Non-profit organizations which do not own or operate vessels
but do offer sail training or sea education programs

ActionQuest/ActionSail Programs

For over 30 years, ActionQuest has been providing high quality, expedition-based summer programs for teenagers. ActionQuest voyages focus on sailing, scuba diving, cultural immersion, marine biology and global exploration – all in a live-aboard environment unlike any other. Through hands-on experiential learning and exceptional global expeditions, ActionQuest challenges young adults with high action, life-changing adventures that promote personal growth, teamwork and leadership. Choose from voyage offerings in the British Virgin Islands, the Caribbean's Leeward Islands, the Mediterranean, Galapagos, Australia or Tahiti, and French Polynesia.

ActionQuest also offers Lifeworks community service summer programs for teens and Sea-mester Programs for college students and high school graduates. Living full-time aboard our traditional schooners and sailing through extraordinary destinations that span the globe, Sea-mester teaches accredited academics unconfined by the four walls of a traditional classroom.

ActionQuest
Mike Meighan and Captain James M. Stoll
PO Box 5517, Sarasota, FL 34277 USA
Tel: 941-924-6789 or 800-317-6789
E-mail: info@actionquest.com
Website: www.actionquest.com

Algonac-Clay Township Historical Society

The "Hospitality Port" of the Great Lakes
N 42 deg. 37' 09.43", W 82 deg 31' 45.50"

Algonac is on the St. Clair River between Lake St. Clair and Lake Huron. Our museum is located in the Waterfront Park that features more than 2,200 feet of riverside boardwalk. Tall ships have enjoyed our Hospitality Port with sufficient water depth, easy docking and convenience of stores within walking distance. We can arrange fueling, pump outs, fresh water, land showers, boat repair, transportation. A Port of Entry is located next to the museum. We have welcomed the *Bluenose II, Picton Castle, Niagara, Pride of Baltimore II, Europa, Nina*, Coast Guard Cutters and many others. If dock side tours or day cruising are available, we will advertise and sell tickets. Some ships have stopped in for a quick trip to the grocery store or a Dairy Queen across the street, changing of crewmembers or passengers, or a safe haven for inclement weather.

Algonac-Clay Township Historical Society
1240 St. Clair River Drive, Algonac, MI 48001 USA
Tel: 810-794-9015
E-mail: achs@algonac-clay-history.com
Website: www.algonac-clay-history.com

Bluenose II Preservation Trust

The Bluenose II Preservation Trust has the mandate to raise funds to ensure that *Bluenose II* continues in full operational status as Canada's sailing monument. The Trust is a non-profit organization and a registered charity. Funds are raised through public donations and sales in the Bluenose II Ship's Company Store in Lunenburg and online at www.bluenose2.ns.ca.

The Trust established the Bluenose II Company Store in Lunenburg in May, 1995. The store is open year round, and the proceeds go to support the *Bluenose* legacy as now represented by *Bluenose II.* The Trust continues to support the ship by paying for capital items as its resources permit. More than simply running the store, the staff provide information to the public regarding the ship's sailing schedule, and answer countless inquiries about the original *Bluenose* and *Bluenose II* from all over the world.

Bluenose II Preservation Trust
c/o Bluenose II Company Store
121 Bluenose Drive, P.O. Box 1963, Lunenburg, Nova Scotia, Canada B0J 2C0
Tel: 800-763-1963
E-mail: store@bluenose2.ns.ca
Website: www.bluenose2.ns.ca

Global Maritime and Transportation School

The Global Maritime and Transportation School (GMATS) provides world-class professional education and training programs (including content design, development, and delivery), instructional services, research studies, and technical assistance that enhance the safety, security, efficiency, and environmental soundness of maritime operations and global transportation systems. GMATS is currently divided into four divisions: Nautical Science and Military Training, Marine Engineering, Transportation Logistics and Management, and Research and Special Projects. Together these divisions offer more than 140 professional education and training programs. In addition, GMATS specializes in developing customized education and training programs that meet the specific needs of any transportation organization. With nearly 4000 students annually attending its programs, GMATS has become an important supplier of maritime and transportation training for personnel from numerous government, military, and commercial entities. GMATS is co-located with the U.S. Merchant Marine Academy (USMMA) on 82 acres overlooking the Long Island Sound in Kings Point, New York.

Global Maritime and Transportation School
300 Steamboat Road - Samuels Hall, Kings Point, NY 11024 USA
Tel: 516-726-6150
Website: www.gmats.usmma.edu

Golden Gate Tall Ships Society

The Golden Gate Tall Ship Society (GGTSS) is a California nonprofit organization dedicated to educating people in nautical skills and supporting the preservation and operation of traditional sailing vessels, particularly tall ships.

Goals and strategies include:
• Provide opportunities for sail training experiences for young people
• Provide sailing and shipboard education for members
• Support shore-side education
• Support tall ships visiting San Francisco Bay

Golden Gate Tall Ships Society provides scholarships for young people aboard tall ships, including high school students in San Francisco.

Golden Gate Tall Ship Society
PO Box 926, Sausalito, CA 94966 USA
Tel: 415-332-6990
E-mail: info@ggtss.org
Website: www.ggtss.org

Gundalow Company

Between 1690 and 1900, gundalows dominated the waters of the Piscataqua region. Captain Edward H. Adams (1860–1950), the builder and captain of the *Fanny M*, the last commercial gundalow, worked hard to generate concern about the health of Great Bay Estuary. His efforts inspired the Piscataqua Gundalow Project, through which a group of visionaries and volunteers built a historically accurate replica gundalow in 1982 that bears his name. Built on the grounds of Strawbery Banke using traditional methods, the *Captain Edward H. Adams* represents 300 years of local maritime heritage. Twenty years later, the Gundalow Company was formed as a nonprofit organization to acquire ownership of the gundalow, and to expand onboard programs.

Today the Gundalow Company's mission – to protect the Piscataqua Region's maritime heritage and environment through education and action– has never been more important. Our programs – held throughout the tidal towns of the Piscataqua – connect our maritime history with contemporary coastal issues such as water quality, habitat restoration, conservation, and stewardship.

Gundalow Company
60 Marcy Street, Portsmouth, NH 03801 USA
Tel: 603-433-9505
Website: www.gundalow.org

Landing School of Boatbuilding and Design

Established in 1978 and located in Kennebunkport, Maine, The Landing School of Boatbuilding and Design is a non-profit post-secondary career school dedicated to providing the highest quality vocational education in boatbuilding, yacht design, and marine systems technology available. The School was created to provide a gateway to the marine industry for students seeking career opportunities in the marine trades focusing on both recreational and commercial watercraft in both power and sail. The Landing School's ability to reinforce and preserve traditional skills and knowledge while advancing the art and science of boat design, construction, outfitting and repair through the integration of modern techniques and contemporary materials is recognized and valued throughout the marine industry. Our school has earned an international reputation for program quality and, as an educational institution, is considered by many in the marine industry to be unequaled. The graduates and hundreds of alumni of the school are highly sought after for their craftsmanship, productivity, work ethic, and passion for their chosen careers in, on, and around boats.

Landing School of Boatbuilding and Design
PO Box 1490, Kennebunkport, Maine 04046 USA
Tel: 207-985-7976 Fax: 207-985-7942
E-mail: landingschool@cybertours.com
Website: www.landingschool.org

Northwest School of Wooden Boatbuilding

The Northwest School of Wooden Boatbuilding, located on the Olympic Peninsula of Washington State, has been teaching the marine trades since 1981. Nationally accredited by ACCSCT, the School grants diplomas and degrees in both traditional and modern wooden boatbuilding techniques, with specialization in yacht interiors and restoration work. Other marine trades taught at the school include sailmaking, rigging, blacksmithing, boat design, and systems. Many tall ship crew members have attended the school and remain active members of our alumni. A boat school education can make you an even more valuable member of your crew and will be one of the most memorable years of your life.

Northwest School of Wooden Boatbuilding
42 N. Water Street Port Hadlock, WA 98339 USA
Tel: 360-385-4948 Fax: 360-385-5089
Website: www.nwboatschool.org

Piscataqua Maritime Commission

The Piscataqua Maritime Commission (PMC) is a non-profit community organization dedicated to promoting awareness and education of the New Hampshire seacoast's rich maritime history through tall ship port calls. Proceeds from ship tours and marketing fund a variety of sail training scholarships for area students and other educational programs. Ships visit for at least a three day weekend anytime between April and October.

With over two decades of experience successfully hosting tall ships annually, the PMC Board and hundreds of PMC members and volunteers make a port call not only a regional event for residents, but also the ship, captain, and crew. Vessels are berthed with the enthusiastic support of the NH Dept. of Ports and Harbors, at docks with full facilities and 24-hour security.

The PMC encourages tall ships whose course takes them near New England to contact us to discuss a visit - and discover why captains recommend Portsmouth as "one of their best port calls ever".

Larry Job, Vice Chairman
Tel: 603-929-4472.
E-mail: lrjob@comcast.net

 # Sea Scouts

Sea Scouting promotes better citizenship and improves members' boating skills and knowledge through instruction and practice in water safety, outdoor, social, and service experiences, and knowledge of our maritime heritage. The program fosters self-esteem as the youth share responsibility for the upkeep of boats and equipment; and the value of teamwork, an important life lesson, receives emphasis every time the boats are underway where the actions of one impacts the safety and well-being of all. Each ship has a unique program designed and implemented by its youth members. Basically, if it is an activity about, on, in, under or through the water, Sea Scouts are involved.

Sea Scouts were organized in 1912 as a "new branch of Boy Scouts of America." The purpose was to serve older boys who were interested in the lore of the sea. Sea Scouting became co-ed in 1968, and since that time, the program has continued to grow nationally and internationally. Today's program provides adventure on land and sea and serves youth ages 14 to 21.

National Director Venturing Division
Boy Scouts of America
1325 Walnut Hill Lane, Irving, Texas 75015-2079 USA
Tel: 972-580-2425
Website: www.seascout.org

US Naval Sea Cadets of Rhode Island

The U.S. Naval Sea Cadets of Rhode Island is a federally-sponsored association for teenagers and pre-teens (age 11 through 17), who have or desire ambition, self-discipline, and a strong academic background. Our primary mission is to instill in Rhode Island youth a desire to succeed as individuals and citizens, beginning with a solid foundation for building academic and social skills, teamwork, and critical thinking.

Our goals include:
• Develop in our youth an appreciation for Naval History, traditions, customs, and their role in national defense.
• Develop in our youth a sense of pride in our nation, positive qualities of patriotism, courage and self-reliance, confidence and strong moral character, and good citizenship traits.
• Develop in our youth an interest and skill in seamanship, seagoing, and aviation subjects. Increase the advancement potential of Cadets who may later elect to serve in the Navy, Marine Corps, Coast Guard or Merchant Marines.

US Naval Sea Cadets of Rhode Island
David R. Kerwood, President
35 Belver Avenue, Suite 001, North Kingstown, RI 02852 USA
Tel: 401-932-2396 Fax: 206-666-3422
E-mail: contact@riseacadets.org
Website: www.riseacadets.org

Yorktown Foundation

Riverwalk Landing is a beautiful waterfront development designed in the spirit of colonial architecture reflected in the town's historic buildings. It features a variety of fine retail shops as well as a conveniently located two-tier 270-space parking terrace. The restored historic Freight Shed may be reserved for small receptions and meetings. The waterfront also features a performance area, an inviting beach and two floating piers – one to support larger vessels such as regional cruise ships and visiting tall ships, and the other for smaller personal watercraft. The pier has more than 1,000 feet of dock frontage and electrical, water, telephone, and sewer pump out hookups all provided pier side. A mile-long pedestrian riverwalk links Yorktown's major attractions and provides exquisite views of the York River. Benches lining the walk offer visitors the chance to sit and admire the natural beauty of the York River. A free trolley runs daily, spring through fall, offering many stops throughout town and arrives approximately every 20 minutes to each stop. On many weekends throughout the year, visitors can enjoy live entertainment.

The Yorktown Foundation is a non-profit organization dedicated to preserve and perpetuate the special historic character of Yorktown (site of the last major battle of the American Revolutionary War in 1781).

Dockmaster
Riverwalk Landing, 425 Water Street, PO Box 219, Yorktown, VA 23690 USA
Tel: 757-890-3370
E-mail: dockmaster@yorkcounty.gov
Website: www.riverwalklanding.com

Business Partner Members

Organizations, corporations, businesses and ports which
do not own or operate a vessel or offer sail training or
sea education programs but which do support
sail training and the Tall Ships America® mission.

Allen Agency Insurance and Financial

Navigate the complexities of marine insurance with help from the professionals at Allen Insurance and Financial, the exclusive endorsed insurance agency of Tall Ships America, providing new, unique and improved coverages for Tall Ships America® members and their crews, including crew health insurance.

Alen Insurance and Financial insurance specialists Gene McKeever and Rick Bagnall are among the world's leaders in tall ship insurance. As part of the company's marine division, they tailor insurance programs for vessels of all sizes, for every need and every circumstance.

Global expertise. Hometown service .With Allen Insurance and Financial, you're covered, the world over.

Established in 1866, Allen Insurance and Financial is an independent, employee-owned, community-minded company with 70 employees and offices in Camden, Rockland and Southwest Harbor, Maine.

Eric (Rick) Bagnall: rbagnall@allenfg.com
Barbara Murray: bmurray@allenfg.com
Gene McKeever: gmckeever@alleninsuranceandfinancial.com
Rebecca Robinson: brobinson@alleninsuranceandfinancial.com
Tel: 800-439-4311
Website: www.alleninsuranceandfinancial.com

Artinium Inc.

Artinium Design, Inc. is a full service creative communications company, that offers the services, talent, and skills you need to drive your business forward. Our marketing and creativity is on target, because we use strategies developed in partnership, by working with and listening to our clients. We're energetic, fun and versatile, which enables us to get any project done, just the way you want it, in the right amount of time.

Since its inception, Artinium has provided unique and professional advertising, graphic design and web development services to numerous clients in the Northeast, Mid-Atlantic and on the West Coast. Some of our exciting clients are Consumer Reports Magazine, Babson College, Dartmouth College, the City of Warwick, Tall Ships America and the Department of Fish and Wildlife Marine Fisheries.

Our services include: Advertising, logos, brochures, website design & development, mobile site design, email marketing, banner ads, trade show graphics.

Artinium Design, Inc.
Darren Marinelli
5 Division Street, Building D, First Floor, Warwick, RI 02818 USA
Tel: 401.729.1997
E-mail: darren@artiniuminc.com
Website: www.artiniuminc.com

Boothbay Harbor Shipyard

Boothbay Harbor Shipyard, formerly Sample's Shipyard, was founded more than 135 years ago. Continuing a local shipbuilding tradition, the yard specializes in the maritime skills and trades that made New England famous. Its 700-ton marine railway has braced tall ships, tugboats, fishing trawlers, Coast Guard vessels and other service craft such as passenger boats and ferries. The 150-ton railway has accommodated sailing yachts, workboats, schooners and motor vessels. Conveniently located at the head of Boothbay Harbor in mid-coast Maine, the shipyard offers a complete range of marine-related repairs and services for all vessel types. The 700-ton railway can haul vessels up to 200-feet, and our skilled labor is available for new building, restoration and repairs in steel and wood. We take pride in doing top-quality work quickly and efficiently.

Boothbay Harbor Shipyard
120 Commercial Street, PO Box 462, Boothbay Harbor, Maine 04538 USA
Tel: 207-633-3171 Fax: 207-633-3824
E-mail: info@boothbayharborshipyard.com
Website: www.boothbayharborshipyard.com

Channel Islands Harbor Department

The Channel Islands Harbor, owned by the County of Ventura, is located 60 miles north of Los Angeles, halfway between Los Angeles and Santa Barbara. The harbor is best known for it's year round events and gateway to a wilderness playground, the Channel Islands National Park. Called the "gateway" to the Channel Islands because of its proximity, the harbor is the perfect location from which to take day or extended trips. Located in a picturesque setting, the harbor is home to nine full-service marinas with more than 2,600 boat slips, three nautically themed shopping centers, yacht clubs, more than a dozen restaurants with spectacular views, a year round water taxi, a weekly Farmers' Market, a waterfront hotel and a variety of shops and services. The harbor is home to one of the country's finest maritime collections housed at the Ventura County Maritime Museum located at Fisherman's Wharf. The museum is a cultural center dedicated to the interpretation of maritime history through interactive exhibits and educational outreach.

The Channel Islands hosts several annual events including Celebration of the Whales, Fireworks by the Sea, Concerts by the Sea, Ventura County Boat Show, Ventura Vintage Rods Harbor Run, Channel Islands Harbor Seafood Festival and Parade of Lights.

The Channel Islands Harbor was proud to become a host port for the TALL SHIPS CHALLENGE® Race Series in 2005, 2008 and 2011.

Channel Islands Harbor Department
3900 Pelican Way, Oxnard, CA 93035 USA
Tel: 805-382-3013 Fax: 805-382-3015
E-mail: Suzy.Watkins@ventura.org
Website: www.channelislandsharbor.org

Eastern Salt Company

Eastern Salt is a family-owned business operating on Boston Harbor in the City of Chelsea. We are Massachusetts' leading importer of road salt, and are able to accommodate all sizes and types of vessels, from tall ships to tankers. Located in a designated port area, our facility is a five-acre site with a low-water depth of 40 feet. The City of Chelsea has always played an important role in the maritime history of Massachusetts, and we at Eastern believe in continuing to connect the citizens of Chelsea with her working ports. To celebrate the relationship of community to ocean, Eastern Salt welcomes tall ships to our dock each summer for community groups, schools, and neighbors to tour.

Paul Lamb
Eastern Salt Company, 37 Marginal Street, Chelsea, MA USA
Tel: 617-884-5201

Flagship Niagara League

The Flagship Niagara League is a 501(c)3, non-profit educational associate organization of the Pennsylvania Historical and Museum Commission (PHMC), chartered to facilitate citizen participation and operation of the Flagship Niagara and its homeport, Erie Maritime Museum.

The League was conceived in the late 1970s, incorporated in 1982 by a group of local historians. With assistance from local educators, politicians and representatives from the business community, the Flagship Niagara League supported PHMC in the restoration, sailing and interpretation of the ship. The League has expanded from the original grassroots group to an annual membership of 600.

Flagship Niagara League
Erie Maritime Museum, 150 East Front Street, Erie, PA 16507 USA
Tel: 814.452-2744
Website: www.eriemaritimemuseum.org/flagship_niagara_league/

Gangplank Marina

The Gangplank Marina is only a day's cruise away from the mighty Chesapeake Bay - the country's largest natural estuary. The Gangplank welcomes boaters eager to explore the District of Columbia's historic, cultural and natural attractions. The peak visiting season is spring to summer and early fall. In April, the Cherry Blossom Festival brings thousands of people to see the blooms on trees which were a gift from the country of Japan before the turn of the century. The District sizzles in the summer for the Fourth of July and the annual Smithsonian Folk Life Festival.

Gangplank Marina
600 Water Street SW, Washington, D.C. 20024 USA
Tel: 202-554-5000
E-mail: gpdockoffice@comcast.net
Coordinates: N 38 degrees 52.600' / W 077 degrees 01.334'

Navy Pier, Inc.

Historic Navy Pier® is Chicago's lakefront playground, and the Midwest's top tourist and leisure destination. This unique facility attracts nearly nine million visitors each year.

From rides to restaurants, exhibitions to entertainment, shopping to dining cruises, Navy Pier has it all - in a location along Lake Michigan that's unlike any other. There's so much to do in our 50 acres of parks, promenades, gardens, shops, eateries and attractions.

Take a ride on our iconic 15-story tall Ferris wheel. Catch a blockbuster movie at the Navy Pier IMAX® Theatre or take in a live performance at the Tony Award-winning Chicago Shakespeare Theater. Visit three floors of hands-on fun at the Chicago Children's Museum inside the Family Pavilion. Experience any one of the cruise boat rides departing from Navy Pier's South Dock. Or stroll through the beautiful Smith Museum of Stain Glass Windows.

In the summer, kick back and enjoy your favorite form of free entertainment - blues, jazz, country, rock or hip-hop - as you sip a cold drink in the Navy Pier Beer Garden. Then, gaze skyward to marvel at our twice weekly, free fireworks show. And when the weather turns colder, come indoors to our annual Winter WonderFest holiday extravaganza. As you can tell, there's so much to do here, guests of all ages have a great experience year-round.

If you get hungry, there are plenty of dining options at Navy Pier. Whether you prefer casual, family-oriented eateries, such as the Bubba Gump Shrimp Company, Harry Caray's Tavern or Jimmy Buffett's Margaritaville or a more romantic, candlelit restaurant, such as Riva, Navy Pier has an exciting roster of restaurants.

Come visit us! Navy Pier is the perfect place for you and your family to "Go A Little Overboard!"

Navy Pier is owned by the Metropolitan Pier and Exposition Authority (MPEA) (www.mpea.com), and operated by the not-for-profit corporation, Navy Pier, Inc. (NPI). Also find us at (www.facebook.com/navypier); (www.Twitter.com/navypier); and (www.YouTube.com/navypiertv).

Contact:
Tony Camarillo
Senior Director of Sales & Events
Tel: 312-595-5057
E-mail: tcamarillo@navypier.com
Website: www.navypier.com

Ocean State Tall Ships®

Ocean State Tall Ships® is a non-profit 501(c)3 organization located in Newport, RI and established in July, 2011. The organization's mission is dedicated to providing and promoting public maritime festivals and events featuring tall ships and other vessels for the purpose of encouraging public appreciation of Rhode Island's rich maritime heritage. Its first public maritime festival will be in Newport, RI from July 6-9th, as an Official Host Port for the TALL SHIPS CHALLENGE® series on the Atlantic Coast in the summer of 2012. By incorporating sail training and education opportunities with community events for Rhode Island families, Ocean State Tall Ships® aims to increase youth involvement and enhance public appreciation of our most beautiful resource.

Erin Donovan
Executive Director
29 Touro Street, Newport, RI 02840 USA
Tel: 401.474.7009
Website: www.oceanstatetallships.com

Old Port of Montreal Corportion

Since May 1992, the Old Port of Montreal has been offering Montrealers, yachting tourists, and tall ships a quality marina, the Port d'Escale. Located in the Jacques Cartier Basin, the Port d'Escale is equipped with a full range of up-to-date facilities to accommodate sailboats over 200 feet, docking on floating docks. Tucked into the heart of the Old Port, a few steps away from downtown Montreal, this secure facility provides a quiet haven for tall ships mooring there. Because of its varied activities and its unique atmosphere, the Old Port is an important site for recreation and tourism in Montreal. Set a heading for the Port d'Escale and discover Montreal in style.

Old Port of Montreal Corporation
333 de la Commune Street West, Montreal, Quebec, Canada H2Y 2E2
Tel: 514-283-5256
Website: www.oldportcorporation.com

Perry Group

The Perry Group is a volunteer, nonprofit organization working with the National Park Service and the local, national and international community. The Perry Group honors Commodore Oliver Hazard Perry, who led the U.S. Navy to victory in the Battle of Lake Erie, and celebrates the long-lasting peace between the United States, Britain and Canada.

Since 1989, The Perry Group has supported Perry's Victory and International Peace Memorial in its educational, historic and peacekeeping goals through the promotion and sponsorship of the Memorial's programs and special events.

Perry's Victory and International Peace Memorial, located in Put-in-Bay, Ohio, was constructed in 1913 to honor those who fought in the Battle of Lake Erie on September 10, 1813. The Battle was a turning point in the War of 1812, securing U.S. control of the Great Lakes, forcing a British retreat and leading to the current peaceful border with Canada.

The Perry Groups's Bicentennial Committee is proud to work with Tall Ships America to reenact the Battle of Lake Erie on September 2, 2013. For more information about the Battle of Lake Erie and its Bicentennial celebration, please visit: www.BattleofLakeErie-Bicentennial.com

Perry Group Officers:

Marc Burr, President: marc@burrservice.com
Kay Drake, Vice-President: cooks4400@aol.com
Susie Cooper, Treasurer: director@leihs.org
David Zavagno, Bicentennial Chairman: drzavagno@cs.com

R & W Traditional Rigging & Outfitting

R & W is a family owned and operated distributor of rope and cordage. Started in 1985 as a "one man" operation out of the trunk of a hand-me-down car, we've grown into one of the most diverse stocking warehouses in the industry.

We've got rope - whether it's small 50 lb test braided line for ice fishing, brightly colored rope for trying your hand at tying a rope halter or a fancy knot, a safety line for a school's challenge course, or a full set of custom spliced docklines, chances are we have it and have it in stock.

We know rope – both the technical side of how it's made and the application side of how its used, and enjoy helping you find just the right product for your needs. And we sell our rope at some of the best prices you'll find anywhere. QUALITY, VALUE, & SERVICE - it's what we expect and it's what you can expect from us.

Distributors of:
• Davey & Co. Marine Hardware
• Meissner Winches,
• Ording Wooden Blocks and Rope of all descriptions.

Choose the best gear from the age of classic yachting and working sail.

R & W Traditional Rigging & Outfitting
39 Tarkiln Place, New Bedford MA 02745 USA
Tel: 866-577-5505 or 508-995-1114
E-mail: mainstay@csolve.net
Website: www.RWrope.com

Sailing Ship Adventures

Sailing Ship Adventures is a specialty travel service that represents sailing ship owners and operators, including some of the sailing world's best-kept secrets. We book voyages for our customers on a wide variety of sailing ships ranging from the largest full rigged tall ship in the world (The *Royal Clipper,* at over 400 feet in length) to smaller vessels (ranging from 60 to 100 feet in length), as well as aboard crewed chartered yachts.

Unlike your local travel agent we do not represent just a few ships and tour providers, but a wide variety of ships in many different destination areas. We have researched tall ships and sailing ship vacations the world over. Our extensive knowledge of sailing ships and the resulting roster of vessels in our fleet means that, no matter where you would like to spend your next vacation or what you would like to do there, we can find the perfect voyage for you.

Our fleet is comprised of more than 100 full rigged tall ships, brigantines, barkentines, schooners, and smaller vessels. This range of ships, from the most luxurious to the more spartan, offers you the widest range of choice available.

Our ships sail to destinations through the world, ranging from popular itineraries in the Caribbean and Mediterranean Seas, to ocean crossings, to exotic areas such as the fjords of Patagonia, the Andaman Sea, and the Queen Charlotte Islands. Sailing to these destinations offers opportunities to experience exotic locations in an up-close and intimate way that is not possible on traditional cruises. Smaller vessels are able to stop at smaller, out-of-the-way ports of call not accessible to large cruise liners.

Climb aboard one of these majestic sailing ships and set sail to exotic locations!

Dexter Donham
Sailing Ship Adventures
Tel: 781-237-4395 or toll free 877-882-4395
Fax: 781-237-3141
E-mail: ddonham@sailingshipadventures.com
Website: www.sailingshipadventures.com

 Tall Ship Celebration: Bay City

Tall Ship Celebration is a non-profit organization producing award-winning maritime festivals in Bay City, Michigan. With a reputation for providing exceptional support and hospitality to visiting vessels and their crews, Bay City was twice named "Port of the Year" by Tall Ships America. Bay City is proud to again serve as Michigan's "Port of Call," the only official host port in the state for the TALL SHIPS CHALLENGE® Great Lakes 2013 series.

Shirley Roberts, Event Coordinator
Tall Ship Celebration: Bay City
1712 Center Avenue, Bay City, MI 48708 USA
Tel: 989-225-7856
E-mail: Shirley.Roberts@charter.net
Website: www.tallshipcelebration.com

Village of Greenport, New York

Located in the beautiful, deep and superbly protected waters of the Gardiners/ Peconic Bay system of eastern Long Island, Greenport Harbor has been a uniquely appealing destination for mariners since the dawn of American history. Modern-day Greenport remains true to this maritime heritage.

Stores, galleries, and services including those catering to mariners, such as welding, hauling, carpentry and marine hardware, even a hospital, are but steps away. Lodging, groceries, restaurants and pubs are conveniently located in the heart of town, within walking distance of the marina.

Deep water dockage for large and small vessels is available at a municipally owned marina in the heart of a downtown waterfront listed on the National Register of Historic Places.

A waterfront park has been developed upland of the marina which boasts a vintage carousel, an outdoor amphitheater and expansive boardwalk, connecting the marina to a transportation hub where bus, rail, and ferry connections are available to Shelter Island, New York City, and destinations throughout the East End. Greenport has a reputation of continuing to welcome tall ships and sail training vessels and will make special arrangements to host traditional sailing vessels, their crews and trainees.

Mayor David Nyce
236 Third Street, Greenport, NY 11944 USA
Tel: 631-477-0248 Fax: 631-477-1877
E-mail: David_Nyce@greenportvillage.org
Website: www.villageofgreenport.org

Visit Duluth

More than a gateway to the Great Lakes and an expansive northern wilderness. This is where activities like climbing, kayaking and kitesurfing are as close at hand as the lively mix of restaurants, concerts and festivals.

It's where rich history intersects with museums and mansions offering glimpses into our nation's industrial age and the living legacy of the region's Ojibwe people.

It's where you can stand on the edge of the pier as 1,000-foot ships glide through the canal, or hang onto the edge of your seat as you race down the mountain, through the forest, and on to the next adventure.

Visit Duluth
Gene Shaw, Director of Public Relations
21 West Superior Street, Suite 100, Duluth, MN 55802 USA
Tel: 218-625-8106 or 1-800-438-5884
E-mail: gshaw@visitduluth.com
Website: www.visitduluth.com

Visit Savannah

Visit Savannah is the destination marketing organization for the City of Savannah and Chatham County. Serving as the regions tourism and convention bureau, Visit Savannah is responsible for selling and marketing the destination for leisure tourists, international visitors, group tours, conventions, meetings and trade shows. We also function in five area visitor information and welcome centers.

To begin your Savannah experience and to learn more for your next visit, please contact:

Ms. Jenny Dent
Office of the President
Visit Savannah
101 East Bay Street, Savannah, GA 31401 USA
Tel: 912.644.6400
E-mail: JDent@VisitSavannah.com

Or visit us online at:
www.VisitSavannah.com
Facebook.com/VisitSavannahGA
Twitter.com/VisitSavannah
Youtube.com/SavannahEst1733

Water's Edge Festivals & Events

Water's Edge Festivals & Events [WEFE] is a not-for-profit corporation responsible for The Redpath Toronto Waterfront Festival [RTWF], an annual event that was created to promote awareness and drive traffic to Toronto's central waterfront. WEFE and RTWF are a collaborative effort of primary stakeholders Redpath Sugar and the Waterfront BIA in association with the Festival Producers Krista Slack + Aylett and Harmony Marketing. The Redpath Toronto Waterfront Festival will annually produce creative on-land and on-water programming that showcases the urban uniqueness of 'being by the water' while connecting visitors with our local and global maritime heritage. WEFE/RTWF is pleased to support The Toronto Brigantine Inc. as the official charity.

Following the enormous success of the 2010 event, RTWF is pleased once again to be the launch port of the TALL SHIPS CHALLENGE® 2013, the next Tall Ships America series tour of the Great Lakes Region that commemorates the Bicentennial Celebrations of the War of 1812.

Krista Slack, KS+A
Producer, Strategic Designer
Redpath Toronto Waterfront Festival
Tel: 416 752-9232
E-mail: Krista@kristaslack.com

Whitworth Marine

Meeting the modern needs of traditional vessels.

Specializing in:
• Diesel Engines • High and Low Voltage DC Electrical Systems
• Chargers, Inverters, Ac & DC Panels • Electrical Wiring and Electronics
• Pumps and Piping • Water Makers • Fuel Systems • Sewage Systems

*** Over ten years experience as Chief Engineer on off-shore vessels ***

Nobby Peers
Tel: 631-804-3077
E-mail: nobby@whitworthmarine.com
Website: www.whitworthmarine.com

Waterfront Development Corporation Limited

The Atlantic Canadian region has incredible cruising grounds - all within reach of Halifax, Nova Scotia – a well-equipped cruising base of operation for visiting vessels on the Atlantic Canadian Coast. Captains and crews find Halifax to be the perfect mix of services, entertainment, recreation, and laid back atmosphere to either rest the crew or entertain the owner. The city and port is also a central point to explore the interior of the province, famous for spectacular scenery and traditional maritime hospitality.

The Halifax Waterfront has over one mile of public berth space including more than 1000 feet of floating docks. Services available include Power, Water, Security, Parking, and Free Wireless Internet. Fueling, pump-out, and other provisioning services can be arranged through the Marina Office.

Visiting Ships Program

In an effort to bring awareness to sail training opportunities for youth and to welcome tall ships to our waterfronts, Waterfront Development offers complimentary berthing to visiting tall ships that open for public tours. Ships are encouraged to work with Waterfront Development marketing and communications staff to maximize the potential of their time in port.

Lunenburg, Nova Scotia- A UNESCO World Heritage Site

Located on Nova Scotia's scenic South Shore, there are numerous sights and sounds that come to life on this historic working waterfront.

Tie up along our floating docks (free daily berthing when available). Dine on a patio, uncover seaside treasures and explore the area. Cycling, golfing, sightseeing, boating, festivals and entertainment are just some of Lunenburg's attractions.

Watch local boat builders all along Lunenburg's historic working waterfront from the wooden schooners being built at The Dory Shop.

Dockmaster: Adam Langley
Waterfront Development
c/o The Cable Wharf, 1751 Lower Water Street, Halifax, Nova Scotia, Canada B3J 1S5
Tel: 902-229-BOAT (2628) Fax 902-422-7582
E-mail: marina@wdcl.ca
VHF 68
Website: www.my-waterfront.ca

Associate Members

A very important factor in our growth over the years has been the strength of our membership. Without the support of our members, the development and implementation of all of our programs, publications, and resources, would not be possible.

Board Members & Commodores

Henry H. Anderson, Jr.
Raymond Ashley
Daveneet Bakhshi
Les Bolton
Jonathan Boulware
Terry Davies
Dexter Donham
Bart Dunbar
Kevin Dykema
John Gaughan
James Gladson
Jen Haddock
Richard H. Hawkins
Deborah Hayes
Karen Helmerson
James W. Hiney
John Jamian
Jonathan Kabak
James Kerr

Norman Lemley
Paul Madden
Ken Neal
David Neibuhr
Caleb Pifer
Doug Prothero
Michael J. Rauworth
Nancy H. Richardson
Bert Rogers
Christopher Rowsom
Eric Shaw
Dan Stetson
Gail Thacher
Alix T. Thorne
Barclay 'Tim' Warburton
Thomas R. Weschler
F. C. 'Bunky' Wichmann
David V. V. Wood
Meghan Wren Briggs

Advisory Board Members

Richard Bailey
Hal G. Barstow
Beth Bonds
Alice Cochran
Chuck Fowler
Chris Freeman
Tom Gochberg
Andrew A. Hammond
Michael Jehle

Perry Lewis
James Lyons
Joseph Maggio
Jeffrey Parker
Jed Pearsall
Nigel Rowe
Walter Rybka
Chris Sinnett
Howard Slotnick

Individual Members

DK Abass
James Abrams
Leith Adams
Mark Adams
Meredith Adams
Mike Albertson
Lawrence & Elizabeth Allen
Cameron Anderson
Erin Anderson
Holley Anderson
Sarah Anderson
Titiana Anderson
WJ Anderson
David & Judith Anderson
John Henry & Jeni Anderson
Townsend & Jodee Anderson
William & Elsie Apthorp
Jose Maria Arozamen
Peder Arstorp
Jeremy Atkins
Hugh D. Auchincloss
Richard Bailey
Thomas E. Baker
Talbot Baker
Daveneet Bakhshi
Virginia T. Baldwin
A. L. Ballard
Mike Bancroft
Mitchell Bandklayder
Anya Bandt
Claudia Bankert
B. J. Barden
B. Devereux & Jilda Barker
Katrina Barnes
John & Mary Barnes
Charlotte Barringer
Bruce Barry
J. Burr Bartram
Anne Beaumont
Robert A. Beaver
Austin Becker
Elizabeth Becker

David Bell
Anne Bell
Nicholas Bell
Samuel Bell
Stephen Benjamin
Sean Bercaw
Captain Erik Berliner
Bruce & Jane Berriman
Arthur Birney
James Bishop
Jim Bishop
Alfred Bisset
E.A. Grosvenor & Elizabeth F. Blair
David H. Blomberg
John R. Bockstoce
John & Ann Bohan
Richard N. & Barbara Bohan
Les Bolton
Beth Bonds
Paul Bonge
Bradford Boss
Jonathan Boulware
Robert Boulware
Chris Bouzaid
Justin Bowe
Mark K. Branse
David Brown
Nicholas Brown
Howard & Doris Browne
Loretta Bruno
James L. Buckley
Mary Buivid
George Bulow
David Burnham
Edward Burns
Andrew & Tami Burton
Paul Buttrose
Charles A. Byrne
Tom & Maura Cahill
James Callahan
Tony Camarillo
John Cameron

Individual Members (continued)

Brian & Mona Carey
George & Judith Carmany
Dayton T. Carr
Jason & Darcy Carr
R. Bruce Carruthers
Ron Casey
Amos & Margaret Cecchi
Thomas Chadwick
Casey Charkowick
G. Andy Chase
Mason Chrisman
Howard Christian
David Cicillini
Alice Collier Cochran
George Cochran
Lyman & Mary Coddington
Nancybell Coe
JT & Gay Coe
Steve Colgate
Lyn & Margaret Comfort
Stephen Connett
Bob & Ann Connor
H. Joseph Coughlin
Kevin Coulombe
Peter L. Crew
George W. & Susie Crowninshield
Matthew Cullen
R. Michael Curran
Kevin Currie
Peter Cusick
William & Margo Dalessi
Blythe Daly
Susan Daly
Charles Dana
Hornor & Frederica Davis
Michael Dawson
Arnie De La Porte
Beth Deal
Dwight Deckelmann
Gerard & Dawn DeModena
Timothy & Lyn Demy
Paul Dennis

C. Mathews Dick
Nicholas B. & Bitten Dill
Bob Dollar
Tim & Becky Dolman
Dexter Donham
Duncan & Nancy Doolittle
Richard Dorfman
Peter & Jennifer Dott
Debbie Doucette
Libby Drew
John R. & Noreen Drexel III
Loraine DuBeau
Marion DuBosque
Michael F Dugan
Bart Dunbar
Shannon Dunfey-Ball
Kevin Dykema
John & Nancy Eills
David & Christy Elwell
Frederick Engerer
Peter Equi
Robert Erskine
Bruce & Katherine Estabrook
Joy Farias
Mohamad & Dorienne Farzan
Peter Favelle
Louis Fazzano
Sarah Felder
Noel Field
Tylor Field II
Kip Files
Lynn Fitzpatrick
Margaret Flanagan
David E. Fleenor
Christopher Fleming
Ronald Lee Fleming
Peter Flint
Thomas & Ingrid Flynn
David Ford
Colin & Cristine Foster
Matthew Francis
Iver C. Franzen

Individual Members (continued)

Chris Freeman
Elliot & Corey Frith
Philip Galluccio
Stephen K. Galpin
John Gaughan
Susan & Peter Geiger
Beverly Ghent-Skrzynski
James Gibson
Thomas & Mary Gilbane
James L. Gladson
Arthur & Louise Gleason
Lawrence R. Glenn
Thomas J. & Leatrice Gochberg
Darlene Godin
Colin Gordon
David Grant
David & Alexandra Gray
Robert Green
Andy Green
Chris Greenman
Donald Grosse
Richard & Margot Grosvenor
Richard & Terry Grosvenor
Helen Hadley
Ben Hale
Darryl Hall
Winthrop & Ann Hall
Cora Haltaufterheid
Andrew A. Hammond
Mike Harding
Karen Hardinge
Brian Hardison
Jonathan & Jan Harley
Thomas Harrington
Samara Haver
Richard H. Hawkins
Janet Hawkins
Michael Hayes
Sydney Heald
John Hele
Meredith Helfrich
Jill Helterline

Bushnell Pearce Henry
Sarah Herard
Nancy & Michael Herde
Halsey Herreshoff
George & Nannette Herrick
Eric Hess
Dana Hewson
Bruce Heyman
EA Hank Hibbard
James Hilton
James E. Hilyard
James W. & Martha Hiney
Cameron & Marilyn Hinman
George & Emilie Hinman
David Hirzel
H. Jochen Hoffmann
Robert P. Hofmann
James & Anne Hogg
Allen Hollifield
Joseph C. & Lesley B. Hoopes
Becca Hopkins
Chandler Hovey
Pamela Howard
Garry & Donna Hoyt
Peter Hunter
George M. Isdale
Peter Isler
Jonathan Jablonowski
Andrew Jagger
Doug James
Oliver James
Nathaniel & Alexandra James III
John Jamian
Oliver Janney
Gary Jobson
Rebecca Johnson
Robert A. Johnson
Stuart Johnson
Troy Johnson
Edward & Tressa Johnson
Noel & Donna Johnson
Platt & Nancy Johnson

Individual Members (continued)

Mark Kallio
Stephanie Katz
Michael Kellick
Donna Kelly
John & Regina Kelly
Alvin Kempf
Jesse Kenworthy
Gerald Kerr
James Kerr
Steve & Barbara Kingsland
Matthew O. & Michelle Kirby
Chester & Suzanne Kitchings
Nat Klein
Bill Koch
James Kruse
Roy H. Kruse
Eugene H. & Barbara Kummel
Cameron La Clair
Charles & Leeanne Langston
Timothea Larr
Helena Lawrence
Bruce Lee
Emile Legault
Charles & Roxanne Leighton
E. Jay Lembeck
Norman Lemley
Zack Leonard
Richard Levine
Perry Lewis
Nancy Linden
David & Lynda Lindh
TL & Harriet Linskey
J. Eric Little
Stanley & Martha Livingston
Richard C. 'Chad' Loebs
John & Loraine Lombard
Patricia R. Longan
A. L. Loomis III
Margaret Lord
Oivind Lorentzen
C.S. Lovelace
Townsend & Jane Ludington

Sally H. Lunt
James Lyon
John MacGowan
Malcolm MacKay
Robert MacKay
James Maclay
William Maclay
Paul Madden
Donald & Molly Magee
Michael Maher
Robert Manice
Robert Margouleff
Wayne Marquardt
Christopher Martin
William & Sally Martin
Paul H. Martinez
Kris Mattes
Geo Matteson
Terry Mattson
Brad Maybury
Dennis C. Mayhew
Roberto Mazzoni
Michael McCaffery
John K. & Sarah McColloch
Robert McCollough
Ian A. & Jane Byrd S. McCurdy
Kitty McKoon-Hennick
Judy McLennan
Stephanie McLennan
John D. McShane
Denise Meagher
Mary Meehan
John Mendez
Pierre F. V. Merle
George Meyer
Willets S. Meyer
Clarence F. Michalis
J. William Middendorf II
Jan Miles
Tim Miller
August Miller
Robert Miorelli

Individual Members (continued)

Anne Mooney
James Mooney
John Mooney
William Mooney
Richard & Lynda Moore
Wilfred P. Moore
Charles Morgan
Harry & Sue Morgan
Lincoln Mossop
Arthur Murphy
Christopher Museler
Ken Neal
Jack Neary
Mimi Neff
Peter Neill
Paul Nicholson
Leonard Nihan
Scott Nolan
Louis Norris
Michael Northup
David Nowlin
Bradley Noyes
John T O'Brien
Patricia Ann O'Donnell
Jonathan & Constance Old
Brian Olson
Martin J. O'Meara
John Osmond
Robert Papp
Jonathan & Bettie Pardee
Matthew Parker
Lea Parrell
Dan Parrott
Jed Pearsall
David Pedrick
Christopher T.H. & Janet Pell
Tom & Aggie Perkins
Edward V. Pietka
Caleb Pifer
George & Sallly Pillsbury
William Poole
E. Clayton Porter

William Post
Rives Potts
Brian A. Pratt
Fanny Pratt
David & Mary Price
Donna Prieur
Doug Prothero
Joyce Pucino
Marguerite Pyron
Andrew & Jill Radel
Michael J. Rauworth
David Warren Ray
Andrew Reay-Ellers
Brendan Reed
David & Leslie Reed
Clark & Mary Lee Reiner
John & Mary Reiner
Nick Remlinger
Alan Rice
Richard 'Rusty' E. Rice Jr.
John W. Richmond
Margaret Riker
Alden T. & Glenda Ring
Lloyd Rives
Shirley Roberts
George Rockwood
Elizabeth E. Roosevelt
Leslie Rosenblatt
Barbara & Harald Rosengren
John Rousmaniere
Nigel Rowe
Edmund S. & Nathalie Rumowicz
Timothy & Laurie Runyan
Diana Russell
Thomas Ryan
Christine Rybak
William Sabatini
H. Alexander Salm
James D. Salmon
Clyde Sanadi
Harold Winthrop Sands
Edith Savage

Individual Members (continued)

Jesse Schaffer
Rousevelle Schaum
Nicholas Schaus
Robin Schimpf
Michael Schoettle
Albert Schofield
Andrew Scholtz
James Schoonmaker II
Gary Schwarzman
R. Strother Scott
Richard Shannon
Eric & Adrienne Shaw
Gene Shaw
Paul H. Sheehan
Bobbi Sheffield
David Sheldon
Albert K. Sherman
Edwin Shuman
Charles Shumway
Stuart Siddons
Jeffrey M. Siegal
Andre Sigourney
Zachary Simonson-Bond
Nicole Singer
Krista Slack
Jan & Caroline Slee
John J. & Diana Slocum
Amelia Smith
Colby Smith
Donald Smith
Karla M. Smith
Ronald Smith
JB Smith
Ralph & Lilian Smith
Matt & Amy Snyder
Edward Solomon
Ann C. Souder
Eve Southworth
Robert Spagnolo
Marjorie & Stephen Spencer
Mark & Dana Spring
James E. & Lynn Spurr

Brian Stagner
M. Jeremy Steele-Perkins
Jonathan Stone
Luise Strauss
Kaari Sullivan
Sarah Swan
Hannah Swett
Gladys V. Szapary
Richard Taylor
Charles & E. Paisley Taylor
Donald F. Teal
Gail Thacher
Ian Thomas
Dave Thompson
Richard Thursby
Richard & Linda Tillman
Briggs & Jessica Tobin
Charles Townsend
Robert Towse
Christopher Trandell
Captain Jamie Trost
Stanley Trotman
Thompson & Maureen Tully
Ted Turner
Daniel C. & Annica C. van Starrenburg
Claiborne & Sidney Van Zandt
Michelle Verdi
Kurt Voss
Steven Walk
Scott Walker
Barclay H. Warburton IV
Peter M. Ward
Quentin Warren
Terri & Ron Weinberg-Bell
Ralph & Florence Weiss
Francis & Elizabeth West
Matthew Wheble
Tom & Betsy Whidden
J. Wilfrid White
F. C. 'Bunky' Wichmann
John C. & Priscilla Wigglesworth
James & Judith Wilson

Individual Members (continued)

Jay & Brenda Wilson
Mary Winder
John Winslow
William & Victoria Winterer

Geralyn Wolf
Meghan Wren Briggs
Karin Wyman
William F. Young

 Crew Members

Gary Akin
Armand Almaraz
Shawn Anderson
Lauren Berdow
Adrienne Bode
Siri Botnen
Paul Bracken
Greg Branan
Nathaniel Bray-Marks
Cindy Buffa
Carlos Canario
Jan Caselli
Stephanie Chambers
Barmettler Christian
Donald Church
Gary Delzer
Francoise Desoutler
Daniel Eden
Kevin Eli
Jon Ford
Kyle Friauf
Jorg Gerdiken
John Giebfried
James Gladson
Nicholas Griffes
Wynne Hedlesley
Isaac Henry
Hannah Higgins
Joe Hopkins
Florian Kette
John A. Kraus
Emilie Larew
Rebecca Libby
Taia Marsters

Christian Mayr
Meredith McKinnon
Diven Mohanlall
Clark Munro
Nadja Nitschke
Adam Opsata
Alex Peacock
Nancy H. Richardson
Alice Moore Robinson
Benjamin Saint
Kay Sandor
Morgan P. Sanger
Katharina Schaal
John Schaumburg
Bas Seesing
Katelinn Shaw
Sam Sikkema
Kevin Slocum
Mark Spoerk
Tammy Spoerk
Ed Steiner
Abigail Stern
Liam Tayler
Julie Vermeer
Katie Abigail Walker
Pania Warren
Michael 'Fred' Weiss
Frank White
Jamie White
Ryan Whitehead
Joe Wilhelm
Bradford Woodworth
Charlie Wright

Youth Members

Blake Cannino
Sari Crawford
Aaron Gralnik
Maia Grodin
Colin Jones
Eleanor Littlestone

Patrick Maher
Saphrona Stetson
Alex Tucci
Nelly Turley
Logan Welborn

Family Members

Amy Albrecht
Edward M. & Bernadette Andrews
Steven H. Baker and Family
Thomas & Phyllis Kelly
Robert Bein
Richard & Anita Canfield
William and Deborah Cooper
Vivian Coxe
George & Pamela Dow
Chuck Fowler
Robert Frost
Don Hardy
Dave Haslam
Steven & Catherine Hertz
Michael & Charlotte Jehle
Eric Jones
Jonathan T. & Jennifer Kabak
Candace Kuchinski
Ivan T. & Susan Luke

Brooks McCutchen
Gene McKeever
Hank & Kaia Moseley
Steve & Ginnie Moulton
Jeffrey N. Parker
Cynthia & Monty Pifer
Octavia Randolph
Dana & Carolyn Rexford
Robert D. Rustchak
Walter Rybka
Glenn & Linda Short
Chris & Kathy Sinnett
Howard Slotnick
J. E. Smith
Johanna & William Strassberg
Brenda Thomas
Jennifer Tobin & Garth Wells
David V. V. & Paula Wood
C. Clair Wylie

Lifetime Members

Henry H. Anderson, Jr.
John Benson
Joseph M. Davis
Robert S. Douglas
Ronald V. Gallo

John M. Hopkins
Thor H. Ramsing
Frederic S. Sater
Cornelius Vanderstar
Robin Wallace

Supporting Members

Raymond Ashley
Hal G. Barstow
John W. & Nancy F. Braitmayer
Jeffrey Davies
Jen Haddock
Deborah Hayes & John Beebe-Center
David Hayes
Karen Helmerson
Joseph Maggio
Doug & Pat McKenzie
Bill Munger

Hisakazu Nakayama
David Niebuhr
Ed & Cindy Olivier
Richard S. Palmer
Bert Rogers
Christopher Rowsom
Stan Selden
Alix T. Thorne
Thomas R. Weschler
Joseph A. Willhelm

Sail Training International

Sail Training International

Sail Training International

Sail Training International is a registered charity (not for profit organization) with worldwide membership and activities whose purpose is the development and education of young people of all nationalities, cultures, religions and social backgrounds through the sail training experience.

Sail Training International offers a range of activities and services including conferences and seminars, races and other events for sail training tall ships, publications and DVD presentations, international research and the Class A Tall Ships Forum (for the operators of big square-rigged sail training ships). Members are made up of the national sail training organizations of Australia, Belgium, Bermuda, Canada, Denmark, Finland, France, Germany, Greece, India, Ireland, Italy, Latvia, Lithuania, Netherlands, New Zealand, Norway, Poland, Portugal, Russia, South Africa, Spain, Sweden, UK and USA. Tall Ships America is a founder member of Sail Training International.

www.sailtraininginternational.org

Member Organizations

AUSTRALIA - Australian Sail Training Association

Founded in 1996, AUSTA represents the interests of 16 sail training organizations and tall ship operators in Australia and New Zealand. Its purpose is to promote the development of sail training with an emphasis on adventure training for young people at sea under sail in Australia and elsewhere. AUSTA also plays a key role in the development (for sail training vessel operators) of safety-related codes of conduct and on-board management systems, trainee and professional crew training programs and other related programs.
www.sailtrainingaustralia.com

BELGIUM - Sail Training Association Belgium

Founded in 1994, STA Belgium is a registered charity with national membership. It restored, owns and operates the T/S *Williwaw* and promotes sail training for young people on many other Belgian vessels.
www.sailtrainingbelgium.org

BERMUDA - Sail Training Association Bermuda

Formed in 2001 following the success of the Tall Ships® 2000 transatlantic race, STA Bermuda promotes and helps to fund the participation of young Bermudians in sail training programs internationally.
stabermuda@logic.bm

CANADA - Canadian Sail Training Association

Founded in 1984, its membership now includes the owner/operators of 18 vessels ranging in size from a six meter open sloop to an 80 meter barquentine and providing sail training programs as diverse in scope as the vessels themselves. A key priority for the organization now is to ensure a regulatory environment that is consistent with the goals and activities of sail training operators and their programs.
www.sailtraining.ca

Denmark - Danish Sail Training Association

Founded in 1996, DSTA represents the interests of 30 members in Denmark, the Faroe Islands and Greenland, including ten sail training vessels (ranging in size from an 18 meter ketch to three Class A full rigged ships) and five ports. The organization operates a grant scheme to assist trainees taking part in The Tall Ships' Races.
www.dsta.dk

Member Organizations

FINLAND - Sail Training Association Finland

STA Finland member sail training vessels have taken more than 16,800 young people to sea since the organization's foundation in 1973. These young trainees have also formed their own organization (The Sail Trainees of Finland Association) which provides opportunities for continuing contact between the trainees and also helps to promote sail training in Finland.
www.staf.fi

FRANCE - Sail Training Association France

Amis des Grands Voiliers: Founded in 1990, STA France represents the interests of around 40 vessels and about 400 members (individuals - associations - charities - vessels operators) in promoting sail training for young persons through exhibitions at various maritime festivals and other events. Through its quarterly publication "Grands Voiliers Infos" and its monthly newsletter, it helps potential young trainees in finding opportunities to embark on sail training vessels around the world.
www.amisdesgrandsvoiliers.org

GERMANY - Sail Training Association Germany

Founded in 1984 as a not-for-profit organization, STAG's main purpose is the education, development and support of young people of all nationalities through sail training. Its members include 50 sail training vessels and over 5,000 individual members. The organization operates a bursary program for sail training vessels and individual trainees.
www.sta-g.de

IRELAND - Coiste an Asgard

Formed in 1968, Coiste an Asgard operates the state owned Class A sail training vessel *Asgard II* and promotes offshore sail training for young people generally in the Republic of Ireland. Coiste an Asgard provides the communications link for offshore sail training interests in Ireland with Sail Training International pending the development of a national sail training organization (as defined by Sail Training International).
www.irishsailtraining.com

Member Organizations

ITALY - Sail Training Association Italy

Founded in 1976 by a partnership of the Italian Navy and the Yacht Club Italiano, its charter is to develop and promote sea training for young people as a means to further their personal development and education. Through the co-operation of the Navy and many owner/operators of other vessels, STA Italy offers a variety of sail training opportunities to young people, including berths at no charge or highly subsidized. The organization also operates an international trainee exchange program which is currently expanding.
www.sta-italia.it

LATVIA - Sail Training Association Latvia

Founded in 2002 by 23 sail training enthusiasts in Latvia, the organization also has three members who own/operate vessels, two yacht clubs and three maritime companies. STA Latvia's principal goals are to develop sail training for young people in Latvia by encouraging other vessel owners to participate in sail training activities and events, and through an international trainee exchange program.
www.sta-latvia.lv

NETHERLANDS - Sail Training Association Netherlands

Founded in 1985, STAN's goals are to encourage and develop sail training off-shore for young people in the Netherlands. In pursuit of this, STAN organizes maritime events and races for sail training and tall ships in The Netherlands.
www.stanetherlands.nl

NEW ZEALAND - Spirit of Adventure Trust

Established in 1972 by Lou Fisher, The Spirit of Adventure Trust was formed to offer equal opportunity to young New Zealanders to gain qualities of independence, leadership and community spirit through the medium of the sea. The Spirit of Adventure Trust is dedicated to the youth of New Zealand. Each year it brings together 1,200 young people throughout the country.
www.spiritofadventure.org.nz

NORWAY - Norwegian Sail Training Association

Founded in 1999, NSTA has four membership categories: sail training vessels, past and prospective host ports for The Tall Ships' Races, individuals and organizations supporting NSTA ideals, and corporate entities. The organization promotes sail training for young people and international friendship through sail training.
www.nsta.no

🚢 Member Organizations

POLAND - Sail Training Association Poland

Established in 1993, STA Poland has more than 100 individual (voting) members and is co-owner and sole operator of the Class A sail training tall ship, *Pogoria*. Supporting (non-voting) members include the Maritime Academy of Gdynia (*Dar Mlodziezy*), the Polish Navy (ORP *Iskra*) the Polish Scouts Union Sea Training Centre (*Zawisza Czarny*) and the Polish Yachting Association (*Kapitan Glowacki*).
www.pogoria.pl

PORTUGAL - Portuguese Sail Training Association

Aporvela – Portuguese STA was founded in 1980 as a registered charity. It has three categories of membership and owns three sail training vessels including the Caravel *Vera Cruz*. The organization's main objectives are to promote off-shore sail training mainly for young people.
www.aporvela.pt

RUSSIA - Admiral Makarov State Maritime Academy

This institution represents the interests of sail training in Russia and operates the 100-metre sail training ship *Mir*. The Academy provides the communications link for all sail training activities in Russia with Sail Training International, pending the development of a national sail training organization (as defined by Sail Training International).
smamir@lek.ru

SPAIN - Sail Training Association España

Created in 2003, STA España membership includes all sail training vessels in Spain, the Spanish Navy and a number of ports.
www.sailtraining.es

SWEDEN - Sail Training Association Sweden

STA Sweden was founded in 1998, initially to support the Tall Ships' Races. Today its members include a number of Swedish ports, the Swedish Navy and some 60 vessels engaged wholly or occasionally in sail training activities.
www.stas.nu

UNITED KINGDOM - Association of Sea Training Organisations

Founded in 1972, ASTO represents the interests of UK sail training organizations. It has 25 full members and 10 associate members operating 55 sail training vessels ranging in size from a 10-metre sloop to a 65-metre barque. The organization grants bursary funding towards the costs of more than 80,000 berth days for young people, including disabled trainees each year.
www.asto.org.uk

Member Organizations

USA - Tall Ships America

Founded in 1973, the organization represents the interests in the US of member sail training vessels from more than 20 countries. as well as affiliate members including museums, schools and universities, and more than 500 individual members who support the organization's mission. Tall Ships America raises funds and administers several scholarship programs as well as a professional development grant program to support the continuing education of professional sail trainers and marine educators.
www.tallshipsamerica.org

Recent Additions to the Membership Include:
Greece, India, Lithuania, South Africa

Sail Training International
5 Mumby Road
Gosport
Hampshire PO12 1AA
UK

Telephone: +44 (0)23 9258 6367
Fax: +44 (0)23 9258 4661
Email: office@sailtraininginternational.org

www.sailtraininginternational.org

Programs and Services

Tall Ships America® Programs foster youth education, leadership development and the preservation of North American maritime heritage. Tall Ships America organizes the TALL SHIPS CHALLENGE® annual series of sail training races, rallies and maritime festivals, hosts an annual Conference on Sail Training and Tall Ships, and publishes SAIL TALL SHIPS! A Directory of Sail Training and Adventure at Sea. Tall Ships America also raises money for scholarships, and administers grants directly supporting youth education and leadership development programs that shape young people's lives and build tomorrow's leaders.

Annual Conference on Sail Training and Tall Ships

The Annual Conference on Sail Training and Tall Ships gathers ships' masters, port representatives, public officials, marine suppliers, naval architects, program administrators, festival managers, preservationists, environmentalists, crewmembers, and educators. Topics concerning vessel operations, regulatory issues, management, educational programming, and safety at sea are addressed each year, as are sessions on media relations, marketing, funding, communications, and port event organization. The Annual Conference on Sail Training and Tall Ships is both fun and informative and offers oceans of networking opportunities.

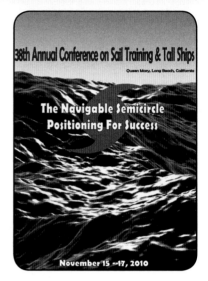

38th Annual Conference on Sail Training & Tall Ships

Queen Mary, Long Beach, California

The Navigable Semicircle
Positioning For Success

November 15 –17, 2010

Education Under Sail Forum

The Education Under Sail Forum made its grand premiere in Chicago in 2000. The first of what has now become a program-focused complement to the Safety Under Sail Forum. The Education Under Sail Forum is held in conjunction with the Annual Conference on Sail Training and Tall Ships. The forum is designed to inform and inspire excellence in the development and delivery of educational experiences under sail, and overflows with creative exchanges among captains, crew, administrators, teachers, program developers, curriculum designers, and others.

Safety Under Sail Forum

Initiated in 1992, the Safety Under Sail Forum expands the international dialogue among professional mariners by presenting case studies of actual incidents at sea, discussing emerging technologies, and sharing "best practices" so as to constantly insure a high level of safety and professionalism in the sail training industry. Professionals engaged in sail training, sea education, vessel operations, and tall ship events from throughout the world participate in this annual symposium. Topics covered have included preparing for heavy weather, hypothermia, technology and forecasting, survival gear and much more. The Safety Forum is held in conjunction with the Annual Conference on Sail Training and Tall Ships.

The Sail Training Rally

In the 1980s, Tall Ships America developed the concept of the Sail Training Rally; a competition among crews, both at sea and ashore. These rallies provide trainees with an opportunity to demonstrate their seamanship skills in a friendly but competitive format by participating in shoreside events such as knot tying, tug-of war, bucket brigade, rowing, walk the plank, and heaving line toss/hawser pull. Most often held in conjunction with the TALL SHIPS CHALLENGE® Race Series, Sail Training Rallies allow the general public to observe the sort of teamwork and maritime skills that are learned on board sail training vessels at sea.

Regional Meetings

Regional-Atlantic, Pacific and Great Lakes-meetings are held annually. These meetings are less formal than our annual conference, but like the conference, we encourage our members to submit ideas for locations and topics. The regional meetings offer an opportunity for the host organization to showcase their facility and programs, while providing an intimate setting for attendees to network.

A typical regional meeting may include a tour, special presentation, workshops, discussion groups, safety demonstration, day sail, luncheon and reception.

If your organization would like to host a regional meeting, please send a letter of interest along with a proposed agenda to Tall Ships America.

2011 Atlantic Regional Meeting aboard the USCGC *Eagle* in New London, CT

The Tall Ships America Website

The Tall Ships America® Website, www.tallshipsamerica.org, links you to the world of sail training and tall ships. The Website combines many exciting features with a fresh look and easy to navigate pages.

A searchable listing of Tall Ships America® member vessels makes it easy to learn more about opportunities under sail, the ships that can take you to sea, and shore-based programs. The Tall Ships America® Website also provides information about Tall Ships® events such as the TALL SHIPS CHALLENGE® Race Series and international sail training associations and resources around the world.

The Tall Ships America Billet Bank

Filter Positions By:

SHOWING ALL POSITIONS

HMS Bounty Organization, LLC www.tallshipbounty.org based in Palm I
Florida, operates Bounty and invites applications for the post of **Engine
Bosun, mates, deckhands**.

The Bounty Organization is looking for crew to be on board for the
winter maintenance months of Bounty in Florida. The duties will
include tours, daily maintenance and possible sailing for private
functions. All positions are open. Those who are hired for the winter
will have first choice for positions during our 2010 sailing season.

This post is Seasonal.

Apply by email to
Contact Name: Margaret Ramsey
Tel: 1 (631) 584-7900
Fax: 1 843 280-6856
email: mramsey@tallshipbounty.org
2806 Ship Wheel Drive , North Myrtle Beach SC 29582 US

An online Billet Bank provides notice of positions available aboard Tall Ships America® member vessels.

The Billet Bank is the most visited section of the Tall Ships America® Website and is the most effective service available for matching professional sail trainers and open positions.

Tall Ships America does not endorse any specific program or individual, but simply shares information as it becomes available.

Crew Membership Program

The Tall Ships America® Crew Membership program allows Tall Ships America® Sail Training Organization members to purchase blocks of 10 membership vouchers at a reduced rate, for distribution to their staff, crew, volunteers and trainees.

Crew memberships must be purchased by the member Sail Training Organization (STO) and are sold in blocks of 10 for US $250. Membership application forms are sent to the member STO who then distributes them to staff and crew. The memberships are valid for one year from the time Tall Ships America receives the completed application form and carry all the same benefits as an individual membership (US $50) plus some added benefits.

Marine Insurance Program

Allen Insurance and Financial of Camden, Maine is the officially-endorsed insurance agency of Tall Ships America. Established in 1866, Allen Insurance and Financial is an independent, employee-owned company with 70 employees specializing in providing vessel owners from around the world with choices in coverage from a variety of the industry's best insurance companies.

Allen Insurance and Financial has insured tall ships for decades. The company's tradition of exemplary service and competitive rates is now available to both new customers and returning ones.   Allen Insurance and Financial's marine insurance experts, back up these offerings with the utmost attention to detail and an emphasis on customer service.

Allen Insurance and Financial offers these products to Tall Ships America® members who qualify: Hull, P&I and related vessel insurance for U.S.-flagged member vessels; hull, P&I and related vessel insurance for foreign-flagged member vessels; non-profit directors and officers liability insurance; events cancellation insurance and events liability insurance; and general business insurance for land-based operations of Tall Ships America® members.

For more information on the Tall Ships America® Marine Insurance program contact Gene McKeever at Allen Insurance and Financial: 800-439-4311 or gmckeever@alleninsuranceandfinancial.com

Marine Medical Coverage Program

Mariners require a medical program they can depend on to protect them as they travel throughout the world. Coverage that provides security, flexibility and benefits unique to today's marine industry demands. Now Tall Ships America® members can sail and travel anywhere with the confidence that they are protected with comprehensive, marine-specific medical coverage.

Allen Insurance and Financial of Camden, the Tall Ships America-endorsed insurance company, are pleased to offer a health/medical program for crew. This special health/medical product protects Tall Ships America® members with full coverage, 24/7, while onboard the vessel and when signed off or on personal leisure time.

Tall Ships America® organizational membership is required to participate.

For more information on the Marine Medical Coverage program contact Rick Bagnall at Allen Insurance and Financial 207-236-8376 X 540 or rbagnall@allenfg.com

Henry H. Anderson, Jr. Sail Training Scholarship Program

The Henry H. Anderson, Jr. Sail Training Scholarship was established in 1999 and is designed to assist young people between the ages of 14 and 19 achieve a sail training experience aboard a USCG inspected Tall Ships America® member vessel. Scholarships are available to both individuals and groups. Scholarships are awarded to individuals and groups who are genuinely interested in experiencing sail training and education under sail. Applicants must show a demonstrated need for financial assistance and must describe, in writing, what they feel they will achieve by participating in the sail training experience.

For details contact the Tall Ships America® office or visit the Tall Ships America® Website at www.tallshipsamerica.org.

Ernestine Bennett Memorial Sail Training Scholarship Program

The Ernestine Bennett Memorial Sail Training Scholarship is designed to assist people to achieve a sail training experience aboard a USCG inspected Tall Ships America® member vessel. Scholarships are available to people ages 14 and above with special consideration going to female applicants from the Pacific Northwest. Scholarships are awarded to individuals who are genuinely interested in experiencing sail training and education under sail. Applicants must show a demonstrated need for financial assistance and must describe, in writing, what they feel they will achieve by participating in the sail training experience.

For details contact the Tall Ships America® office or visit the Tall Ships America® Website at www.tallshipsamerica.org.

Ernestine Bennett Memorial Sail Training Scholarship Program

The Tall Ships America® Professional/Crew Development Grant has been established to provide financial assistance to professional crewmembers of Tall Ships America® member vessels in order to meet new and existing requirements for maintaining as well as advancing their USCG licenses, and to encourage the highest possible standards of safety training for individuals or groups of Tall Ships America® members. Applicants must be a Tall Ships America® Associate or Crew Member in good standing.

For details contact the Tall Ships America® office or visit the Tall Ships America® Website at www.tallshipsamerica.org.

Publications

Sail Tall Ships! A Directory of Sail Training and Adventure at Sea first appeared in 1980, and is now in its nineteenth edition. The directory provides program and contact information for Tall Ships America® member vessels and sail training associations throughout the world. To help fulfill the mission of Tall Ships America, the directory is also distributed through maritime museums and their affiliated shops, marinas, maritime events, and sail training programs, as well as bookstores, libraries, high school guidance counselors, university career resource centers, and education conferences throughout the United States and Canada. 436 pages. Soft cover, 9 by 6 inches. US $14.95

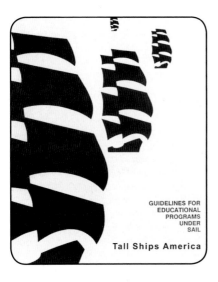

Guidelines for Educational Programs Under Sail defines Tall Ships America® standards for sail training and sea education within the framework of the Sailing School Vessels Act. This manual defines criteria and indicators of effectiveness for the design, delivery, and evaluation of curricula, instruction, and program administration. In addition to the core of safe seamanship education, the guidelines apply to all aspects of sail training: adventure, education, environmental science, maritime heritage, and leadership development. US $12.00

Conferences and Events

Tall Ships America®
Conferences, Fundraisers, Receptions
and other events

2009 Annual Conference on Sail Training and Tall Ships

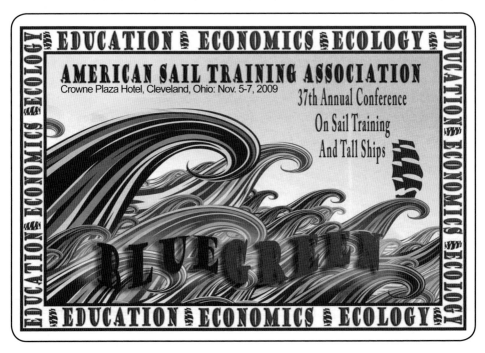

The 37th Annual Conference on Sail Training and Tall Ships took place at the Crowne Plaza Hotel in Cleveland, Ohio on November 5 and 6, 2009. It was followed by the Safety Under Sail Forum on November 7.

Gary Jobson of Jobson Sailing Inc. opened the conference with his keynote address, *Sailing: Speed and Passion*. Through a series of personal stories and video clips, Jobson illustrated the transformative themes of sail training and how it can alter the mind and attitude beyond the boat and into the entirety of life. His speech was received with a standing ovation at its conclusion.

Dr. Eric Shaw closed the conference with an engaging and positive presentation, *Riding the Trough: Successes in Hard Times,* highlighting how, despite lackluster economic times, many member organizations are making great strides forward.

In between we heard from Brent Gibson, Director of Communications for Great Lakes United, our partner for the Great Lakes United TALL SHIPS CHALLENGE®2010 *Race to Save the Lakes* series, who spoke about the past pollution in the Great Lakes, how far we have come, and how the partnership between Great Lakes United and the tall ships will help reintroduce inhabitants of the Great Lakes area to their lakes.

2009 Annual Conference on Sail Training and Tall Ships

RADM Peter V. Neffenger, Commander, 9th Coast Guard District, gave a brief talk emphasizing his personal connection to the Great Lakes region and the goal of the US Coast Guard to assist the ships leading up to and during the Great Lakes United TALL SHIPS CHALLENGE®2010 *Race to Save the Lakes* series.

Sixteen focus sessions were offered, covering everything from medical preparedness to how to spin your online social web to appeal to trainees, to how to put on a succsessful Tall Ships® event.

The Safety Under Sail Forum included a case study presented by Dr. Eric Shaw, *Personnel Injuries at Sea: An EAGLE Case Study.* Attorney Reb Gregg spoke about *Legal Issues in an E-world* and Captains Jonathan Kabak and Jonathan Boulware brought us up to speed on where things stand in the development of rig inspection protocols that, if approved by the USCG, could preclude a requirement for a 3rd party professional rig inspector.

Allen Agency Insurance and Financial treated delegates to a fabulous evening dinner and reception at the Rock and Roll Hall of Fame, including free passes to the museum, and the Annual Sail Training Awards Banquet was a lively affair followed by dancing to the tunes of The BackBeats, a Beatles tribute band complete with authentic period instruments and costumes.

2009 Focus Sessions

Navigating the Regulatory Seas

Asking For Money: Grantwriting 101

Sail Training For Students With Learning Differences

Ingredients For A Succsessful Tall Ships® Event

Medical Preparedness A

Medial Preparedness B

New Program Showcase

Getting Youth Onboard

Building a Successful Marketing Strategy in Harsh Economic Weather

Rethinking the Three Hour Daysail

Health Insurance Program For Crew

Navigating the Regulatory Seas: License Tracking

Don't Fall Through the Cracks: Are you Protected Where the Land Meets the Sea? (Insurance)

Defensive Paperwork: Law 101

Recruiting Trainees Using YouTube

Clean Boating Practices: Making a Difference Onboard and in the Classroom

2010 Annual Conference on Sail Training and Tall Ships

The 2010 Annual Conference on Sail Training and Tall Ships took place on November 15 and 16, aboard the Queen Mary in Long Beach, California. It was followed by the Safaty Under Sail Forum and the Education Under Sail Forum on November 17. Delegates were welcomed aboard by the ship's captain at a reception, hosted by the Queen Mary and the Long Beach CVB, the evening preceding the conference.

CAPT Eric Jones, USCG, Commanding Officer of the USCGC EAGLE, opened the conference with a keynote address titled *Take Stock of the Ship and Keep the Destination in Mind.*

Attorney Reb Gregg presented the general session, *Did You Really Say That? A discussion of marketing, applications, medical and other documents,* looking at the language used on various forms used by member programs and the hazards of exaggeration and unsupported claims or promises.

Dr. Ray Ashley, Executive Director of the San Diego Maritime Museum, provided the closing address, *Tall Ships as Allegory.*

Eighteen focus sessions, covering a wide variety of topics, were offered over the course of the two day conference.

2010 Annual Conference on Sail Training and Tall Ships

Education Under Sail Forum sessions included *Improving Practice and Impact: The Sail Training Program Evaluation Self Assessment Toolkit, Models of Educational Daysails,* and *Linking Shipboard Programs with Schools: Where is Education in Your Mission?*

The Safety Under Sail Forum opened with a session on *Risk/Benefit Analysis: How to Make Safety Reviews Work* followed by *S/V Concordia Total Loss: Operator Crisis Management Timeline.* Joe Sienkiewicz, Chief of the Ocean Applications Branch of the NOAA Ocean Prediction Center, talked to us about *Ship Killers: A Look at Thunderstorm Outflow -What Every Mariner Needs to Know and* Gene McKeever of Allen Agency Insurance and Financial closed the day with *Now What? Dealing With Total Loss.*

Sponsored evening receptions gave delegates the opportunity to experience the Queen Mary in all her vast glory and the Annual Awards Banquet was an elegant affair, taking place in the Grand Salon, and featuring "The Swing Dolls", an Andrews Sisters tribute show.

2009 Focus Sessions

Navigating the Regulatory Seas

Perils of Plastic Pacific Pollution: Facts, Myths, and How You Can Help

Update: Tall Ships America's Marine Health Insurance Program

Beyond Pirates: Showcasing Your Maritime Heritage at Port Events

License Guidance for Captains: What the Old Guard Needs to Know

Hot Topics in Marine Biology/Oceanography

The Business of Ship-Port Appearance Agreements

Updating Your Release Agreement: (It's Been Quite a Year!)

Website Analytics 101: Measuring the Effectiveness of Your Website

New Program Showcase

The Maritime Industry: Careers at Sea for You and your Trainees

Marketing and Social Media—What's New?

What You Need to Know: Strategies for Psychotropic Med Management in Remote Programming

Making Educators Out of Sailors

Building a Strong Annual Giving Program

The Future of Marine Weather Prediction Technology

Working with Volunteers: How our volunteer program validates, vindicates or violates accepted principles of volunteer program administration.

Finding the Right Insurance and Understanding What You Have

2011 Harry Anderson 90th Birthday Gam and Endowment Fundraiser

Over 350 people celebrated the 90th birthday of Henry H. ("Harry") Anderson, Jr. at an evening "gam" and fundraiser for Tall Ships America held at the New York Yacht Club's Harbour Court, Saturday, June 18th in Newport, RI. The event honored Commodore Anderson's unwavering commitment to sailing and sail training, while at the same time allowing friends and family to shower him with well deserved accolades. It was a truly a special night.

"Having been Chairman of Tall Ships America, now Commodore emeritus, I hope to use the occasion of my 90th to provide a legacy to establish a robust endowment of $1.5 million in support of the mission of Tall Ships America, *to encourage character building through sail training, promote sail training to the North American* public, and support education under sail. What greater accolade to a chap in his twilight years?"

Harbour Court, overlooking Newport Harbor, was the perfect setting and it was a beautiful summer night for a party. Cocktails were served on the lawn while guests perused the silent auction tables. During dinner, Harry shared some personal stories of sailing, a bust of his likeness was revealed, and Gary Jobson, Master of Ceremonies, showed a special video he produced highlighting Harry's amazing contributions to the sailing world. Later in the evening, a live auction was held for which Mr. Jobson filled the role of auctioneer. The evening was capped off with music and dancing to the tunes of the Alex Donner Orchestra. It was a festive night celebrating the life and accomplishments of a remarkable individual and sailor as well as raising awareness of the mission of Tall Ships America. Proceeds from the event combined with donations to the Henry H. Anderson, Jr. Endowment Fund totaled $400,000.

2011 Harry Anderson 90th Birthday Gam and Endowment Fundraiser

Henry H. ("Harry") Anderson, Jr. has dedicated his life to sailing and along the way has inspired many young people to follow his course. Commodore Anderson's first competitive sailing event was the 1936 Newport – Bermuda Race in which he sailed at the age of 15. That early adventure began what has become a highly distinguished and internationally renowned avocation. Commodore Anderson has served as Chairman of Tall Ships America, Commodore of the New York Yacht Club and on several America's Cup Race Committees, once as Chairman. He worked as one of the first Executive Directors of the North American Yacht Racing Union and later as a member of US Sailing's Appeals Committee. He is co-author of *The Centennial History of the United States Sailing Association*. A co-founder of Yale Sailing Associates, Commodore Anderson sailed for Yale from 1939 to 1943 and is also well-known in international circles as a past vice-president of the International Yacht Racing Union and as a judge on the international collegiate racing circuit for more than 52 years. A strong supporter of youth competitive sailing, Commodore Anderson played a critical role in establishing the University of Rhode Island's Sailing Center and fleet of 420s. He has served for more than 30 years on the Board of Directors of his high school alma mater, Ransom Everglades School in Coconut Grove, Florida, which hosted the 1997 Interscholastic Sailing Championships, and has named both its Sailing Center and its Gymnasium in his honor.

Henry H. Anderson, Jr. was presented with a Lifetime Achievement Award by Tall Ships America at its 1998 Annual Conference on Sail Training and Tall Ships and ten years later, at the 2008 Annual Conference, was presented with a Special Recognition Award for his continuing achievements and support. Commodore Anderson has also been awarded the Nathanael G. Herreshoff Trophy by US Sailing for his "outstanding contribution to sailing in America" in 1979, and he received the Beppe Croce Award from the International Sailing Federation in 1996. He has also received the Richard S. Nye Trophy from Cruising Club of America and been awarded an Honorary Degree from the University of Rhode Island.

MOONRAKER ($100,000+)
Henry H. Anderson, Jr.

SKYSAIL ($50,000+)
Dayton Carr

ROYAL ($10,000+)
James Hilton
William & Victoria Winterer

TOPGALLANT ($5,000+)
Lawrence Glenn
Thomas Gochberg
John Hele
Mr. & Mrs. Chester Kitchings
Dr. & Mrs. Charles Langston
Honorable Juliette McLennan
Captain Michael J. Rauworth, Esq.
Lloyd M. Rives
Mr. & Mrs. Bert Rogers
James "Ding" Schoonmaker
Jeffrey Siegal

TOPSAIL ($1,000+)
Lawrence Allen
Leslie Ballard
James D. Bishop
David Brown
Nicholas Brown
Loretta Bruno
Nancybell Coe
JT & Gay Coe
Matthew Dick, Jr.
Dexter Donham
Lisa Lewis & Bart Dunbar
David Elwell
Louis A. Fazzano
Michael & Nancy Herde
Mr. & Mrs. Joseph Hoopes
Garry J. Hoyt
Oliver Janney
James Kerr
Stanley Livingston, Jr.
AL "Chip" Loomis III
Robert G. Manice
Geo Matteson & Adele Ursone
Clarence Michales
Charles F. Morgan
Lincoln Mossop III
George Pillsbury
Fanny Gray Pratt
Mr. & Mrs. David Reed
Harald Rosengren
Peter Dirk Siemsen
Luise Strauss
Hannah Swett
Alix T. Thorne
Charles Townsend
Ted Turner
Barclay "Tim" Warburton IV
VADM Thomas Weschler, USN (ret.)

MAINSAIL ($275+)
Mr. & Mrs. Ed Adams
Leith Adams
Honorable & Mrs. David Anderson
Jose Arozamen
Peder Arstorp
Jeremy Atkins
Hugh D. Auchincloss
Mr. & Mrs. B. Devereux Barker
John A. Barnes
Nicholas Bell
Anne Bell
Alfred G. Bisset
Richard N. Bohan
Mr. & Mrs. John F. Bohan
Christopher Bouzaid
George M. Bulow
Mr. & Mrs. Andrew Burton
Paul D. Buttrose
Charles Byrne
James Byrne Callahan
Brian J. Carey
Mr. & Mrs. George W. Carmany
Mason R. Chrisman
Howard Christian
Captain George Crowninshield
Peter Cusick
Susan Daly
Mr. & Mrs. Horner Davis
Captain Joseph M. Davis, Jr.
Timothy Demy
Nicholas B. Dill
JP Tim Dolman
Mr. & Mrs. Duncan Doolittle
Peter Dott
Mrs. John R. Drexel III
Kevin Dykema
Mr. & Mrs. Mohamad Farzan
Tylor "Toby" Field
Lynn Fitzpatrick
Mr. & Mrs. Thomas K. Flynn
David B. Ford
Colin Foster
Stephen Galpin
Susan Geiger
Mary Gilbane
Captain James Gladson
Winthrop Hall, Jr.
Thomas J. Harrington
Richard H. Hawkins
Michael Hayes
Karen Helmerson
Jill Helterline
Dana Hewson
James W. Hiney
Commodore & Mrs. George R. Hinman
Chandler "Bee" Hovey
Gary Jobson
Mr. & Mrs. Platt Johnson
Stuart F. Johnson
Troy Johnson
Captain & Dr. Jonathan Kabak

JIB (under $275)
Oliver Burr James III
CAPT & Mrs. Nathaniel James III
Ed Johnson
Eugene H. Kummel
Cameron LaClair, Jr.
Norman Lemley
Mr. & Mrs. David Lindh
Tom & Harriet Linskey
Richard C. Loebs, Jr.
Oivind Lorentzen, Jr.
CS Lovelace
Townsend Ludington, Jr.
Sally H. Lunt
James B. Lyon
Malcolm Mackay
Robert B. Mackay
James Maclay
William C. Martin
Mr. & Mrs. John M. Mendez
George S. Meyer
Willetts S. Meyer
Captain Jan Miles
James D. Mooney
Mrs. W.P. Neff
Peter Neill
Leonard Nihan
Bradley P. Noyes
Patricia O'Donnell
Constance Old
Jonathan H. Pardee
David R. Pedrick
Monty & Cynthia Pifer
William W. Poole
Clayton Porter

JIB (under $275)
R&W Traditional Rigging
Day Ravenscroft
John & Mary Reiner
Nancy H. Richardson
Margaret Riker
Alden T. Ring
George Rockwood
John P. Rousmaniere
Timothy Runyan
Edith Savage
Nicholas Schaus
Michael B. Schoettle
Andrew A. Scholtz
Struther Scott
Arthur Edwin A. Shuman III
Amelia Smith
Mr. & Mrs. Ralph Smith
Mr. & Mrs. Stephen W. Spencer
Daniel T. Stetson
Richard L. Tillman
Mr. & Mrs. Briggs Tobin
Commodore Robert C. Towse
C.C. van Zandt, Jr.
Mr. & Mrs. Daniel van Starrenburg
Mr. & Mrs. Chad Verdi
Dr. ARG Wallace
Quentin Warren
Terri Weinberg-Bell
Ralph Weiss
Francis West, Jr.
Captain John C. Wigglesworth
Right Rev. Geralyn Wolf
Meghan Wren

Indices

Geographical
and
Alphabetical

Photo by Thad Koza

Directory Sponsors

Tall Ships America would like to thank our sponsors. Their support made the production of this Directory possible.

Allen Insurance and Financial
Boothbay Harbor Shipyard
Epifanes
Gangplank Marina
Global Maritime and Training School
Maine Maritime Academy
N & D Sports
Navy Pier/Tall Ships® Chicago
Newport Marriott
Northeast Maritime Institute
Northwest Wooden Boat School
Ocean Classroom Foundation
Ocean State Tall Ships®
Oceanus Sailcloth
Perry Group
Picton Castle
R & W Traditional Rigging & Outfitting
Sailing Ship Adventures
Scarano Boat
Sea Education Association (SEA)
Sea History Magazine
Star Clippers
Tall Ship Celebration Bay City
Tall Ships® Erie
Tall Ships® Nova Scotia
Tall Ships® Savannah
Taylor Made Destinations
The Sailing Channel
The Spar Shop
Flagship Niagara League
Village of Greenport, NY
Visit Duluth

Photo by Thad Koza

Geographical Index

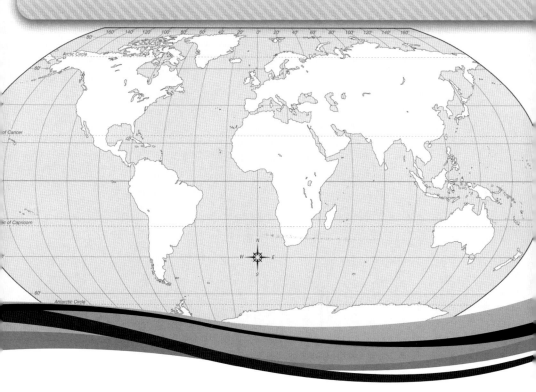

New England

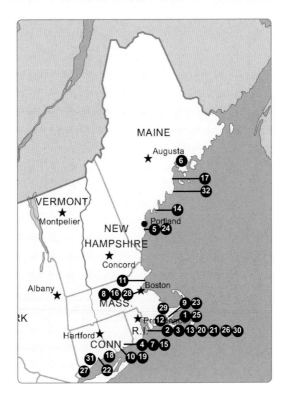

🏴 New England

	Vessel Name	Homeport		Page #
1	ALABAMA	Vineyard Haven	MA	131
2	ADIRONDACK II	Newport	RI	127
3	AQUIDNECK	Newport	RI	140
4	ARGIA	Mystic	CT	141
5	BAGHEERA	Portland	ME	144
6	BOWDOIN	Castine	ME	150
7	BRILLIANT	Mystic	CT	151
8	CONSTITUTION	Charlestown	MA	160
9	CORWITH CRAMER	Woods Hole	MA	161
10	EAGLE	New London	CT	168
11	FRIENDSHIP OF SALEM	Salem	MA	179
12	FRITHA	Fairhaven	MA	180
13	GERONIMO	Middletown	RI	182
14	HARVEY GAMAGE	Boothbay Harbor	ME	189
15	JOSEPH CONRAD	Mystic	CT	195
16	LIBERTY CLIPPER	Boston	MA	206
17	MARY DAY	Camden	ME	212
18	MARY E	Essex	CT	213
19	MYSTIC WHALER	New London	CT	217
20	OLIVER HAZARD PERRY	Newport	RI	223
21	PROVIDENCE	Newport	RI	238
22	QUINNIPIACK	New Haven	CT	239
23	ROBERT C SEAMANS	Woods Hole	MA	242
24	SAMANA	Portland	ME	246
25	SHENANDOAH	Vineyard Haven	MA	250
26	SIGHTSAILER	Newport	RI	251
27	SOUNDWATERS	Stamford	CT	255
28	SPIRIT OF MASSACHUSETTS	Boston	MA	258
29	TABOR BOY	Marion	MA	270
30	TREE OF LIFE	Newport	RI	274
31	UNICORN	Bridgeport	CT	275
32	WESTWARD	Rockland	ME	278

Mid Atlantic and Florida

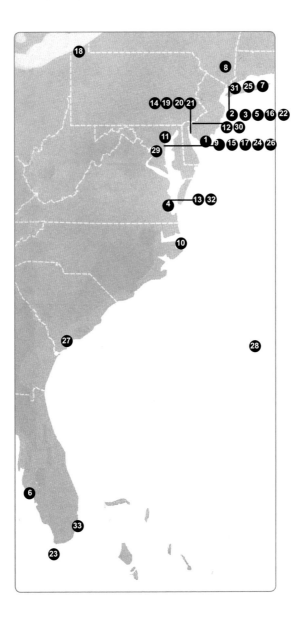

🚢 Mid Atlantic and Florida

	Vessel Name	Homeport		Page #
1	AJ MEERWALD	Bivalve	NJ	130
2	ADIRONDACK	New York	NY	126
3	ADIRONDACK III	New York	NY	128
4	ALLIANCE	Yorktown	VA	132
5	AMERICA 2.0	New York	NY	135
6	ARGO	Sarasota	FL	142
7	BOUNTY	Greenport	NY	149
8	CLEARWATER	Beacon	NY	158
9	CONSTELLATION	Baltimore	MD	159
10	ELIZABETH II	Manteo	NC	170
11	FAREWELL	Dundalk	MD	177
12	GAZELA	Philadelphia	PA	181
13	GODSPEED	Williamsburg	VA	185
14	KALMAR NYCKEL	Wilmington	DE	199
15	LADY MARYLAND	Baltimore	MD	202
16	LETTTIE G. HOWARD	New York	NY	204
17	MINNIE V	Baltimore	MD	214
18	NIAGARA	Erie	PA	219
19	NINA	Wilmington	DE	220
20	NORSEMAN	Wilmington	DE	221
21	PINTA	Wilmington	DE	232
22	PIONEER	New York	NY	233
23	PIRATES LADY	Marathon	FL	234
24	PRIDE OF BALTIMORE II	Baltimore	MD	237
25	SAIL'S UP	Port Jefferson	NY	245
26	SIGSBEE	Baltimore	MD	252
27	SPIRIT OF SOUTH CAROLINA	Charleston	SC	259
28	SPIRIT OF BERMUDA	Hamilton	Bermuda	256
29	SULTANA	Chestertown	MD	263
30	SUMMER WIND	Philadelphia	PA	265
31	SUMMERWIND	Kings Point	NY	264
32	SUSAN CONSTANT	Williamsburg	VA	268
33	YANKEE	Miami	FL	280

Gulf of Mexico

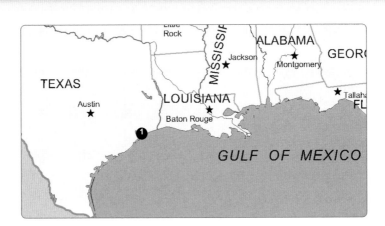

	Vessel Name	Homeport		Page #
1	ELISSA	Galveston	TX	169

California & Hawaii

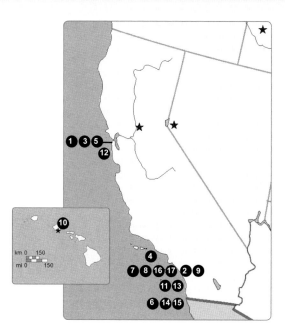

	Vessel Name	Homeport		Page #
1	ALMA	San Francisco	CA	133
2	AMERICAN PRIDE	Yorba Linda	CA	136
3	BALCLUTHA	San Francisco	CA	145
4	BILL OF RIGHTS	Oxnard	CA	146
5	CA THAYER	San Francisco	CA	152
6	CALIFORNIAN	San Diego	CA	153
7	EXY JOHNSON	San Pedro	CA	174
8	IRVING JOHNSON	San Pedro	CA	193
9	LYNX	Newport Beach	CA	207
10	MAKANI OLU	Kaneohe Bay	HI	209
11	PILGRIM	Dana Point	CA	231
12	SEAWARD	Sausalito	CA	247
13	SPIRIT OF DANA POINT	Dana Point	CA	257
14	STAR OF INDIA	San Diego	CA	261
15	SURPRISE	San Diego	CA	267
16	SWIFT OF IPSWICH	San Pedro	CA	269
17	TOLE MOUR	Long Beach	CA	273

Pacific Northwest

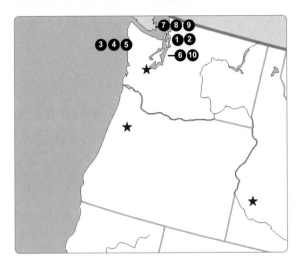

	Vessel Name	Homeport			Page #
1	ADVENTURESS	Port Townsend	WA		129
2	CUTTY SARK	Coupeville	WA		164
3	HAWAIIAN CHIEFTAIN	Aberdeen	WA		190
4	HEWITT R JACKSON	Aberdeen	WA		191
5	LADY WASHINGTON	Aberdeen	WA		203
6	MALLORY TODD	Seattle	WA		210
7	ORIOLE	Esquimalt	BC	Canada	224
8	PACIFIC GRACE	Victoria	BC	Canada	225
9	PACIFIC SWIFT	Victoria	BC	Canada	226
10	ZODIAC	Seattle	WA		283

Great Lakes USA & Canada

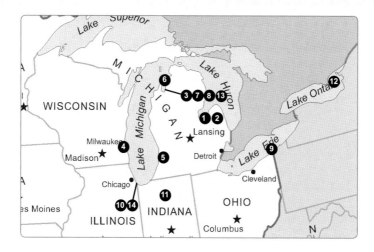

	Vessel Name	Homeport			Page#
1	APPLEDORE IV	Bay City	MI		138
2	APPLEDORE V	Bay City	MI		139
3	CHAMPION	Traverse City	MI		155
4	DENIS SULLIVAN	Milwaukee	WI		166
5	FRIENDS GOOD WILL	South Haven	MI		178
6	INLAND SEAS	Suttons Bay	MI		192
7	MADELINE	Traverse City	MI		208
8	MANITOU	Traverse City	MI		211
9	NIAGARA	Erie	PA		219
10	RED WITCH	Chicago	IL		241
11	R.H. LEDBETTER	Culver	IN		240
12	ST. LAWRENCE II	Kingston	ON	Canada	260
13	WELCOME	Traverse City	MI		277
14	WINDY	Chicago	IL		279

Canadian Maritimes & St. Lawrence Seaway

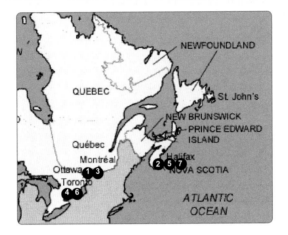

	Vessel Name	Homeport			Page #
1	BLACK JACK	Ottawa	ON	Canada	147
2	BLUENOSE II	Lunenburg	NS	Canada	148
3	FAIR JEANNE	Ottawa	ON	Canada	175
4	PATHFINDER	Toronto	ON	Canada	229
5	PICTON CASTLE	Lunenburg	NS	Canada	230
6	PLAYFAIR	Toronto	ON	Canada	235
7	SORCA	Lunenburg	NS	Canada	254

Mexico

South America and Caribbean

	Vessel Name	Homeport		Page #
1	ARGO	Road Harbour	BVI	142
2	CAPITAN MIRANDA	Montevideo	Uruguay	154
3	CISNE BRANCO	Rio de Janeiro	Brazil	157
4	ESMERALDA	Valparaiso	Chile	171
5	GLORIA	Cartegena	Colombia	184
6	GUAYAS	Guayquil	Ecuador	188
7	KAISEI	St John's	Antigua	197
8	LIBERTAD	Buenos Aires	Argentina	205
9	OCEAN STAR	Road Town	Tortola, BVI	222
10	ROSEWAY	St. Croix	USVI	243
11	SIMON BOLIVAR	La Guaira	Venezuela	253

Asia and South Pacific

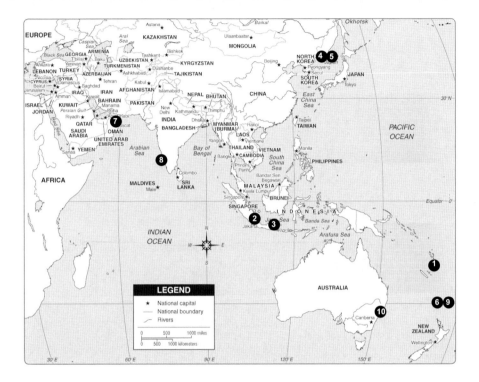

	Vessel Name	Homeport		Page #
1	ALVEI	Nelson	New Zealand	134
2	ARUNG SAMUDERA	Jakarta	Indonesia	143
3	DEWARUCI	Surabaya	Indonesia	167
4	NADEZHDA	Vladivostok	Russia	218
5	PALLADA	Vladivostok	Russia	228
6	PICTON CASTLE	Avatui, Rarotonga	Cook Islands	230
7	SHABAB OF OMAN	Muscat	Oman	249
8	TARANGINI	Kochi	India	271
9	TIARE TAPORO	Avatui, Rarotonga	Cook Islands	272
10	YOUNG ENDEAVOUR	Sydney	Australia	281

Europe

Europe

	Vessel Name	Homeport		Page #
1	AMERIGO VESPUCCI	La Spezia	Italy	137
2	CHRISTIAN RADICH	Oslo	Norway	156
3	CREOULA	Lisbon	Portugal	162
4	DAR MLODZIEZY	Gdynia	Poland	165
5	ETOILE	Brest	France	172
6	EUROPA	Rotterdam	The Netherlands	173
7	FALKEN	Karlskrona	Sweden	176
8	GLADEN	Karlskrona	Sweden	183
9	GORCH FOCK II	Kiel	Germany	186
10	GÖTHEBORG	Goteborg	Sweden	187
11	ISKRA	Gdynia	Poland	194
12	JUAN SEBASTIAN DE ELCANO	Cadiz	Spain	196
13	KALIAKRA	Varna	Bulgaria	198
14	KRUZENSHTERN	Kalingrad	Russia	200
15	LA BELLE POULE	Brest	France	201
16	MIR	St. Petersburg	Russia	215
17	MIRCEA	Constanta	Romania	216
18	PALINURO	La Maddalena, Sardinia	Italy	227
19	POGORIA	Gdynia	Poland	236
20	SAGRES	Lisbon	Portugal	244
21	SEDOV	Murmansk	Russia	248
22	STATSRAAD LEHMKUHL	Bergen	Norway	262
23	URANIA	Den Helder	The Netherlands	276
24	ZENOBE GRAMME	Zeebruge	Belgium	282

Photo by Thad Koza

Alphabetical Index

From A - Z
everything you always
wanted to know about
tall ships and sail training

S (continued)

Membership Opportunities

TALL SHIPS
AMERICA.

Associate and Organizational
Memberships

Associate Membership

Associate memberships are renewable on date of anniversary.

Individual - $50 per year

Benefits:
- Complimentary copy of Sail Tall Ships! A Directory of Sail Training and Adventure at Sea.
- Subscription to e-Running Free, Tall Ships America's monthly e-mail newsletter covering tall ships news and events.
- Discounts to attend the Annual Conference on Sail Training and Tall Ships.
- Discounts to attend Regional Meetings, Education and Safety Forums.
- Invitations to attend Tall Ships America® special events and friendraisers.

Youth - $25 per year
Open to sailors 25 years of age or younger

Benefits:
- All of the benefits of Individual Membership above

Family - $75 per year
Open to two members at the same address

Benefits:
- All of the benefits of Individual Membership above

Supporting - $250 per year

Benefits:
- All of the benefits of Membership above
- A Tall Ships America® Burgee (New members only)

Patron - $1,000 per year
For individuals wishing to express a greater commitment to the Tall Ships America® mission

Benefits:

- All of the benefits of Supporting Membership above

Organizational Membership

Dues are based on a calendar year January 1 – December 31

Business Partners - $550 per year
For ports, businesses, and associates of sail training and tall ships.

Corporate - $1000 per year
For ports, businesses and associates of sail training and tall ships wishing to express a greater commitment to the Tall Ships America® mission.

Affiliate Membership - $375 per year
Open to non-profit organizations which do not operate their own sail training vessel, but do offer sail training, sea education or maritime history programs (Scouts, schools, colleges, etc.)

Benefits:
- A 150-word listing in the directory Sail Tall Ships! *
- A listing of your Organization on the Tall Ships America® Website. We provide a hot link to your Website and appreciate reciprocity.
- The opportunity to post help wanted ads in the very popular Billet Bank on the Tall Ships America® Website. The Billet Bank is the most visited section of the Tall Ships America® Website and is the most effective service for matching professional sail trainers and open positions.
- 10 complimentary copies of Sail Tall Ships! for your staff and volunteers.
- Subscription to e-Running Free, Tall Ships America's monthly e-mail newsletter covering tall ships news and events.
- Discounts for staff to attend the Annual Conference on Sail Training and Tall Ships.
- Discounts for staff to attend Regional Meetings, Education and Safety Forums.
- Invitations to attend Tall Ships America® special events and friendraisers.
- 15% discount on sponsorship displays in Sail Tall Ships!*
- Additional copies of Sail Tall Ships! at production cost (plus shipping) for resale.**

* In those membership years when a printed directory is produced.

** We anticipate production cost to be less than $6.00 per book. Therefore, when you sell them at the suggested retail price of $14.95 you will not only be raising revenue for your program but equally important, you will be assisting us in spreading the word about the power of sail training.

Prices subject to change

Organizational Membership (continued)

Sail Training Organizations/ Historic/Educational Vessels

Open to those organizations operating vessels. Membership dues are based on the organization's annual budget. STO1: Less than $250,000 / $525 per year, STO2: $250,000-$500,000 / $675 per year, STO3: Over $500,000 / $775 per year.

Benefits:
- Sail Training Organizations/ Historic / Educational Vessels - A full page listing, including a photo of your vessel, in the directory Sail Tall Ships! (additional vessel listings are available for additional charges.) Distribution is 7,500 copies.*
- A listing of your vessel(s) on the Tall Ships America® Website.
- Eligibility for the Henry H. Anderson, Jr. Sail Training Scholarship and the Ernestine Bennett Memorial Sail Training Scholarship programs for trainees that sail aboard your vessel(s).**
- Eligibility for the Professional Crew Development Grant Program.
- Eligibility for the Crew Membership Program.**
- Eligibility for the Marine Health Insurance Program.**
- Eligibility for the Marine Insurance Program.**
- The opportunity to post help wanted ads in the very popular Billet Bank on the Tall Ships America® Website. The Billet Bank is the most visited section of the Tall Ships America® Website and is the most effective service for matching professional sail trainers and open positions.
- 10 complimentary copies of Sail Tall Ships! for your staff and volunteers
- Subscription to e-Running Free, Tall Ships America's monthly e-mail newsletter covering tall ships news and events.
- Discounts for staff to attend the Annual Conference on Sail Training and Tall Ships.
- Discounts for staff to attend Regional Meetings, Education and Safety Forums.
- Invitations to attend Tall Ships America® special events and friendraisers.
- Complimentary Tall Ships America® Flag (new members only)
- 15% discount on sponsorship displays in Sail Tall Ships!*
- Additional copies of Sail Tall Ships! at production cost (plus shipping) for resale.***

* In those membership years when a printed directory is produced. Membership includes listing for one vessel. Additional vessel listings are $100 each.

**Some restrictions apply

***We anticipate production cost to be less than $6.00 per book. Therefore, when you sell them at the suggested retail price of $14.95 you will not only be raising revenue for your program but equally important, you will be assisting us in spreading the word about the power of sail training.

Prices subject to change

🚢 Crew Membership

Tall Ships America's Crew Membership Program

Sail Training Organization members may purchase blocks of 10 individual crew membership vouchers at a reduced rate, for distribution to their staff, crew, volunteers and trainees.

Crew memberships must be purchased by the member Sail Training Organization and are sold in blocks of 10 for US $250. Membership application forms are sent to the member STO who then distributes them to staff and crew. The individual crew memberships are valid for one year from the time Tall Ships America receives the completed individual crew member application form and carry all the same benefits as an individual membership (US $50) plus some added benefits.

Benefits per individual crew membership:
- Complimentary copy of Sail Tall Ships! A Directory of Sail Training and Adventure at Sea.
- Subscription to e-Running Free, Tall Ships America's monthly e-mail newsletter covering tall ships news and events.
- Discounts to attend the Annual Conference on Sail Training and Tall Ships.
- Discounts to attend Tall Ships America's Regional Meetings, Education and Safety Forums.
- Invitations to attend Tall Ships America® special events and friendraisers.
- Individual health insurance plans available to eligible crew members.
- Professional Crew Development Grants available to eligible crew members.

In addition to the above direct benefits, Tall Ships America works on a regular basis with the Coast Guard, Customs and Immigration and other government agencies on behalf of the sail training industry.

We look forward to having you come aboard with the membership that best suits your interest and budget! Not only will you become a member of the largest sail training association in the world, but you will be supporting the youth education and leadership development programs that can help shape young people's lives!

To become a member please mail or fax the form on the following page to:

Tall Ships America
PO Box 1459
Newport, RI 02840 USA
Fax: +1 401.849.5400

Organizational Crew Membership Application

Please sign us up in the Crew Membership Program!
(Available to Tall Ships America® Sail Training Organization Members only.)

Package of ten (10) Individual Crew Memberships US $250.00

Benefits per individual crew membership:
- Complimentary copy of Sail Tall Ships! A Directory of Sail Training and Adventure at Sea.
- Subscription to e-Running Free, our monthly e-mail newsletter.
- Discounts to attend the Annual conference on Sail Training and Tall Ships.
- Discounts to attend Regional Meetings, Education and Safety Forums and other special events.
- Individual health insurance plans available to eligible crew members.
- Professional Crew Development Grants available to eligible crew members.

(Individual Crew Memberships are activated when the crew member submits to Tall Ships America the membership form issued to them through the participating Sail Training Organization member. Membership is good for one year from the activation date.)

Member Organization: _____

Vessel(s): _____

Contact Name: _____

Mailing Address: _____

City: _____ State/Province: _____ Postal/Zip: _____

Country: _____

Phone: _____ Fax: _____

E-Mail: _____

Payment of dues:

___Check or money order enclosed (US dollars please)

___Visa or MasterCard (We do not accept AMEX)

Card number:_____ Expires:_____ CCV#:_____

NOC: _____ Signature: _____

Associate/Organizational Membership Application

Name: _____

Organization: _____

Vessel(s): _____

Mailing Address: _____

City: _____ State/Province: _____ Postal/Zip: _____

Country: _____ *

Phone: _____ Fax: _____

E-Mail: _____

Please enroll me/us in the following membership category:

Associate Memberships* (renewable on date of anniversary)

__Individual $50 __Youth $25 __Family $75 __ Supporting $250 __Patron $1,000

* For addresses in Canada or Mexico, please add US $16 to cover additional postage and handling costs. For addresses outside of North America, please add US $24.

Organizational Memberships** (January 1 through December 31).

___Corporate $1000 ___Business Partner $550 ___Affiliate $375

Sail Training Organizations/Historic/Educational Vessels:

___Budget less than $250,000: $525

___Budget between $250,000 and $500,000: $675

___Budget greater than $500,000: $775

** For addresses in Canada or Mexico, please add US $35 to cover additional postage and handling costs. For addresses outside of North America, please add US $75.

Payment of dues:

___Check or money order enclosed (US dollars please)

___Visa or MasterCard (We do not accept AMEX)

Card number:_____ Expires:_____ CCV#:____

NOC: _____ Signature: _____

The mission of Tall Ships America
is to encourage character building
through sail training,
promote sail training to the
North American public,
and support education under sail.